Biological Psychology

CUSTOM EDITION

James W. Kalat

CENGAGE
Learning·

Australia • Brazil • Japan • Korea • Mexico • Singapore • Spain • United Kingdom • United States

CENGAGE
Learning·

Biological Psychology: Custom Edition

BIOLOGICAL PSYCHOLOGY, ELEVENTH EDITION
Kalat

© 2013, 2009 Cengage Learning. All rights reserved.

Senior Project Development Manager:
  Linda deStefano

Market Development Manager:
  Heather Kramer

Senior Production/Manufacturing Manager:
  Donna M. Brown

Production Editorial Manager:
  Kim Fry

Sr. Rights Acquisition Account Manager:
  Todd Osborne

For product information and technology assistance, contact us at
Cengage Learning Customer & Sales Support, 1-800-354-9706

For permission to use material from this text or product, submit all requests online at **cengage.com/permissions**
Further permissions questions can be emailed to
permissionrequest@cengage.com

This book contains select works from existing Cengage Learning resources and was produced by Cengage Learning Custom Solutions for collegiate use. As such, those adopting and/or contributing to this work are responsible for editorial content accuracy, continuity and completeness.

Compilation © 2013 Cengage Learning
ISBN-13: 978-1-285-91885-3

ISBN-10: 1-285-91885-1

Cengage Learning
5191 Natorp Boulevard
Mason, Ohio 45040
USA

Cengage Learning is a leading provider of customized learning solutions with office locations around the globe, including Singapore, the United Kingdom, Australia, Mexico, Brazil, and Japan. Locate your local office at:

international.cengage.com/region.

Cengage Learning products are represented in Canada by Nelson Education, Ltd.
For your lifelong learning solutions, visit **www.cengage.com/custom.**
Visit our corporate website at **www.cengage.com.**

Printed in the United States of America

Brief Contents

Nerve Cells and Nerve Impulses

2

CHAPTER OUTLINE

MAIN IDEAS

1. The nervous system is composed of two kinds of cells: neurons and glia. Only the neurons transmit impulses from one location to another.

2. The larger neurons have branches, known as axons and dendrites, that can change their branching pattern as a function of experience, age, and chemical influences.

3. Many molecules in the bloodstream that can enter other body organs cannot enter the brain.

4. The action potential, an all-or-none change in the electrical potential across the membrane of a neuron, is caused by the sudden flow of sodium ions into the neuron and is followed by a flow of potassium ions out of the neuron.

5. Local neurons are small and do not have axons or action potentials. Instead, they convey information to nearby neurons by graded potentials.

OPPOSITE: An electron micrograph of neurons, magnified tens of thousands of times. The color is added artificially. For objects this small, it is impossible to focus light to obtain an image. It is possible to focus an electron beam, but electrons do not show color.

I f you lived entirely alone, how long could you survive? If you are like most people, you have never hunted your own meat. Maybe you have occasionally caught your own fish. You have probably never grown enough fruits or vegetables to meet your needs. Could you build your own house? Have you ever made your own clothing? Of all the activities necessary for your survival, are there *any* that you could do entirely on your own, other than breathe? People can do an enormous amount together, but very little by themselves.

The cells of your nervous system are like that, too. Together they accomplish amazing things, but one cell by itself is helpless. We begin our study of the nervous system by examining single cells. Later, we examine how they act together.

Advice: Parts of this chapter and the next assume that you understand the basic principles of chemistry. If you have never studied chemistry, or if you have forgotten what you did study, read Appendix A.

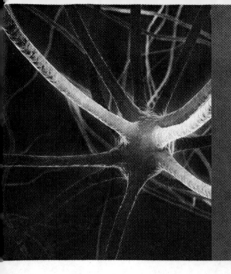

The Cells of the Nervous System

You think of yourself—I assume—as a single individual. You don't think of your mental experience as being composed of pieces... but it is. Your experiences depend on the activity of a huge number of separate cells. The activity of one cell, by itself, accomplishes almost nothing and means almost nothing, but this vast array of cells working together constitutes *you*. Researchers are far from fully understanding how that happens, but the place to begin is by trying to understand what each cell does.

▌Anatomy of Neurons and Glia

The nervous system consists of two kinds of cells: neurons and glia. **Neurons** receive information and transmit it to other cells. Glia serve many functions that are difficult to summarize, and we shall defer that discussion until later in the chapter. According to one estimate, the adult human brain contains approximately 100 billion neurons (R. W. Williams & Herrup, 1988) (Figure 2.1). An accurate count would be more difficult than it is worth, and the exact number varies from person to person.

The idea that the brain is composed of individual cells is now so well established that we take it for granted. However, the idea was in doubt as recently as the early 1900s. Until then, the best microscopic views revealed little detail about the brain. Observers noted long, thin fibers between one neuron's cell body and another, but they could not see whether each fiber merged into the next cell or stopped before it (Albright, Jessell, Kandel, & Posner, 2001). Then, in the late 1800s, Santiago Ramón y Cajal used newly developed staining techniques to show that a small gap separates the tips of one neuron's fibers from the surface of the next neuron. The brain, like the rest of the body, consists of individual cells.

Cerebral cortex and associated areas:12 to 15 billion neurons

Cerebellum: 70 billion neurons

Spinal cord: 1 billion neurons

FIGURE 2.1 Estimated numbers of neurons in humans
Because of the small size of many neurons and the variation in cell density from one spot to another, obtaining an accurate count is difficult. *(Source: R. W. Williams & Herrup, 1988)*

APPLICATIONS AND EXTENSIONS

Santiago Ramón y Cajal, a Pioneer of Neuroscience

Two scientists are widely recognized as the main founders of neuroscience: Charles Sherrington, whom we shall discuss in Chapter 3, and the Spanish investigator Santiago Ramón y Cajal (1852–1934). Cajal's early career did not progress altogether smoothly. At one point, he was imprisoned in a solitary cell, limited to one meal a day, and taken out daily for public floggings—at the age of 10—for the crime of not paying attention during his Latin class (Cajal, 1901–1917/1937). (And *you* complained about *your* teachers!)

Cajal wanted to become an artist, but his father insisted that he study medicine as a safer way to make a living. He managed to combine the two fields, becoming an outstanding anatomical researcher and illustrator. His detailed drawings of the nervous system are still considered definitive today.

Before the late 1800s, microscopy revealed few details about the nervous system. Then the Italian investigator Camillo Golgi found a way to stain nerve cells with silver salts. This method, which completely stained some cells without affecting others at all, enabled researchers to examine the structure of a single cell. Cajal used Golgi's methods but applied them to infant brains, in which the cells are smaller and therefore easier to examine on a single slide. Cajal's research demonstrated that nerve cells remain separate instead of merging into one another.

Philosophically, we see the appeal of the old idea that neurons merge. We describe our experience as undivided, not the sum of separate parts, so it seems right that all the cells in the brain might be joined together as one unit. How the separate cells combine their influences is a complex and still mysterious process. ■

Santiago Ramón y Cajal
(1852–1934)
How many interesting facts fail to be converted into fertile discoveries because their first observers regard them as natural and ordinary things! . . . It is strange to see how the populace, which nourishes its imagination with tales of witches or saints, mysterious events and extraordinary occurrences, disdains the world around it as commonplace, monotonous and prosaic, without suspecting that at bottom it is all secret, mystery, and marvel. (Cajal, 1937, pp. 46-47).

The Structures of an Animal Cell

Figure 2.2 illustrates a neuron from the cerebellum of a mouse (magnified enormously, of course). Neurons have much in common with the rest of the body's cells. The surface of a cell is its **membrane** (or *plasma membrane*), a structure that separates the inside of the cell from the outside environment. It is composed of two layers of fat molecules that are free to flow around one another, as illustrated in Figure 2.3. Most chemicals cannot cross the membrane, but specific protein channels in the membrane permit a controlled flow of water, oxygen, sodium, potassium, calcium, chloride, and other important chemicals.

Except for mammalian red blood cells, all animal cells have a **nucleus**, the structure that contains the chromosomes. A **mitochondrion** (pl.: mitochondria) is the structure that performs metabolic activities, providing the energy that the cell requires for all other activities. Mitochondria require fuel and oxygen to function. **Ribosomes** are the sites at which the cell synthesizes new protein molecules. Proteins provide building materials for the cell and facilitate various chemical reactions. Some ribosomes float freely within the cell. Others are attached to the **endoplasmic reticulum**, a network of thin tubes that transport newly synthesized proteins to other locations.

The Structure of a Neuron

The most distinctive feature of neurons is their shape, which varies enormously from one neuron to another (Figure 2.4). Unlike most other body cells, neurons have long branching extensions. The larger neurons have these components: dendrites, a soma (cell body), an axon, and presynaptic terminals.

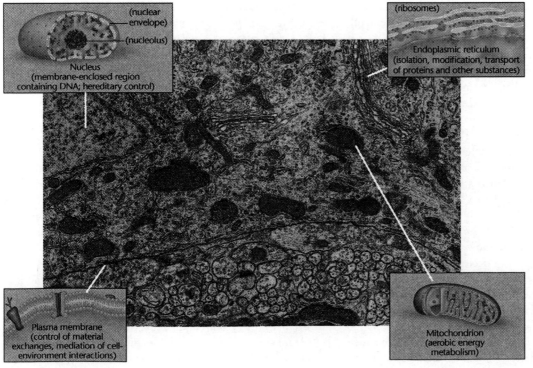

(nuclear envelope)
(nucleolus)
Nucleus
(membrane-enclosed region containing DNA; hereditary control)

(ribosomes)
Endoplasmic reticulum
(isolation, modification, transport of proteins and other substances)

Plasma membrane
(control of material exchanges, mediation of cell-environment interactions)

Mitochondrion
(aerobic energy metabolism)

FIGURE 2.2 An electron micrograph of parts of a neuron from the cerebellum of a mouse
The nucleus, membrane, and other structures are characteristic of most animal cells. The plasma membrane is the border of the neuron. Magnification approximately x 20,000. *(Source: Micrograph courtesy of Dennis M. D. Landis)*

Bettmann/CORBIS

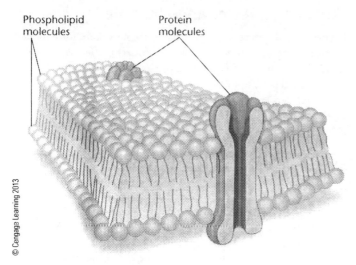

FIGURE 2.3 **The membrane of a neuron**
Embedded in the membrane are protein channels that permit
certain ions to cross through the membrane at a controlled rate.

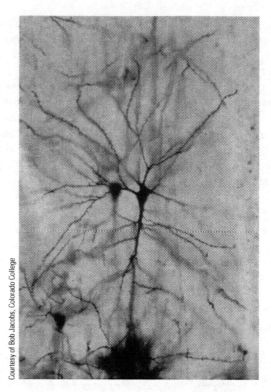

FIGURE 2.4 **Neurons, stained to appear dark**
Note the small fuzzy-looking spines on the dendrites.

(The tiniest neurons lack axons, and some lack well-defined
dendrites.) Contrast the motor neuron in Figure 2.5 and the
sensory neuron in Figure 2.6. A **motor neuron** has its soma
in the spinal cord. It receives excitation from other neurons
through its dendrites and conducts impulses along its axon
to a muscle. A **sensory neuron** is specialized at one end to
be highly sensitive to a particular type of stimulation, such as
light, sound, or touch. The sensory neuron shown in Figure
2.6 is a neuron conducting touch information from the skin to
the spinal cord. Tiny branches lead directly from the receptors
into the axon, and the cell's soma is located on a little stalk off
the main trunk.

Dendrites are branching fibers that get narrower near
their ends. (The term *dendrite* comes from a Greek root
word meaning "tree." A dendrite branches like a tree.) The
dendrite's surface is lined with specialized *synaptic receptors*,
at which the dendrite receives information from other neurons. (Chapter 3 concerns synapses.) The greater the surface
area of a dendrite, the more information it can receive. Some
dendrites branch widely and therefore have a large surface
area. Many also contain **dendritic spines**, the short outgrowths that increase the surface area available for synapses
(Figure 2.7).

The **cell body**, or **soma** (Greek for "body"; pl.: somata),
contains the nucleus, ribosomes, and mitochondria. Most of
the metabolic work of the neuron occurs here. Cell bodies of
neurons range in diameter from 0.005 mm to 0.1 mm in
mammals and up to a full millimeter in certain invertebrates.
Like the dendrites, the cell body is covered with synapses on
its surface in many neurons.

The **axon** is a thin fiber of constant diameter, in most
cases longer than the dendrites. (The term *axon* comes from

a Greek word meaning "axis.") The axon is the neuron's information sender, conveying an impulse toward other neurons or an organ or muscle. Many vertebrate axons are covered with an insulating material called a **myelin sheath**
with interruptions known as **nodes of Ranvier** (RAHN-
vee-ay). Invertebrate axons do not have myelin sheaths. An
axon has many branches, each of which swells at its tip,
forming a **presynaptic terminal**, also known as an *end bulb*
or *bouton* (French for "button"). This is the point from
which the axon releases chemicals that cross through the
junction between one neuron and the next.

A neuron can have any number of dendrites. It has only
one axon, but that axon may have branches far from the
soma. Axons can be a meter or more in length, as in the case
of axons from your spinal cord to your feet. That is, in many
cases the length of an axon is enormous in comparison to its
width—like that of a narrow highway that stretches across
a continent.

Other terms associated with neurons are *afferent, efferent,* and *intrinsic*. An **afferent axon** brings information into
a structure; an **efferent axon** carries information away from
a structure. Every sensory neuron is an afferent to the rest
of the nervous system, and every motor neuron is an efferent from the nervous system. Within the nervous system, a
given neuron is an efferent from one structure and an afferent

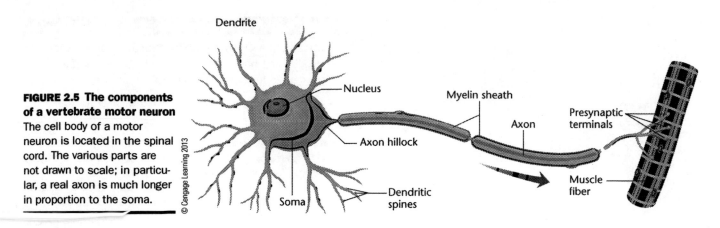

FIGURE 2.5 The components of a vertebrate motor neuron
The cell body of a motor neuron is located in the spinal cord. The various parts are not drawn to scale; in particular, a real axon is much longer in proportion to the soma.

© Cengage Learning 2013

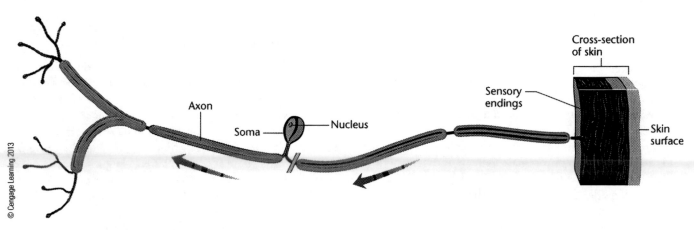

© Cengage Learning 2013

FIGURE 2.6 A vertebrate sensory neuron
Note that the soma is located on a stalk off the main trunk of the axon. (As in Figure 2.5, the various structures are not drawn to scale.)

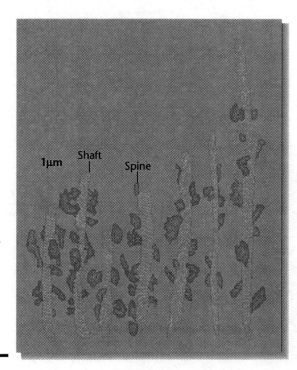

FIGURE 2.7 Dendritic spines
The dendrites of certain neurons are lined with spines, short outgrowths that receive specialized incoming information. That information apparently plays a key role in long-term changes in the neuron that mediate learning and memory. *(Source: From K. M. Harris and J. K. Stevens, Society for Neuroscience, "Dendritic Spines of CA1 Pyramidal Cells in the Rat Hippocampus: Serial Electron Microscopy With Reference to Their Biophysical Characteristics." Journal of Neuroscience, 9, 1989, 2982–2997. Copyright © 1989 Society for Neuroscience. Reprinted by permission.)*

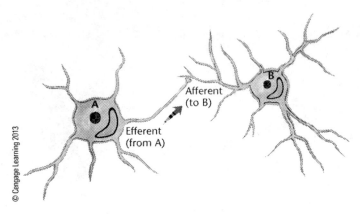

© Cengage Learning 2013

FIGURE 2.8 Cell structures and axons
It all depends on the point of view. An axon from A to B is an efferent axon from A and an afferent axon to B, just as a train from Washington to New York is exiting Washington and approaching New York.

to another. (You can remember that *efferent* starts with *e* as in *exit; afferent* starts with *a* as in *admit.*) For example, an axon might be efferent from the thalamus and afferent to the cerebral cortex (Figure 2.8). If a cell's dendrites and axon are entirely contained within a single structure, the cell is an **interneuron** or **intrinsic neuron** of that structure. For example, an intrinsic neuron of the thalamus has its axon and all its dendrites within the thalamus.

1.   What are the widely branching structures of a neuron called? And what is the long thin structure that carries information to another cell called?

2.   Which animal species would have the longest axons?

ANSWERS   1. The widely branching structures of a neuron are called *dendrites*, and the long thin structure that carries information to another cell is called an *axon*. 2. The longest axons occur in the largest animals. For example, giraffes and elephants have axons that extend from the spinal cord to the feet, nearly two meters away.

Variations Among Neurons

Neurons vary enormously in size, shape, and function. The shape of a given neuron determines its connections with other neurons and thereby determines its contribution to the nervous system. Neurons with wider branching connect with more targets.

The function of a neuron relates to its shape (Figure 2.9). For example, the widely branching dendrites of the Purkinje cell of the cerebellum (Figure 2.9a) enable it to receive a huge number of inputs—up to 200,000 in some cases. By contrast, certain cells in the retina (Figure 2.9d) have only short

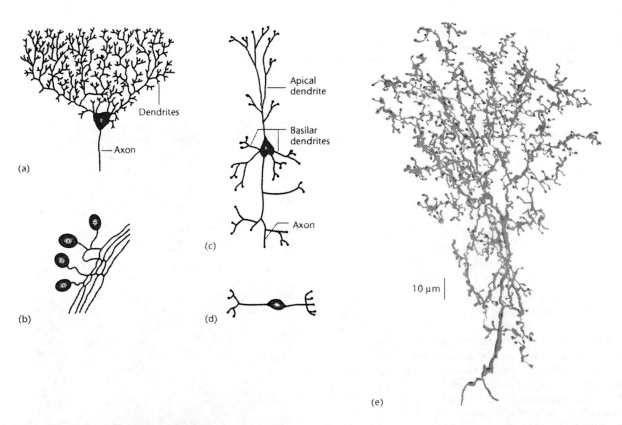

FIGURE 2.9 The diverse shapes of neurons
(a) Purkinje cell, a cell type found only in the cerebellum; (b) sensory neurons from skin to spinal cord; (c) pyramidal cell of the motor area of the cerebral cortex; (d) bipolar cell of retina of the eye; (e) Kenyon cell, from a honeybee. *(Source: Part e courtesy of R. G. Goss)*

branches on their dendrites and therefore pool input from only a few sources.

Glia

Glia (or neuroglia), the other major components of the nervous system, do not transmit information over long distances as neurons do, although they perform many other functions. The term *glia*, derived from a Greek word meaning "glue," reflects early investigators' idea that glia were like glue that held the neurons together (Somjen, 1988). Although that concept is obsolete, the term remains. Glia are smaller but more numerous than neurons (Figure 2.10).

The brain has several types of glia with different functions (Haydon, 2001). The star-shaped **astrocytes** wrap around the presynaptic terminals of a group of functionally related axons, as shown in Figure 2.11. By taking up ions released by axons and then releasing them back to axons, an astrocyte helps synchronize the activity of the axons, enabling them to send messages in waves (Angulo, Kozlov, Charpak, & Audinat, 2004; Antanitus, 1998). Astrocytes also remove waste material created when neurons die and control the amount of blood flow to each brain area (Mulligan & MacVicar, 2004). An additional function is that during periods of heightened activity in some brain areas, astrocytes dilate the blood vessels to bring more nutrients into that area (Filosa et al., 2006; Takano et al., 2006). Uncertainty surrounds another possible function: Neurons communicate by releasing certain transmitters, such as *glutamate*. After a neuron releases much glutamate, nearby glia cells absorb some of the excess. We know that the glia convert most of this glutamate into a related chemical, *glutamine*, and then pass it back to the neurons, which convert it back to glutamate, which they get ready for further release. (It's a recycling system.) The uncertain question is whether glia cells also release glutamate and other chemicals themselves. If so, they could be part of the brain's signaling system (Hamilton & Attwell, 2010).

Microglia, very small cells, also remove waste material as well as viruses, fungi, and other microorganisms. In effect, they function like part of the immune system (Davalos et al., 2005). **Oligodendrocytes** (OL-i-go-DEN-druh-sites) in the brain and spinal cord and **Schwann cells** in the periphery of the body are specialized types of glia that build the myelin sheaths that surround and insulate certain vertebrate axons. **Radial glia** guide the migration of neurons and their axons and dendrites during embryonic development. When embryological development finishes, most radial glia differentiate into neurons, and a smaller number differentiate into astrocytes and oligodendrocytes (Pinto & Götz, 2007).

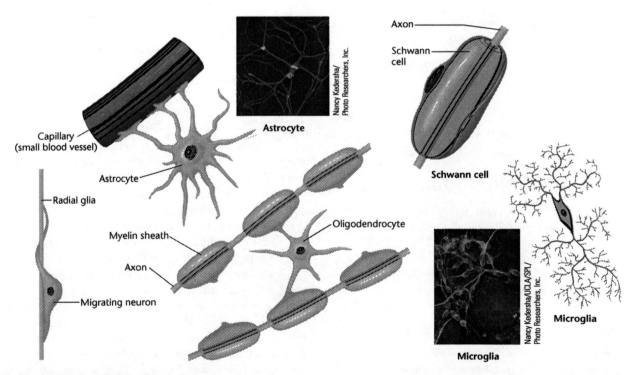

FIGURE 2.10 Shapes of some glia cells
Oligodendrocytes produce myelin sheaths that insulate certain vertebrate axons in the central nervous system; Schwann cells have a similar function in the periphery. The oligodendrocyte is shown here forming a segment of myelin sheath for two axons; in fact, each oligodendrocyte forms such segments for 30 to 50 axons. Astrocytes pass chemicals back and forth between neurons and blood and among neighboring neurons. Microglia proliferate in areas of brain damage and remove toxic materials. Radial glia (not shown here) guide the migration of neurons during embryological development. Glia have other functions as well. (© *Cengage Learning 2013*)

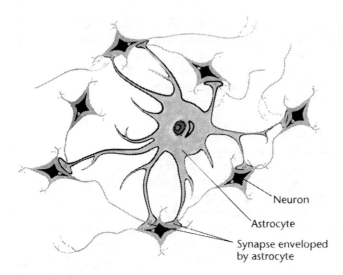

Neuron

Astrocyte

Synapse enveloped
by astrocyte

FIGURE 2.11 How an astrocyte synchronizes associated axons
Branches of the astrocyte (in the center) surround the presynaptic terminals of related axons. If a few of them are active at once, the astrocyte absorbs some of the chemicals they release. It then temporarily inhibits all the axons to which it is connected. When the inhibition ceases, all of the axons are primed to respond again in synchrony. *(Source: Based on Antanitus, 1998)*

Stop & Check

3. Identify the four major structures that compose a neuron.

4. Which kind of glia cell wraps around the synaptic terminals of axons?

ANSWERS

3. Dendrites, soma (cell body), axon, and presynaptic terminal. 4. Astrocytes.

The Blood–Brain Barrier

Although the brain, like any other organ, needs to receive nutrients from the blood, many chemicals cannot cross from the blood to the brain (Hagenbuch, Gao, & Meier, 2002). The mechanism that excludes most chemicals from the vertebrate brain is known as the **blood–brain barrier**. Before we examine how it works, let's consider why we need it.

Why We Need a Blood–Brain Barrier

When a virus invades a cell, mechanisms within the cell extrude virus particles through the membrane so that the immune system can find them. When the immune system cells identify a virus, they kill it and the cell that contains it. In effect, a cell exposing a virus through its membrane says, "Look, immune system, I'm infected with this virus. Kill me and save the others."

This plan works fine if the virus-infected cell is, say, a skin cell or a blood cell, which the body replaces easily. However, with few exceptions, the vertebrate brain does not replace damaged neurons. To minimize the risk of irreparable brain damage, the body builds a wall along the sides of the brain's blood vessels. This wall keeps out most viruses, bacteria, and harmful chemicals.

"What happens if a virus does enter the nervous system?" you might ask. Certain viruses, such as the rabies virus, evade the blood–brain barrier, infect the brain, and lead to death. For several other viruses that enter the nervous system, microglia and other mechanisms attack the viruses or slow their reproduction without killing the neurons they invaded (Binder & Griffin, 2001). However, a virus that enters your nervous system probably remains with you for life. For example, the virus responsible for chicken pox and shingles enters spinal cord cells. No matter how effectively the immune system attacks that virus outside the nervous system, virus particles remain in the spinal cord, from which they can emerge decades later. The same is true for the virus that causes genital herpes.

How the Blood–Brain Barrier Works

The blood–brain barrier (Figure 2.12) depends on the endothelial cells that form the walls of the capillaries (Bundgaard, 1986; Rapoport & Robinson, 1986). Outside the brain, such cells are separated by small gaps, but in the brain, they are joined so tightly that virtually nothing passes between them.

"If the blood–brain barrier is such a good defense," you might ask, "why don't we have similar walls around our other organs?" The answer is that the barrier keeps out useful chemicals as well as harmful ones. Those useful chemicals include all fuels and amino acids, the building blocks for proteins. For the brain to function, it needs special mechanisms to get these chemicals across the blood–brain barrier.

The brain has several such mechanisms. First, *small uncharged molecules*, including oxygen and carbon dioxide, cross freely. Water crosses through special protein channels in the wall of the endothelial cells (Amiry-Moghaddam & Ottersen, 2003). Second, *molecules that dissolve in the fats of the membrane* also cross passively. Examples include vitamins A and D and all the drugs that affect the brain—from antidepressants and other psychiatric drugs to illegal drugs such as heroin.

For a few other chemicals, the brain uses **active transport**, a protein-mediated process that expends energy to pump chemicals from the blood into the brain. Chemicals that are actively transported into the brain include glucose (the brain's main fuel), amino acids (the building blocks of proteins), purines, choline, a few vitamins, iron, and certain hormones (Abbott, Rönnback, & Hansson, 2006; A. R. Jones & Shusta, 2007).

The blood–brain barrier is essential to health. In people with Alzheimer's disease or similar conditions, the endothelial cells lining the brain's blood vessels shrink, and harmful

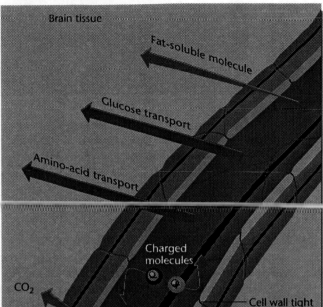

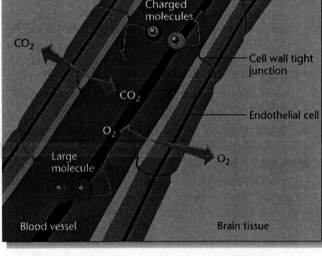

FIGURE 2.12 The blood–brain barrier
Most large molecules and electrically charged molecules cannot cross from the blood to the brain. A few small, uncharged molecules such as O_2 and CO_2 cross easily; so can certain fat-soluble molecules. Active transport systems pump glucose and certain amino acids across the membrane. (© Cengage Learning 2013)

chemicals enter the brain (Zipser et al., 2006). However, the barrier also poses a difficulty in medicine because it keeps out many medications. Brain cancers are difficult to treat because nearly all the drugs used for chemotherapy fail to cross the blood–brain barrier.

5. Identify one major advantage and one disadvantage of having a blood–brain barrier.

6. Which chemicals cross the blood–brain barrier passively?

7. Which chemicals cross the blood–brain barrier by active transport?

ANSWERS **5.** The blood–brain barrier keeps out viruses (an advantage) and also most nutrients (a disadvantage). **6.** Small, uncharged molecules such as oxygen, carbon dioxide, and water cross the blood–brain barrier passively. So do chemicals that dissolve in the fats of the membrane. **7.** Glucose, amino acids, purines, choline, certain vitamins, iron, and a few hormones.

Nourishment in Vertebrate Neurons

Most cells use a variety of carbohydrates and fats for nutrition, but vertebrate neurons depend almost entirely on **glucose,** a sugar. (Cancer cells and the testis cells that make sperm also rely overwhelmingly on glucose.) Because the metabolic pathway that uses glucose requires oxygen, neurons need a steady supply of oxygen (Wong-Riley, 1989). The brain uses about 20% of all the oxygen consumed in the body.

Why do neurons depend so heavily on glucose? Although neurons have the enzymes necessary to metabolize other fuels, glucose is practically the only nutrient that crosses the blood–brain barrier after infancy, except for *ketones* (a kind of fat), and ketones are seldom available in large amounts (Duelli & Kuschinsky, 2001).

Although neurons require glucose, glucose shortage is rarely a problem. The liver makes glucose from many kinds of carbohydrates and amino acids, as well as from glycerol, a breakdown product from fats. The only likely problem is an inability to *use* glucose. To use glucose, the body needs vitamin B_1, **thiamine.** Prolonged thiamine deficiency, common in chronic alcoholism, leads to death of neurons and a condition called *Korsakoff's syndrome,* marked by severe memory impairments (Chapter 13).

Neurons

What does the study of individual neurons tell us about behavior? One important principle is that our experience and behavior *do not* follow from the properties of any one neuron. Just as a chemist must know about atoms to make sense of compounds, a biological psychologist or neuroscientist must know about cells to understand the nervous system. However, the nervous system is more than the sum of the individual cells, just as water is more than the sum of oxygen and hydrogen. Our behavior emerges from the communication among neurons.

SUMMARY

1. Neurons receive information and convey it to other cells. The nervous system also contains *glia*.   28

2. In the late 1800s, Santiago Ramón y Cajal used newly discovered staining techniques to establish that the nervous system is composed of separate cells, now known as neurons.   28

3. Neurons contain the same internal structures as other animal cells.   29

4. Neurons have four major parts: a cell body, dendrites, an axon, and presynaptic terminals. Their shapes vary greatly depending on their functions and their connections with other cells.   29

5. Because of the blood–brain barrier, many molecules cannot enter the brain. The barrier protects the nervous system from viruses and many dangerous chemicals.

    The blood–brain barrier consists of an unbroken wall of cells that surround the blood vessels of the brain and spinal cord. A few small uncharged molecules, such as water, oxygen, and carbon dioxide, cross the barrier freely. So do molecules that dissolve in fats.   34

6. Active transport proteins pump glucose, amino acids, and a few other chemicals into the brain and spinal cord.   34

7. Adult neurons rely heavily on glucose, the only nutrient that can cross the blood–brain barrier. They need thiamine (vitamin B_1) to use glucose.   35

KEY TERMS

Terms are defined in the module on the page number indicated. They're also presented in alphabetical order with definitions in the book's Subject Index/Glossary, which begins on page 561. Interactive flashcards and crossword puzzles are among the online resources available to help you learn these terms and the concepts they represent.

active transport 34	glia 33	nodes of Ranvier 30
afferent axon 30	glucose 35	nucleus 29
astrocytes 33	interneuron 32	oligodendrocytes 33
axon 30	intrinsic neuron 32	presynaptic terminal 30
blood–brain barrier 34	membrane 29	radial glia 33
cell body (soma) 30	microglia 33	ribosomes 30
dendrites 30	mitochondrion 29	Schwann cells 33
dendritic spines 30	motor neuron 30	sensory neuron 30
efferent axon 32	myelin sheath 30	thiamine 35
endoplasmic reticulum 30	neurons 28	

THOUGHT QUESTION

Although heroin and morphine are similar in many ways, heroin exerts faster effects on the brain. What can we infer about those drugs with regard to the blood–brain barrier?

The Nerve Impulse

Think about the axons that convey information from your feet's touch receptors toward your spinal cord and brain. If the axons used electrical conduction, they could transfer information at a velocity approaching the speed of light. However, given that your body is made of water and carbon compounds instead of copper wire, the strength of the impulse would decay rapidly as it traveled. A touch on your shoulder would feel stronger than a touch on your abdomen. Short people would feel their toes more strongly than tall people could—if either could feel their toes at all!

The way your axons actually function avoids these problems. Instead of conducting an electrical impulse, the axon regenerates an impulse at each point. Imagine a long line of people holding hands. The first person squeezes the second person's hand, who then squeezes the third person's hand, and so forth. The impulse travels along the line without weakening because each person generates it anew.

Although the axon's method of transmitting an impulse prevents a touch on your shoulder from feeling stronger than one on your toes, it introduces a different problem: Because axons transmit information at only moderate speeds (varying from less than 1 meter/second to about 100 m/s), a touch on your shoulder will reach your brain *sooner* than will a touch on your toes. If you get someone to touch you simultaneously on your shoulder and your toe, you will not notice that your brain received one stimulus before the other, because the difference is small. In fact, if someone touches you on one hand and then the other, you won't be sure which hand you felt first, unless the delay between touches exceeds 70 milliseconds (ms) (S. Yamamoto & Kitazawa, 2001). Your brain is not set up to register small differences in the time of arrival of touch messages. After all, why should it be? You almost never need to know whether a touch on one part of your body occurred slightly before or after a touch somewhere else.

ONLINE

In vision, however, your brain *does* need to know whether one stimulus began slightly before or after another one. If two adjacent spots on your retina—let's call them A and B—send impulses at almost the same time, an extremely small difference in timing indicates whether light moved from A to B or from B to A. To detect movement as accurately as possible, your visual system compensates for the fact that some parts of

the retina are slightly closer to your brain than other parts are. Without some sort of compensation, simultaneous flashes arriving at two spots on your retina would reach your brain at different times, and you might perceive movement inaccurately. What prevents this illusion is the fact that axons from more distant parts of your retina transmit impulses slightly faster than those closer to the brain (Stanford, 1987)!

In short, the properties of impulse conduction in an axon are well adapted to the exact needs for information transfer in the nervous system. Let's examine the mechanics of impulse transmission.

The Resting Potential of the Neuron

Messages in a neuron develop from disturbances of the resting potential. Let's begin by understanding the resting potential.

All parts of a neuron are covered by a membrane about 8 nanometers (nm) thick (just less than 0.00001 mm), composed of two layers (an inner layer and an outer layer) of phospholipid molecules (containing chains of fatty acids and a phosphate group). Embedded among the phospholipids are cylindrical protein molecules through which various chemicals can pass (see Figure 2.3 on page 30). The structure of the membrane provides it with a combination of flexibility and firmness and controls the flow of chemicals between the inside and outside of the cell.

In the absence of any outside disturbance, the membrane maintains an **electrical gradient**, also known as **polarization**—a difference in electrical charge between the inside and outside of the cell. The neuron inside the membrane has a slightly negative electrical potential with respect to the outside, mainly because of negatively charged proteins inside the cell. This difference in voltage in a resting neuron is called the **resting potential**.

Researchers measure the resting potential by inserting a very thin *microelectrode* into the cell body, as Figure 2.13 shows. The diameter of the electrode must be as small as possible so that it enters the cell without causing damage. The most common electrode is a fine glass tube filled with a con-

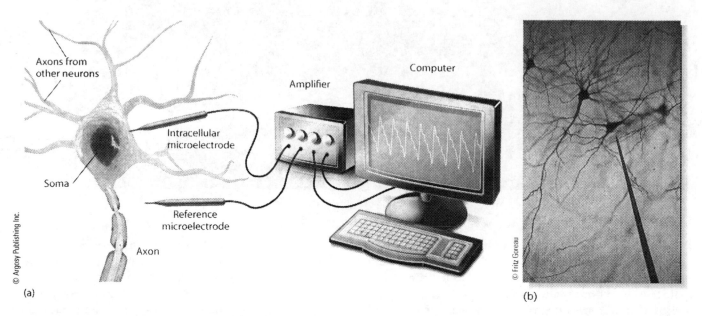

FIGURE 2.13 Methods for recording activity of a neuron
(a) Diagram of the apparatus and a sample recording. (b) A microelectrode and stained neurons magnified hundreds of times by a light microscope.

centrated salt solution and tapering to a tip diameter of 0.0005 mm or less. A reference electrode outside the cell completes the circuit. Connecting the electrodes to a voltmeter, we find that the neuron's interior has a negative potential relative to its exterior. A typical level is −70 millivolts (mV), but it varies from one neuron to another.

Forces Acting on Sodium and Potassium Ions

If charged ions could flow freely across the membrane, the membrane would depolarize. However, the membrane is **selectively permeable.** That is, some chemicals pass through it more freely than others do. Oxygen, carbon dioxide, urea, and water cross freely through channels that are always open. Most large or electrically charged ions and molecules do not cross the membrane at all. A few biologically important ions, such as sodium, potassium, calcium, and chloride, cross through membrane channels (or gates) that are sometimes open and sometimes closed. When the membrane is at rest, the sodium channels are closed, preventing almost all sodium flow, as shown on the right side of Figure 2.14. Certain kinds of stimulation can open the sodium channels, as in the center of that figure. When the membrane is at rest, potassium channels are nearly but not entirely closed, so potassium flows slowly. Stimulation opens them more widely also, as it does for sodium channels.

The **sodium–potassium pump,** a protein complex, repeatedly transports three sodium ions out of the cell while drawing two potassium ions into it. The sodium–potassium pump is an active transport that requires energy. As a result of the sodium–potassium pump, sodium ions are more than 10 times more concentrated outside the membrane than inside,

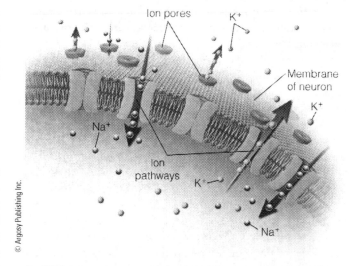

FIGURE 2.14 Ion channels in the membrane of a neuron
When a channel opens, it permits one kind of ion to cross the membrane. When it closes, it prevents passage of that ion.

and potassium ions are similarly more concentrated inside than outside.

The sodium–potassium pump is effective only because of the selective permeability of the membrane, which prevents the sodium ions that were pumped out of the neuron from leaking right back in again. When sodium ions are pumped out, they stay out. However, some of the potassium ions pumped into the neuron slowly leak out, carrying a positive charge with them. That leakage increases the electrical gradient across the membrane, as shown in Figure 2.15.

When the neuron is at rest, two forces act on sodium, both tending to push it *into* the cell. First, consider the electrical gradient. Sodium is positively charged and the inside of the cell is negatively charged. Opposite electrical charges attract, so the electrical gradient tends to pull sodium into the cell. Second, consider the **concentration gradient,** the difference in distribution of ions across the membrane. Sodium is more concentrated outside than inside, so just by the laws of probability, sodium is more likely to enter the cell than to leave it. (By analogy, imagine two rooms connected by a door. There are 100 cats in room A and only 10 in room B. Cats are more likely to move from A to B than from B to A. The same principle applies to the movement of ions across a membrane.) Given that both the electrical gradient and the concentration gradient tend to move sodium ions into the cell, sodium would move rapidly if it could. However, the sodium channels are closed when the membrane is at rest, and almost no sodium flows except for the sodium pushed *out of* the cell by the sodium–potassium pump.

Potassium is subject to competing forces. Potassium is positively charged and the inside of the cell is negatively charged, so the electrical gradient tends to pull potassium in. However, potassium is more concentrated inside the cell than outside, so the concentration gradient tends to drive it out. (Back to our cat analogy: Imagine some female cats tethered inside a room. Male cats can enter the room or leave through a narrow door. They are attracted to the female cats, but when the males get too crowded, some of them leave.)

If the potassium channels were wide open, potassium would have a small net flow out of the cell. That is, the electrical gradient and concentration gradient for potassium are almost in balance, but not quite. The sodium–potassium pump pulls more potassium into the cell as fast as it flows out of the cell, so the two gradients cannot get completely in balance.

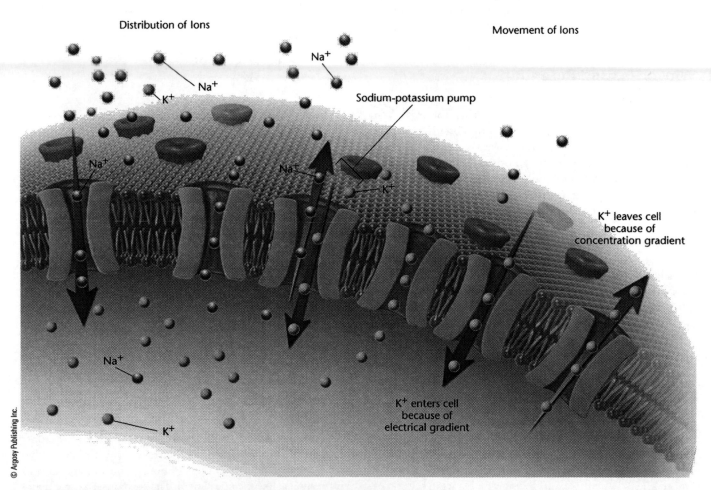

FIGURE 2.15 The sodium and potassium gradients for a resting membrane
Sodium ions are more concentrated outside the neuron. Potassium ions are more concentrated inside. Protein and chloride ions (not shown) bear negative charges inside the cell. At rest, very few sodium ions cross the membrane except by the sodium–potassium pump. Potassium tends to flow into the cell because of an electrical gradient but tends to flow out because of the concentration gradient. However, potassium gates retard the flow of potassium when the membrane is at rest.

The cell has negative ions, too. Negatively charged proteins inside the cell are responsible for the membrane's polarization. Chloride ions, being negatively charged, are mainly outside the cell. When the membrane is at rest, the concentration gradient and electrical gradient balance, so opening chloride channels produces little effect. However, chloride does have a net flow when the membrane's polarization changes.

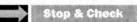

Stop & Check

8. When the membrane is at rest, are the sodium ions more concentrated inside the cell or outside? Where are the potassium ions more concentrated?

9. When the membrane is at rest, what tends to drive the potassium ions out of the cell? What tends to draw them into the cell?

ANSWERS
8. Sodium ions are more concentrated outside the cell; potassium is more concentrated inside. **9.** When the membrane is at rest, the concentration gradient tends to drive potassium ions out of the cell; the electrical gradient draws them into the cell. The sodium–potassium pump also draws them into the cell.

Why a Resting Potential?

The body invests much energy to operate the sodium–potassium pump, which maintains the resting potential. Why is it worth so much energy? The resting potential prepares the neuron to respond rapidly. As we shall see in the next section, excitation of the neuron opens channels that allow sodium to enter the cell rapidly. Because the membrane did its work in advance by maintaining the concentration gradient for sodium, the cell is prepared to respond vigorously to a stimulus.

Compare the resting potential of a neuron to a poised bow and arrow: An archer who pulls the bow in advance and then waits is ready to fire at the appropriate moment. The neuron uses the same strategy. The resting potential remains stable until the neuron is stimulated. Ordinarily, stimulation of the neuron takes place at synapses, which we consider in Chapter 3. In the laboratory, it is also possible to stimulate a neuron by inserting an electrode into it and applying current.

▌ The Action Potential

Messages sent by axons are called **action potentials**. To understand action potentials, let's begin by considering what happens when the resting potential is disturbed. We can measure a neuron's potential with a microelectrode, as shown in Figure 2.13b. When an axon's membrane is at rest, the recordings show a negative potential inside the axon. If we now use another electrode to apply a negative charge, we can further increase the negative charge inside the neuron. The change is called **hyperpolarization**, which means increased polariza-

tion. When the stimulation ends, the charge returns to its original resting level. The recording looks like this:

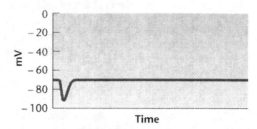

Now let's apply a current to **depolarize** the neuron—that is, reduce its polarization toward zero. If we apply a small depolarizing current, we get a result like this:

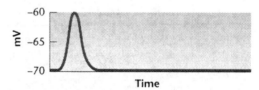

With a slightly stronger depolarizing current, the potential rises slightly higher but again returns to the resting level as soon as the stimulation ceases:

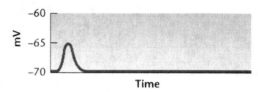

Now let's apply a still stronger current: Stimulation beyond the **threshold of excitation** produces a massive depolarization of the membrane. When the potential reaches the threshold, the membrane opens its sodium channels and permits sodium ions to flow into the cell. The potential shoots up far beyond the strength of the stimulus:

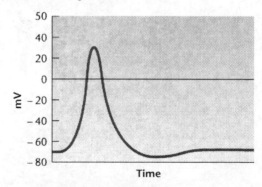

Any *subthreshold* stimulation produces a small response proportional to the amount of current. Any stimulation beyond the threshold, regardless of how far beyond, produces a big response like the one shown. That response, a rapid depolarization and then reversal of the usual polarization, is the action potential. The peak of the action potential, shown as +30 mV in this illustration, varies from one axon to another, but it is consistent for a given axon.

Stop & Check

10. What is the difference between a hyperpolarization and a depolarization?

11. What is the relationship between the threshold and an action potential?

ANSWERS

10. A hyperpolarization is an exaggeration of the usual negative charge within a cell (to a more negative level than usual). A depolarization is a decrease in the amount of negative charge within the cell. **11.** A depolarization that passes the threshold produces an action potential. One that falls short of the threshold does not produce an action potential.

The Molecular Basis of the Action Potential

The chemical events behind the action potential make sense if you remember these principles:

1. At the start, sodium ions are mostly outside the neuron and potassium ions are mostly inside.
2. When the membrane is depolarized, sodium and potassium channels in the membrane open.
3. At the peak of the action potential, the sodium channels close.

A neuron's membrane contains several types of cylindrical proteins, like the one in Figure 2.3, that can open or close. When one of these proteins is open, it allows a particular type of ion to cross the membrane. (Which ion crosses depends on the exact size and shape of the opening.) A protein that allows sodium to cross is called a sodium channel, one that allows potassium to cross is a potassium channel, and so forth. The ones regulating sodium and potassium are **voltage-gated channels.** That is, their permeability depends on the voltage difference across the membrane. At the resting potential, the sodium channels are closed (permitting no sodium to cross) and the potassium channels are almost closed (allowing only a little flow of potassium). As the membrane becomes depolarized, both the sodium and the potassium channels begin to open, allowing freer flow. At first, opening the potassium channels makes little difference, because the concentration gradient and electrical gradient are almost in balance anyway. However, opening the sodium channels makes a big difference, because both the electrical gradient and the concentration gradient tend to drive sodium ions into the neuron. When the depolarization reaches the threshold of the membrane, the sodium channels open wide enough for sodium to flow freely. Driven by both the concentration gradient and the electrical gradient, the sodium ions enter the cell rapidly, until the electrical potential across the membrane passes beyond zero to a reversed polarity, as shown in the following diagram:

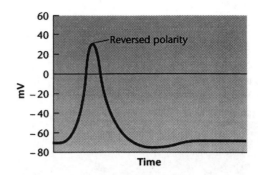

Compared to the total number of sodium ions in and around the axon, less than 1% of them cross the membrane during an action potential. Even at the peak of the action potential, sodium ions continue to be far more concentrated outside the neuron than inside. Because of the persisting concentration gradient, sodium ions should still tend to diffuse into the cell. However, at the peak of the action potential, the sodium gates snap shut and resist reopening for the next millisecond.

Then what happens? Remember that depolarizing the membrane also opens potassium channels. At first, opening those channels made little difference. However, after so many sodium ions have crossed the membrane, the inside of the cell has a slight positive charge instead of its usual negative charge. At this point both the concentration gradient and the electrical gradient drive potassium ions out of the cell. As they flow out of the axon, they carry with them a positive charge. Because the potassium channels remain open after the sodium channels close, enough potassium ions leave to drive the membrane beyond its usual resting level to a temporary hyperpolarization. Figure 2.16 summarizes the key movements of ions during an action potential.

At the end of this process, the membrane has returned to its resting potential, but the inside of the neuron has slightly more sodium ions and slightly fewer potassium ions than before. Eventually, the sodium–potassium pump restores the original distribution of ions, but that process takes time. After an unusually rapid series of action potentials, the pump cannot keep up with the action, and sodium accumulates within the axon. Excessive buildup of sodium can be toxic to a cell. (Excessive stimulation occurs only under abnormal conditions, however, such as during a stroke or after the use of certain drugs. Don't worry that thinking too hard will explode your brain cells!)

Action potentials require the flow of sodium and potassium. **Local anesthetic** drugs, such as Novocain and Xylocaine, attach to the sodium channels of the membrane, preventing sodium ions from entering, and thereby stopping action potentials (Ragsdale, McPhee, Scheuer, & Catterall, 1994). When a dentist administers Novocain before drilling into one of your teeth, your receptors are screaming, "pain, pain, pain!" but the axons can't transmit the message to your brain, and so you don't feel it.

To explore the action potential further and try some virtual experiments on the membrane, use the online MetaNeuron program available through the Department of Neuroscience at the University of Minnesota: http://www2.neuroscience.umn.edu/eanwebsite/metaneuron.htm

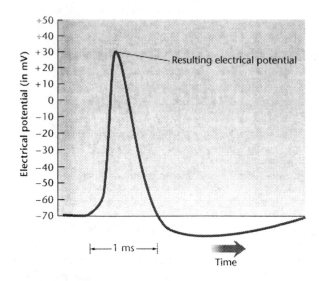

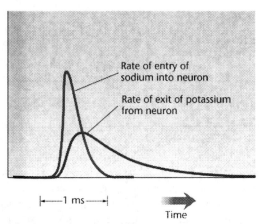

FIGURE 2.16 The movement of sodium and potassium ions during an action potential
Sodium ions cross during the peak of the action potential and potassium ions cross later in the opposite direction, returning the membrane to its original polarization. (© *Cengage Learning 2013*)

Stop & Check

12. During the rise of the action potential, do sodium ions move into the cell or out of it? Why?

13. As the membrane reaches the peak of the action potential, what brings the membrane down to the original resting potential?

ANSWERS

12. During the action potential, sodium ions move into the cell. The voltage-dependent sodium gates have opened, so sodium can move freely. Sodium is attracted to the inside of the cell by both an electrical and a concentration gradient. 13. After the peak of the action potential, potassium ions exit the cell, driving the membrane back to the resting potential. Important note: The sodium–potassium pump is NOT responsible for returning the membrane to its resting potential. The sodium–potassium pump is too slow for this purpose.

The All-or-None Law

An action potential always starts in an axon and propagates without loss along the axon. However, once it starts, in many cases it "back-propagates" into the cell body and dendrites (Lorincz & Nusser, 2010). The cell body and dendrites do not conduct action potentials in the same way that axons do, but they passively register the electrical event happening in the nearby axon. This back-propagation is important in some neurons, as we shall see in Chapter 13: When an action potential back-propagates into a dendrite, the dendrite becomes more susceptible to the structural changes responsible for learning.

Here, we concentrate on the axon: When the voltage across an axon membrane reaches the threshold, voltage-gated sodium channels open wide enough to let sodium ions enter, and the incoming sodium depolarizes the membrane enough to produce an action potential. For a given neuron, all action potentials are approximately equal in amplitude (intensity) and velocity. More properly stated, the **all-or-none law** is that the amplitude and velocity of an action potential are independent of the intensity of the stimulus that initiated it, provided that the stimulus reaches the threshold. By analogy, imagine flushing a toilet: You have to make a press of at least a certain strength (the threshold), but pressing harder does not make the toilet flush faster or more vigorously.

Although the amplitude, velocity, and shape of action potentials are consistent over time for a given axon, they vary from one neuron to another. The earliest studies dealt with squid axons because squid have very thick axons that are easy to study. More recent studies of mammalian axons have found much variation in the types of protein channels and therefore in the characteristics of the action potentials (Bean, 2007).

The all-or-none law puts constraints on how an axon can send a message. To signal the difference between a weak stimulus and a strong stimulus, the axon can't send bigger or faster action potentials. All it can change is the timing. By analogy, suppose you agree to exchange coded messages with someone who can see your window when you flick the lights on and off. The two of you might agree, for example, to indicate some kind of danger by the frequency of flashes. (The more flashes, the more danger.) Much of the brain's signaling follows the principle that more frequent action potentials signal a greater intensity of stimulus.

You could also convey information by a rhythm.

Flash-flash . . .   [long pause] . . .   flash-flash

might mean something different from

Flash . . . [pause] . . . flash . . . [pause] . . . flash . . . [pause] . . . flash.

In some cases, the nervous system uses this kind of coding. For example, a taste axon shows one rhythm of responses for sweet tastes and a different rhythm for bitter tastes (Di Lorenzo, Leshchinskiy, Moroney, & Ozdoba, 2009).

The Refractory Period

While the electrical potential across the membrane is returning from its peak toward the resting point, it is still above the threshold. Why doesn't the cell produce another action potential during this period? (If it did, of course, it would go into a permanent repetition of one action potential after another.) Immediately after an action potential, the cell is in a **refractory period** during which it resists the production of further action potentials. In the first part of this period, the **absolute refractory period**, the membrane cannot produce an action potential, regardless of the stimulation. During the second part, the **relative refractory period**, a stronger than usual stimulus is necessary to initiate an action potential. The refractory period has two mechanisms: The sodium channels are closed, and potassium is flowing out of the cell at a faster than usual rate.

In most of the neurons that researchers have tested, the absolute refractory period is about 1 ms and the relative refractory period is another 2–4 ms. (To return to the toilet analogy, there is a short time right after you flush a toilet when you cannot make it flush again—an absolute refractory period. Then follows a period when it is possible but difficult to flush it again—a relative refractory period—before it returns to normal.)

Stop & Check

14. State the all-or-none law.

15. Does the all-or-none law apply to dendrites? Why or why not?

16. Suppose researchers find that axon A can produce up to 1,000 action potentials per second (at least briefly, with maximum stimulation), but axon B can never produce more than 100 per second (regardless of the strength of the stimulus). What could we conclude about the refractory periods of the two axons?

ANSWERS   **14.** According to the all-or-none law, the size and shape of the action potential are independent of the intensity of the stimulus that initiated it. That is, every depolarization beyond the threshold of excitation produces an action potential of about the same amplitude and velocity for a given axon. **15.** The all-or-none law does not apply to dendrites because they do not have action potentials. **16.** Axon A must have a shorter absolute refractory period, about 1 ms, whereas B has a longer absolute refractory period, about 10 ms.

Propagation of the Action Potential

Up to this point, we have considered how the action potential occurs at one point on the axon. Now let us consider how it moves down the axon. Remember, it is important for axons to convey impulses without any loss of strength over distance.

In a motor neuron, an action potential begins on the **axon hillock**, a swelling where the axon exits the soma (Figure 2.5). During the action potential, sodium ions enter a point on the axon. Temporarily, that spot is positively charged in comparison with neighboring areas along the axon. The positive ions flow within the axon to neighboring regions. The positive charges slightly depolarize the next area of the membrane, causing it to reach its threshold and open its voltage-gated sodium channels. Therefore, the membrane regenerates the action potential at that point. In this manner, the action potential travels along the axon, as in Figure 2.17.

The term **propagation of the action potential** describes the transmission of an action potential down an axon. The propagation of an animal species is the production of offspring. In a sense, the action potential gives birth to a new action potential at each point along the axon. As a result, the action potential is just as strong at the end of the axon as it was at the beginning.

Let's reexamine Figure 2.17 for a moment. What is to prevent the electrical charge from flowing in the direction opposite that in which the action potential is traveling? Nothing. In fact, the electrical charge does flow in both directions. Then what prevents an action potential near the center of an axon from reinvading the areas that it has just passed? The answer is that the areas just passed are still in their refractory period.

Let's review the action potential:

- When an area of the axon membrane reaches its threshold of excitation, sodium channels and potassium channels open.
- At first, the opening of potassium channels produces little effect.
- Opening sodium channels lets sodium ions rush into the axon.
- Positive charge flows down the axon and opens voltage-gated sodium channels at the next point.
- At the peak of the action potential, the sodium gates snap shut. They remain closed for the next millisecond or so, despite the depolarization of the membrane.
- Because the membrane is depolarized, voltage-gated potassium channels are open.
- Potassium ions flow out of the axon, returning the membrane toward its original depolarization.
- A few milliseconds later, the voltage-dependent potassium channels close.

All of this may seem like a lot to memorize, but it is not. Everything follows logically from the facts that voltage-gated sodium and potassium channels open when the membrane is depolarized and that sodium channels snap shut at the peak of the action potential.

The Myelin Sheath and Saltatory Conduction

In the thinnest axons, action potentials travel at a velocity of less than 1 m/s. Increasing the diameter brings conduction velocity up to about 10 m/s. At that speed, an impulse along an axon to or from a giraffe's foot takes about half a second. To increase the speed still more, vertebrate axons evolved a

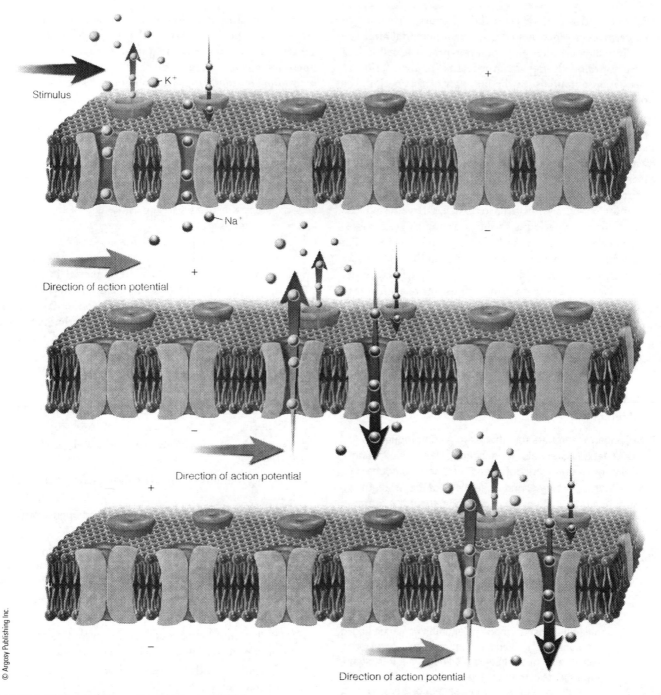

Stimulus

K⁺

Direction of action potential

Na⁺

Direction of action potential

Direction of action potential

© Argosy Publishing Inc.

FIGURE 2.17 Propagation of an action potential
As an action potential occurs at one point on the axon, enough sodium enters to depolarize the next point to its threshold, producing an action potential at that point. In this manner the action potential flows along the axon. Behind each area of sodium entry, potassium ions exit, restoring the resting potential.

special mechanism: sheaths of **myelin,** an insulating material composed of fats and proteins.

Consider the following analogy. Suppose your job is to take written messages over a long distance without using any mechanical device. Taking each message and running with it would be reliable but slow, like the propagation of an action potential along an unmyelinated axon. If you tied each message to a ball and threw it, you could increase the speed, but your throws would not travel far enough. The best solution is to station people at moderate distances along the route and throw the message-bearing ball from person to person until it reaches its destination.

The same principle applies to **myelinated axons,** those covered with a myelin sheath. Myelinated axons, found only in vertebrates, are covered with layers of fats and proteins. The myelin sheath is interrupted periodically by short sections of axon called nodes of Ranvier, each one about 1 micrometer wide, as shown in Figure 2.18. In most cases, the action potential starts at the axon hillock, but in some cases it starts at the first node of Ranvier (Kuba, Ishii, & Ohmari, 2006).

Suppose an action potential starts at the axon hillock and propagates along the axon until it reaches the first myelin segment. The action potential cannot regenerate along the membrane between nodes because sodium channels are virtually absent between nodes (Catterall, 1984). After an action potential occurs at a node, sodium ions enter the axon and diffuse within the axon, pushing a chain of positive ions along the axon to the next node, where they regenerate the action potential (Figure 2.19). This flow of ions is considerably faster than the regeneration of an action potential at each point along the axon. The jumping of action potentials from node to node is referred to as **saltatory conduction**, from the Latin word *saltare*, meaning "to jump." (The same root shows up in the word *somersault*.) In addition to providing rapid conduction of impulses, saltatory conduction conserves energy: Instead of admitting sodium ions at every point along the axon and then having to pump them out via the sodium–potassium pump, a myelinated axon admits sodium only at its nodes.

In multiple sclerosis, the immune system attacks myelin sheaths. An axon that never had a myelin sheath conducts impulses slowly but steadily. An axon that has lost its myelin is not the same. After myelin forms along an axon, the axon loses its sodium channels under the myelin (Waxman & Ritchie,

1985). If the axon later loses its myelin, it still lacks sodium channels in the areas previously covered with myelin, and most action potentials die out between one node and the next. People with multiple sclerosis suffer a variety of impairments, ranging from visual impairments to poor muscle coordination.

Stop & Check

17. In a myelinated axon, how would the action potential be affected if the nodes were much closer together? How might it be affected if the nodes were much farther apart?

ANSWER 17. If the nodes were closer, the action potential would travel more slowly. If they were much farther apart, the action potential would be faster if it could successfully jump from one node to the next. When the distance becomes too great, the current cannot diffuse from one node to the next and still remain above threshold, so the action potentials would stop.

Local Neurons

Axons produce action potentials. However, many small neurons have no axon. Neurons without an axon exchange information with only their closest neighbors. We therefore call them **local neurons**. Because they do not have an axon, they do not follow the all-or-none law. When a local neuron receives information from other neurons, it has a **graded potential**, a

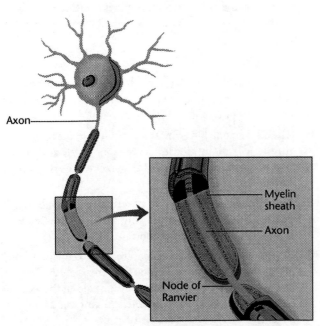

FIGURE 2.18 An axon surrounded by a myelin sheath and interrupted by nodes of Ranvier
The inset shows a cross-section through both the axon and the myelin sheath. Magnification approximately x 30,000. The anatomy is distorted here to show several nodes; in fact, the distance between nodes is generally at least 100 times as long as the nodes themselves. (© Cengage Learning 2013)

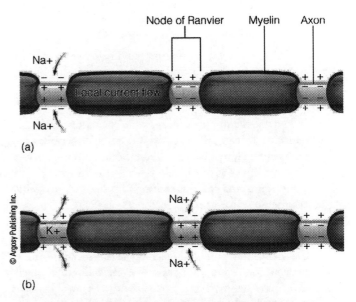

FIGURE 2.19 Saltatory conduction in a myelinated axon
An action potential at the node triggers flow of current to the next node, where the membrane regenerates the action potential. In reality, a myelin sheath is much longer than shown here, relative to the size of the nodes of Ranvier and to the diameter of the axon.

membrane potential that varies in magnitude in proportion to the intensity of the stimulus. The change in membrane potential is conducted to adjacent areas of the cell, in all directions, gradually decaying as it travels. Those various areas of the cell contact other neurons, which they excite or inhibit through synapses (which we consider in the next chapter).

Local neurons are difficult to study because it is almost impossible to insert an electrode into a tiny cell without damaging it. Most of our knowledge, therefore, has come from large neurons, and that bias in our research methods may have led to a misconception. Many years ago, all that neuroscientists knew about local neurons was that they were small. Given their focus on larger neurons, many scientists assumed that the small neurons were immature. As one textbook author put it, "Many of these [neurons] are small and apparently undeveloped, as if they

constituted a reserve stock not yet utilized in the individual's cerebral activity" (Woodworth, 1934, p. 194). In other words, the small cells would contribute to behavior only if they grew.

Perhaps this misunderstanding was the origin of that widespread, nonsensical belief that "they say we use only 10% of our brain." (Who are "they," incidentally?) Other origins have also been suggested for this belief. Regardless of how it started, it has been remarkably persistent, given its total lack of justification. Surely, it can't be true that someone could lose 90% of the brain and still behave normally. Nor is it true that only 10% of neurons are active at any given moment. The belief that we use only a small part of the brain became popular, presumably because people wanted to believe it. Eventually, people were simply quoting one another long after everyone forgot where the idea originated.

MODULE 2.2 ■ IN CLOSING
Neural Messages

In this chapter, we have examined what happens within a single neuron, as if each neuron acted independently. It does not, of course. All of its functions depend on communication with other neurons, which we will consider in the next chapter. We may as well admit from the start, however, that neural communication is amazing. Unlike human communication, in which a speaker sometimes presents a complicated

message to an enormous audience, a neuron delivers only an action potential—a mere on/off message—to only that modest number of other neurons that receive branches of its axon. At various receiving neurons, an "on" message can be converted into either excitation or inhibition (yes or no). From this limited system, all of our behavior and experience emerge.

SUMMARY

1. The action potential transmits information without loss of intensity over distance. The cost is a delay between the stimulus and its arrival in the brain. **37**

2. The inside of a resting neuron has a negative charge with respect to the outside. Sodium ions are actively pumped out of the neuron, and potassium ions are pumped in. **37**

3. When the membrane is at rest, the electrical gradient and concentration gradient act in competing directions for potassium, almost balancing out. Potassium ions have a slow net flow out of the cell. Both gradients tend to push sodium into the cell, but sodium ions do not cross while the membrane is at rest. **39**

4. When the charge across the membrane is reduced, sodium and potassium channels begin to open. When the membrane potential reaches the threshold of the neuron, sodium ions enter explosively, suddenly reducing and reversing the charge across the membrane. This event is known as the action potential. **41**

5. After the peak of the action potential, the membrane returns to its original level of polarization because of the outflow of potassium ions. **41**

6. The all-or-none law: For any stimulus greater than the threshold, the amplitude and velocity of the action potential are independent of the size of the stimulus that initiated it. **42**

7. Immediately after an action potential, the membrane enters a refractory period during which it is resistant to starting another action potential. **42**

8. The action potential is regenerated at successive points along the axon as sodium ions flow through the core of the axon and stimulate the next point along the axon to its threshold. The action potential maintains a constant magnitude as it passes along the axon. **43**

9. In axons that are covered with myelin, action potentials form only in the nodes that separate myelinated segments. Transmission in myelinated axons is faster than in unmyelinated axons. **43**

KEY TERMS

Terms are defined in the module on the page number indicated. They're also presented in alphabetical order with definitions in the book's Subject Index/Glossary, which begins on page 561. Interactive flashcards and crossword puzzles are among the online resources available to help you learn these terms and the concepts they represent.

absolute refractory period 43	hyperpolarization 40	relative refractory period 43
action potential 40	local anesthetic 41	resting potential 37
all-or-none law 42	local neurons 45	saltatory conduction 45
axon hillock 43	myelin 44	selectively permeable 38
concentration gradient 39	myelinated axons 44	sodium–potassium pump 38
depolarize 40	polarization 37	threshold 40
electrical gradient 37	propagation of the action potential 43	voltage-gated channels 41
graded potentials 45	refractory period 43	

THOUGHT QUESTIONS

1. Suppose the threshold of a neuron were the same as its resting potential. What would happen? At what frequency would the cell produce action potentials?

2. In the laboratory, researchers can apply an electrical stimulus at any point along the axon, making action potentials travel in both directions from the point of stimulation. An action potential moving in the usual direction, away from the axon hillock, is said to be traveling in the *orthodromic* direction. An action potential traveling toward the axon hillock is traveling in the *antidromic* direction. If we started an orthodromic action potential at the axon hillock and an antidromic action potential at the opposite end of the axon, what would happen when they met at the center? Why?

3. If a drug partly blocks a membrane's potassium channels, how does it affect the action potential?

CHAPTER 2 Interactive Exploration and Study

The **Psychology CourseMate** for this text brings chapter topics to life with interactive learning, study, and exam preparation tools, including quizzes and flashcards for the Key Concepts that appear throughout each module, as well as an interactive media-rich eBook version of the text that is fully searchable and includes highlighting and note-taking capabilities and interactive versions of the book's **Stop & Check** quizzes and **Try It Yourself Online** activities. The site also features **Virtual Biological Psychology Labs, videos,** and **animations** to help you better understand concepts—log on and learn more at **www.cengagebrain.com**, which is your gateway to all of this text's complimentary and premium resources, including the following:

Virtual Biological Psychology Labs

Explore the experiments that led to modern-day understanding of biopsychology with the Virtual Biological Psychology Labs, featuring a realistic lab environment that allows you to conduct experiments and evaluate data to better understand how scientists came to the conclusions presented in your text. The labs cover a range of topics, including perception, motivation, cognition, and more. You may purchase access at **www.cengagebrain.com**, or login at **login.cengagebrain.com** if an access card was included with your text.

Animations

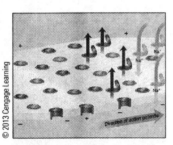

Propogation of the Action Potential

Also available—

- Parts of the Neuron
- Neuron Membrane at Rest
- Saltatory Conduction

Suggestions for Further Exploration

Websites

The Psychology CourseMate for this text provides regularly updated links to relevant online resources for this chapter, such as the **University of Minnesota's MetaNeuron Program.**

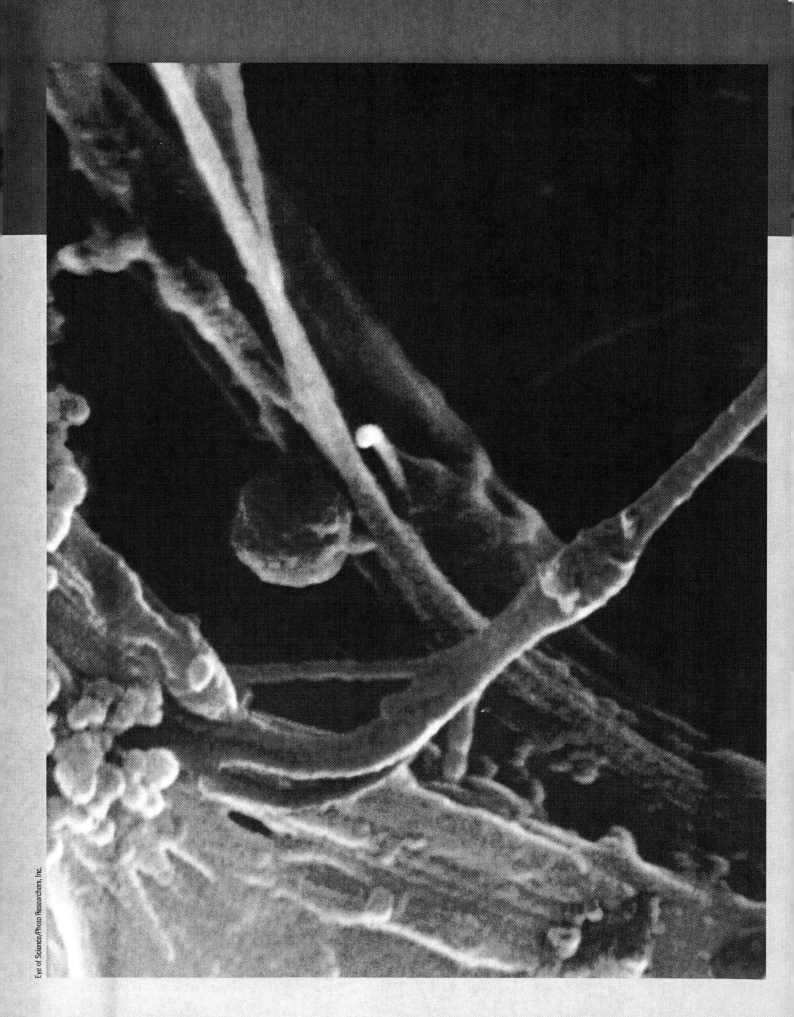

Synapses

3

CHAPTER OUTLINE

MAIN IDEAS

1. At a synapse, a neuron releases chemicals called neurotransmitters that excite or inhibit another cell.

2. In most cases, a single release of neurotransmitter produces only a subthreshold response in the receiving cell. This response summates with other subthreshold responses to determine whether or not the cell produces an action potential.

3. Transmission at synapses goes through many steps, and interference at any of them can alter the outcome.

4. Nearly all drugs that affect behavior or experience do so by acting at synapses.

5. Nearly all abused drugs increase the release of dopamine in certain brain areas.

6. Addiction changes certain brain areas, increasing the tendency to seek the addictive substance and decreasing the response to other kinds of reinforcement.

I f you had to communicate with someone without sight or sound, what would you do? Chances are, your first choice would be a touch code or a system of electrical impulses. You might not even think of passing chemicals back and forth. Chemicals are, however, the main way your neurons communicate. Neurons communicate by transmitting chemicals at specialized junctions called *synapses*.

OPPOSITE: This electron micrograph, with color added artificially, shows that the surface of a neuron is practically covered with synapses, the connections it receives from other neurons.

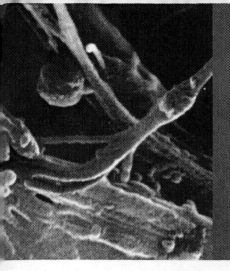

MODULE 3.1

The Concept of the Synapse

I n the late 1800s, Ramón y Cajal anatomically demonstrated a narrow gap separating one neuron from another. In 1906, Charles Scott Sherrington physiologically demonstrated that communication between one neuron and the next differs from communication along a single axon. He inferred a specialized gap between neurons and introduced the term **synapse** to describe it. Cajal and Sherrington are regarded as the great pioneers of modern neuroscience, and their nearly simultaneous discoveries supported each other: If communication between one neuron and another was special in some way, then there could be no doubt that neurons were anatom-ically separate from one another. Sherrington's discovery was an amazing feat of scientific reasoning, as he used behavioral observations to infer the major properties of synapses half a century before researchers had the technology to measure those properties directly.

The Properties of Synapses

Sherrington studied **reflexes**—automatic muscular responses to stimuli. In a leg flexion reflex, a sensory neuron excites a second neuron, which in turn excites a motor neuron, which excites a muscle, as in Figure 3.1. The circuit from sensory neuron to muscle response is called a **reflex arc**. If one neuron is separate from another, as Cajal had demonstrated, a reflex must require communication between neurons, and therefore, measurements of reflexes might reveal some of the special properties of that communication.

Sherrington strapped a dog into a harness above the ground and pinched one of the dog's feet. After a fraction of a second, the dog *flexed* (raised) the pinched leg and *extended* the other legs. Sherrington found the same reflexive movements after he made a cut that disconnected

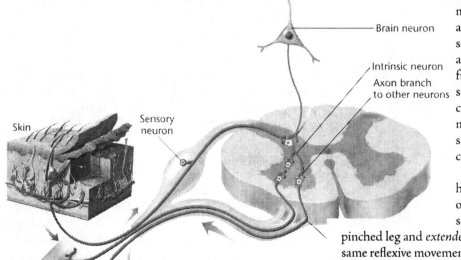

FIGURE 3.1 A reflex arc for leg flexion
Anatomy has been simplified to show the relationship among sensory neuron, intrinsic neuron, and motor neuron. (© Argosy Publishing Inc.)

Charles Scott Sherrington (1857–1952)
A rainbow every morning who would pause to look at? The wonderful which comes often or is plentifully about us is soon taken for granted. That is practical enough. It allows us to get on with life. But it may stultify if it cannot on occasion be thrown off. To recapture now and then childhood's wonder is to secure a driving force for occasional grown-up thoughts. (Sherrington, 1941, p. 104.)

52

the spinal cord from the brain. Evidently, the spinal cord controlled the flexion and extension reflexes. In fact, the movements were more consistent after he separated the spinal cord from the brain. (In an intact animal, messages descending from the brain modify the reflexes, making them stronger at some times and weaker at others.)

Sherrington observed several properties of reflexes suggesting special processes at the junctions between neurons: (a) Reflexes are slower than conduction along an axon. (b) Several weak stimuli presented at slightly different times or locations produce a stronger reflex than a single stimulus does. (c) When one set of muscles becomes excited, a different set becomes relaxed. Let's consider each of these points and their implications.

Speed of a Reflex and Delayed Transmission at the Synapse

When Sherrington pinched a dog's foot, the dog flexed that leg after a short delay. During that delay, an impulse had to travel up an axon from the skin receptor to the spinal cord, and then an impulse had to travel from the spinal cord back down the leg to a muscle. Sherrington measured the total distance that the impulse traveled from skin receptor to spinal cord to muscle and calculated the speed at which the impulse must have traveled to produce the response. He found that the speed of conduction through the reflex arc varied but was never more than about 15 meters per second (m/s). In contrast, previous research had measured action potential velocities along sensory or motor nerves at about 40 m/s. Sherrington concluded that some process was slowing conduction through the reflex, and he inferred that the delay must occur where one neuron communicates with another (Figure 3.2). This idea is critical, as it established the existence of synapses. Sherrington, in fact, introduced the term *synapse*.

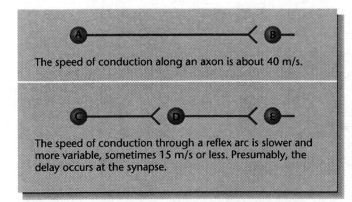

The speed of conduction along an axon is about 40 m/s.

The speed of conduction through a reflex arc is slower and more variable, sometimes 15 m/s or less. Presumably, the delay occurs at the synapse.

FIGURE 3.2 Sherrington's evidence for synaptic delay
An impulse traveling through a synapse in the spinal cord is slower than one traveling a similar distance along an uninterrupted axon. (© Cengage Learning 2013)

Stop & Check

1. What evidence led Sherrington to conclude that transmission at a synapse is different from transmission along an axon?

ANSWER
1. Sherrington found that the velocity of conduction through a reflex arc was significantly slower than the velocity of an action potential along an axon. Therefore, some delay must occur at the junction between one neuron and the next.

Temporal Summation

Sherrington found that repeated stimuli within a brief time have a cumulative effect. He referred to this phenomenon as **temporal summation** (summation over time). A light pinch of the dog's foot did not evoke a reflex, but a few rapidly repeated pinches did. Sherrington surmised that a single pinch did not reach the threshold of excitation for the next neuron. The neuron that delivers transmission is the **presynaptic neuron**. The neuron that receives it is the **postsynaptic neuron**. Sherrington proposed that this subthreshold excitation in the postsynaptic neuron decays over time, but it can combine with a second excitation that follows it quickly. With a rapid succession of pinches, each adds its effect to what remained from the previous ones, until the combination exceeds the threshold of the postsynaptic neuron, producing an action potential.

Decades later, John Eccles (1964) attached microelectrodes to stimulate axons of presynaptic neurons while he recorded from the postsynaptic neuron. For example, after he had briefly stimulated an axon, Eccles recorded a slight depolarization of the membrane of the postsynaptic cell (point 1 in Figure 3.3).

Note that this partial depolarization is a graded potential. Unlike action potentials, which are always depolarizations, graded potentials may be either depolarizations (excitatory) or hyperpolarizations (inhibitory). A graded depolarization is known as an **excitatory postsynaptic potential (EPSP)**. It results from a flow of sodium ions into the neuron. If an EPSP does not cause the cell to reach its threshold, the depolarization decays quickly.

When Eccles stimulated an axon twice, he recorded two EPSPs. If the delay between EPSPs was short enough, the second EPSP added to what was left of the first one (point 2 in Figure 3.3), producing temporal summation. At point 3 in Figure 3.3, a quick sequence of EPSPs combines to exceed the threshold and produce an action potential.

Spatial Summation

Sherrington also found that synapses have the property of **spatial summation**—that is, summation over space. Synaptic inputs from separate locations combine their effects on a neuron. Sherrington again began with a pinch too weak to

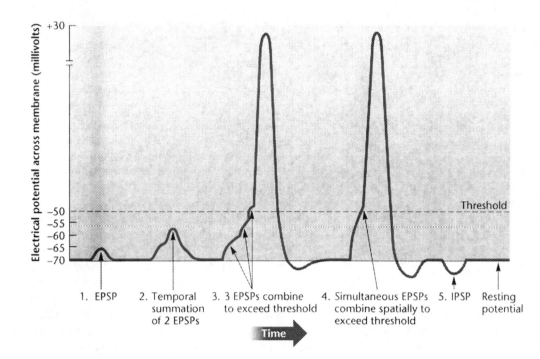

FIGURE 3.3 Recordings from a postsynaptic neuron during synaptic activation *(© Cengage Learning 2013)*

elicit a reflex. This time, instead of pinching one point twice, he pinched two points at once. Although neither pinch alone produced a reflex, together they did. Sherrington concluded that pinching two points activated separate sensory neurons, whose axons converged onto a neuron in the spinal cord. Excitation from either sensory axon excited that spinal neuron, but not enough to reach the threshold. A combination of excitations exceeded the threshold and produced an action potential (point 4 in Figure 3.3). Again, Eccles confirmed Sherrington's inference, demonstrating that EPSPs from several axons summate their effects on a postsynaptic cell (Figure 3.4).

Spatial summation is critical to brain functioning. Sensory input to the brain arrives at synapses that individually produce weak effects. However, each neuron receives many incoming axons that frequently produce synchronized responses (Bruno & Sakmann, 2006). Spatial summation ensures that a sensory stimulus stimulates neurons enough to activate them.

Temporal summation and spatial summation ordinarily occur together. That is, a neuron might receive input from several axons at approximately, but not exactly, the same time. Integrating these inputs provides complexity. As Figure 3.5

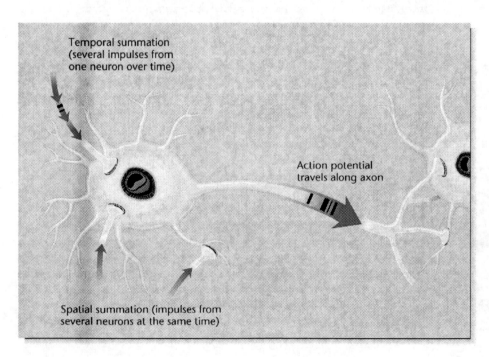

FIGURE 3.4 Temporal and spatial summation *(© Cengage Learning 2013)*

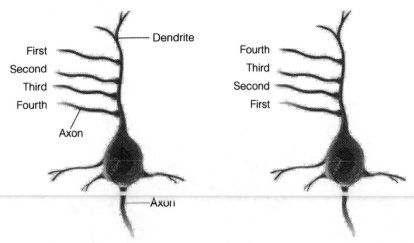

First
Second
Third
Fourth

Dendrite

Axon

Fourth
Third
Second
First

Axon

Summation in this direction
produces greater depolarization.

Summation in this direction
produces less depolarization.

FIGURE 3.5 Summation effects can depend on the order of stimuli. *(© Argosy Publishing Inc.)*

shows, a series of axons active in one order can have a different result from the same axons in a different order. For example, a neuron in the visual system could respond to light moving in one direction and not another (Branco, Clark, & Häusser, 2010).

Stop & Check

2. What is the difference between temporal summation and spatial summation?

ANSWER

2. Temporal summation is the combined effect of quickly repeated stimulation at a single synapse. Spatial summation is the combined effect of several nearly simultaneous stimulations at several synapses onto one neuron.

Inhibitory Synapses

When Sherrington vigorously pinched a dog's foot, the flexor muscles of that leg contracted, and so did the extensor muscles of the other three legs (Figure 3.6). Also, the dog relaxed the extensor muscles of the stimulated leg and the flexor muscles of the other legs. Sherrington's explanation assumed certain connections in the spinal cord: A pinch on the foot sends a message along a sensory neuron to an *interneuron* (an intermediate neuron) in the spinal cord, which in turn excites the motor neurons connected to the flexor muscles of that leg (Figure 3.7). Sherrington surmised that the interneuron also sends a message to block activity of motor neurons to the extensor muscles in the same leg and the flexor muscles of the three other legs.

Later researchers physiologically demonstrated the inhibitory synapses that Sherrington had inferred. At these synapses, input from an axon hyperpolarizes the postsynap-

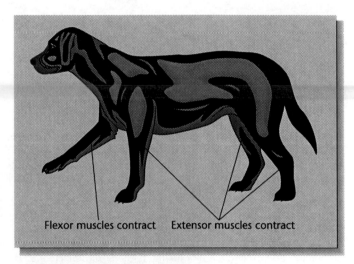

Flexor muscles contract   Extensor muscles contract

FIGURE 3.6 Antagonistic muscles
Flexor muscles draw an extremity toward the trunk of the body, whereas extensor muscles move an extremity away from the body. *(© Cengage Learning 2013)*

tic cell. That is, it increases the negative charge within the cell, moving it further from the threshold and decreasing the probability of an action potential (point 5 in Figure 3.3). This temporary hyperpolarization of a membrane—called an **inhibitory postsynaptic potential,** or **IPSP**—resembles an EPSP. An IPSP occurs when synaptic input selectively opens the gates for potassium ions to leave the cell (carrying a positive charge with them) or for chloride ions to enter the cell (carrying a negative charge).

Today, we take for granted the concept of inhibition, but at Sherrington's time, the idea was controversial, as no one could imagine a mechanism to accomplish it. Establishing the idea of inhibition was critical not just for neuroscience but for psychology as well.

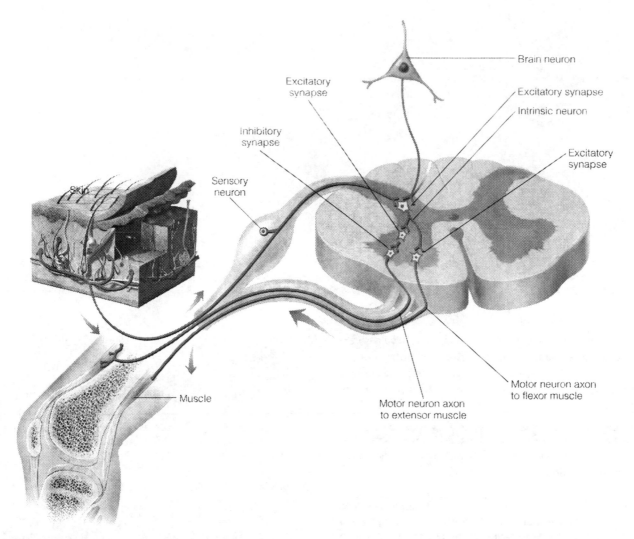

FIGURE 3.7 Sherrington's inference of inhibitory synapses
When a flexor muscle is excited, the probability of excitation decreases in the paired extensor muscle. Sherrington inferred that the interneuron that excited a motor neuron to the flexor muscle also inhibited a motor neuron connected to the extensor muscle. (© Argosy Publishing Inc.)

Stop & Check

3. What was Sherrington's evidence for inhibition in the nervous system?

4. What ion gates in the membrane open during an EPSP? What gates open during an IPSP?

5. Can an inhibitory message flow along an axon?

ANSWERS

[rotated answers text]
3. Sherrington found that a reflex that stimulates a flexor muscle prevents contraction of the extensor muscles of the same limb. He therefore inferred that an axon sending an excitatory message for the flexor muscle also sent an inhibitory message for the extensor muscle. **4.** During an EPSP sodium gates open. During an IPSP potassium or chloride gates open. **5.** No. Only action potentials propagate along an axon. Inhibitory messages—IPSPs—decay over time and distance.

Relationship Among EPSP, IPSP, and Action Potentials

Sherrington's work opened the way to exploring the wiring diagram of the nervous system. Consider the neurons shown in Figure 3.8. When neuron 1 excites neuron 3, it also excites neuron 2, which inhibits neuron 3. The excitatory message reaches neuron 3 faster because it goes through just one synapse instead of two. The result is brief excitation (EPSP) in neuron 3, which stops quickly. You see how the inhibitory neurons, which are typically very small, can regulate the timing of activity.

The nervous system is full of complex patterns of connections, which produce an unending variety of responses. To see how the synaptic wiring diagram controls responses, consider Figures 3.9 through 3.11. In Figure 3.9, either the axon from cell A or the axon from cell B stimulates cell X enough to reach its threshold. Therefore cell X responds to

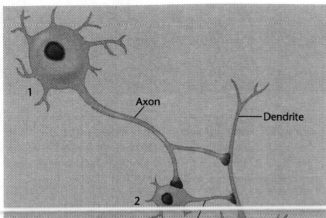
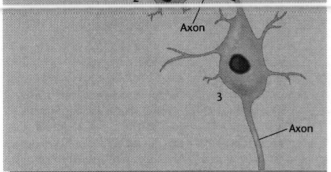

FIGURE 3.8 One of many possible wiring diagrams for synapses
Excitatory synapses are in green, and inhibitory synapses in red. In the circuit shown here, excitation would reach the dendrite before inhibition. (Remember, any transmission through a synapse produces a delay.) Therefore, the result would be brief excitation of the dendrite and then a stop. Inhibitory synapses serve many other functions, too. *(Based on Kullmann & Lamsa, 2007)*

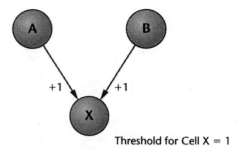

FIGURE 3.9 Wiring diagram for an "A or B" response
The axon from either A or B stimulates cell X enough to reach its threshold. *(© Cengage Learning 2013)*

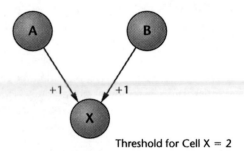

FIGURE 3.10 Wiring diagram for an "A and B" response
The axons from A and B stimulate cell X but neither one by itself reaches the threshold for X. The combination of both at the same time reaches the threshold. *(© Cengage Learning 2013)*

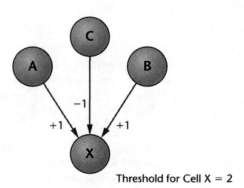

FIGURE 3.11 Wiring diagram for an "A and B if not C" response
The axons from A and B can combine to reach the threshold for X, but the axon from C can inhibit X enough to prevent a response. *(© Cengage Learning 2013)*

"A or B." In Figure 3.10, neither A nor B stimulates cell X enough to reach its threshold, but the two can summate to reach the threshold. (Remember spatial summation.) Therefore in this case cell X responds to "A and B." In Figure 3.11, cell X responds to "A and B if not C." With a little imagination, you can construct other possibilities. In reality, the possibilities are vast. Sherrington assumed—as did many people who have proposed mathematical models of the nervous system since then—that synapses simply produce on and off responses. In fact, synapses vary enormously in their duration of effects. Furthermore, many inputs interact in ways that are not quite additive. The effect of two synapses at the same time can be more than double the effect of either one, or less than double (Silver, 2010).

Most neurons have a **spontaneous firing rate**, a periodic production of action potentials even without synaptic input. In such cases, the EPSPs increase the frequency of action potentials above the spontaneous rate, whereas IPSPs decrease it. For example, if the neuron's spontaneous firing rate is 10 action potentials per second, a stream of EPSPs might increase the rate to 15 or more, whereas a preponderance of IPSPs might decrease it to 5 or fewer.

The Neuron as Decision Maker

Synapses are where the action is. Transmission along an axon merely sends information from one place to another. Synapses determine whether to send the message. The EPSPs and IPSPs reaching a neuron at a given moment compete with one another, and the net result is a complicated, not exactly algebraic summation of their effects. We could regard the summation of EPSPs and IPSPs as a "decision" because it determines whether or not the postsynaptic cell fires an action potential. However, do not imagine that any single neuron decides what to eat for breakfast. Complex behaviors depend on the contributions from a huge network of neurons.

SUMMARY

1. The synapse is the point of communication between two neurons. Charles S. Sherrington's observations of reflexes enabled him to infer the properties of synapses.   **52**

2. Because transmission through a reflex arc is slower than transmission through an equivalent length of axon, Sherrington concluded that some process at the synapses delays transmission.   **53**

3. Graded potentials (EPSPs and IPSPs) summate their effects. The summation of graded potentials from stimuli at different times is temporal summation. The summation of graded potentials from different locations is spatial summation.   **53**

4. Inhibition is more than just the absence of excitation; it is an active "brake" that suppresses excitation. Within the nervous system, inhibition is just as important as excitation. Stimulation at a synapse produces a brief graded potential in the postsynaptic cell. An excitatory graded potential (depolarizing) is an EPSP. An inhibitory graded potential (hyperpolarizing) is an IPSP. An EPSP occurs when gates open to allow sodium to enter the neuron's membrane. An IPSP occurs when gates open to allow potassium to leave or chloride to enter.   **55**

5. The EPSPs on a neuron compete with the IPSPs; the balance between the two increases or decreases the neuron's frequency of action potentials.   **56**

KEY TERMS

Terms are defined in the module on the page number indicated. They're also presented in alphabetical order with definitions in the book's Subject Index/Glossary, which begins on page 561. Interactive flashcards and crossword puzzles are among the online resources available to help you learn these terms and the concepts they represent.

excitatory postsynaptic potential (EPSP)   53   reflex arc   52   synapse   52
inhibitory postsynaptic potential (IPSP)   55   reflexes   52   temporal summation   53
postsynaptic neuron   53   spatial summation   53
presynaptic neuron   55   spontaneous firing rate   57

THOUGHT QUESTIONS

1. When Sherrington measured the reaction time of a reflex (i.e., the delay between stimulus and response), he found that the response occurred faster after a strong stimulus than after a weak one. Can you explain this finding? Remember that all action potentials—whether produced by strong or weak stimuli—travel at the same speed along a given axon.

2. A pinch on an animal's right hind foot excites a sensory neuron that excites an interneuron that excites the motor neurons to the flexor muscles of that leg. The interneuron also inhibits the motor neurons connected to the extensor muscles of the leg. In addition, this interneuron sends impulses that reach the motor neuron connected to the extensor muscles of the left hind leg. Would you expect the interneuron to excite or inhibit that motor neuron? (Hint: The connections are adaptive. When an animal lifts one leg, it must put additional weight on the other legs to maintain balance.)

3. Suppose neuron X has a synapse onto neuron Y, which has a synapse onto Z. Presume that no other neurons or synapses are present. An experimenter finds that stimulating neuron X causes an action potential in neuron Z after a short delay. However, she determines that the synapse of X onto Y is inhibitory. Explain how the stimulation of X might produce excitation of Z.

4. Figure 3.11 shows synaptic connections to produce a cell that responds to "A and B if not C." Construct a wiring diagram so that a cell responds to "A or B if not C." This is much trickier than it sounds. If you simply shift the threshold of cell X to 1, it will respond to "A if not C, or B if not C, or A and B even if C." Can you get X to respond to either A or B, but only if C is inactive? (Hint: You might need to introduce one or two additional cells on the way to X.)

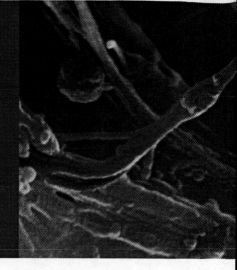

Chemical Events at the Synapse

Although Charles Sherrington accurately inferred many properties of the synapse, he was wrong about one important point: Although he knew that synaptic transmission was slower than transmission along an axon, he thought it was still too fast to depend on a chemical process and therefore concluded that it must be electrical. We now know that the great majority of synapses rely on chemical processes, which are much faster and more versatile than Sherrington or anyone else of his era would have guessed. Over the years, our concept of activity at synapses has grown in many ways.

The Discovery of Chemical Transmission at Synapses

A set of nerves called the sympathetic nervous system accelerates the heartbeat, relaxes the stomach muscles, dilates the pupils of the eyes, and regulates other organs. T. R. Elliott, a young British scientist, reported in 1905 that applying the hormone *adrenaline* directly to the surface of the heart, the stomach, and the pupils produces the same effects as those of the sympathetic nervous system. Elliott therefore suggested that the sympathetic nerves stimulate muscles by releasing adrenaline or a similar chemical.

However, Elliott's evidence was not convincing. Perhaps adrenaline merely mimicked effects that are ordinarily electrical in nature. At the time, Sherrington's prestige was so great that most scientists ignored Elliott's results and continued to assume that synapses transmitted electrical impulses. Otto Loewi, a German physiologist, liked the idea of chemical synapses but did not see how to demonstrate it more decisively. Then in 1920, he awakened one night with an idea. He wrote himself a note and went back to sleep. Unfortunately, the next morning he could not read his note. The following night he awoke at 3 A.M. with the same idea, rushed to the laboratory, and performed the experiment.

Loewi repeatedly stimulated a frog's vagus nerve, thereby decreasing the heart rate. He then collected fluid from that heart, transferred it to a second frog's heart, and found that the second heart also decreased its rate of beating, as shown in Figure 3.12. Then Loewi stimulated the accelerator nerve to the first frog's heart, increasing the heart rate. When he collected fluid from that heart and transferred it to the second frog's heart, its heart rate increased. That is, stimulating one nerve released something that inhibited heart rate, and stimulating a different nerve released something that increased heart rate. He knew he was collecting and transferring chemicals, not loose electricity. Therefore, Loewi concluded, nerves send messages by releasing chemicals.

Loewi later remarked that if he had thought of this experiment in the light of day, he probably would not have tried it (Loewi, 1960). Even if synapses did release chemicals, his daytime reasoning went, they probably did not release much. Fortunately, by the time he realized that the experiment should not work, he had already completed it, and it did work. It earned him a Nobel Prize.

Despite Loewi's work, most researchers over the next three decades continued to believe that most synapses were electrical and that chemical synapses were the exception. Finally, in the 1950s, researchers established that chemical transmission predominates throughout the nervous system. That discovery revolutionized our understanding and led to research developing drugs for psychiatric uses (Carlsson, 2001). (A small number of electrical synapses do exist, however, as discussed at the end of this module.)

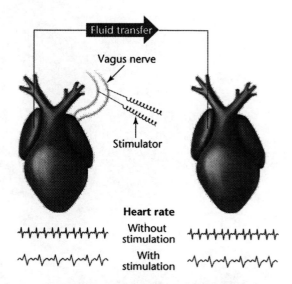

FIGURE 3.12 Loewi's experiment demonstrating that nerves send messages by releasing chemicals
Loewi stimulated the vagus nerve to one frog's heart, decreasing the heartbeat. When he transferred fluid from that heart to another frog's heart, he observed a decrease in its heartbeat. Why does he insist on doing this to me. (© Cengage Learning 2013)

Stop & Check

6. What was Loewi's evidence that neurotransmission depends on the release of chemicals?

ANSWER

6. When Loewi stimulated a nerve that increased or decreased a frog's heart rate, he could withdraw some fluid from the area around the heart, transfer it to another frog's heart, and thereby increase or decrease its rate also.

The Sequence of Chemical Events at a Synapse

Understanding the chemical events at a synapse is fundamental to understanding the nervous system. Every year, researchers discover more and more details about synapses, their structure, and how those structures relate to function. Here are the major events:

1. The neuron synthesizes chemicals that serve as neurotransmitters. It synthesizes the smaller neurotransmitters in the axon terminals and synthesizes neuropeptides in the cell body.

2. Action potentials travel down the axon. At the presynaptic terminal, an action potential enables calcium to enter the cell. Calcium releases neurotransmitters from the terminals and into the *synaptic cleft*, the space between the presynaptic and postsynaptic neurons.

3. The released molecules diffuse across the cleft, attach to receptors, and alter the activity of the postsynaptic neuron.

4. The neurotransmitter molecules separate from their receptors.

5. The neurotransmitter molecules may be taken back into the presynaptic neuron for recycling or they may diffuse away.

6. Some postsynaptic cells send reverse messages to control the further release of neurotransmitter by presynaptic cells.

Figure 3.13 summarizes these steps. Let's now consider each step in more detail.

Types of Neurotransmitters

At a synapse, a neuron releases chemicals that affect another neuron. Those chemicals are known as **neurotransmitters**. A hundred or so chemicals are believed or suspected to be neurotransmitters, as shown in Table 3.1 (Borodinsky et al., 2004). Here are the major categories:

amino acids acids containing an amine group (NH_2)

monoamines chemicals formed by a change in certain amino acids

acetylcholine (a one-member "family") a chemical similar to an amino acid, except that it includes an $N(CH_3)_3$ group instead of an NH_2

neuropeptides chains of amino acids

purines a category of chemicals including adenosine and several of its derivatives

gases nitric oxide and possibly others

The oddest transmitter is **nitric oxide** (chemical formula NO), a gas released by many small local neurons. (Do not confuse nitric oxide, NO, with nitrous oxide, N_2O, sometimes known as "laughing gas.") Nitric oxide is poisonous in large quantities and difficult to make in a laboratory. Yet, many neurons contain an enzyme that enables them to make it efficiently. One special function of nitric oxide relates to blood flow: When a brain area becomes highly active, blood flow to that area increases. How does the blood "know" which brain area has become more active? The message comes from nitric oxide. Many

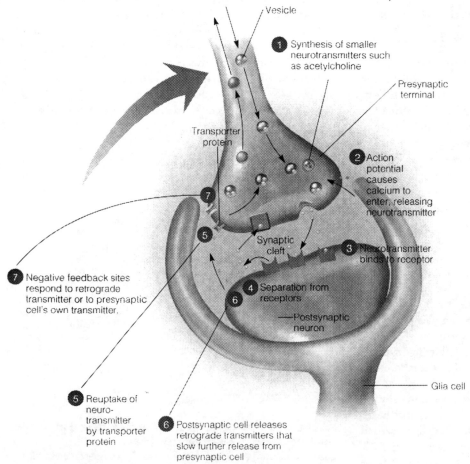

Vesicle

1 Synthesis of smaller neurotransmitters such as acetylcholine

Presynaptic terminal

Transporter protein

2 Action potential causes calcium to enter, releasing neurotransmitter

Synaptic cleft

3 Neurotransmitter binds to receptor

4 Separation from receptors

Postsynaptic neuron

7 Negative feedback sites respond to retrograde transmitter or to presynaptic cell's own transmitter.

5 Reuptake of neurotransmitter by transporter protein

6 Postsynaptic cell releases retrograde transmitters that slow further release from presynaptic cell

Glia cell

FIGURE 3.13 Some major events in transmission at a synapse (© Argosy Publishing Inc.)

TABLE 3.1	Neurotransmitters
Amino Acids	glutamate, GABA, glycine, aspartate, maybe others
A Modified Amino Acid	acetylcholine
Monoamines (also modified from amino acids)	indoleamines: serotonin catecholamines: dopamine, norepinephrine, epinephrine
Neuropeptides (chains of amino acids)	endorphins, substance P, neuropeptide Y, many others
Purines	ATP, adenosine, maybe others
Gases	NO (nitric oxide), maybe others

© Cengage Learning 2013

neurons release nitric oxide when they are stimulated. In addition to influencing other neurons, nitric oxide dilates the nearby blood vessels, thereby increasing blood flow to that brain area (Dawson, Gonzalez-Zulueta, Kusel, & Dawson, 1998).

Stop & Check

7. What does a highly active brain area do to increase its blood supply?

ANSWER 7. In a highly active brain area, many stimulated neurons release nitric oxide, which dilates the blood vessels in the area and thereby increases blood flow to the area.

Synthesis of Transmitters

Neurons synthesize nearly all neurotransmitters from amino acids, which the body obtains from proteins in the diet. Figure

3.14 illustrates the chemical steps in the synthesis of acetylcholine, serotonin, dopamine, epinephrine, and norepinephrine. Note the relationship among epinephrine, norepinephrine, and dopamine—compounds known as **catecholamines**, because they contain a catechol group and an amine group, as shown here:

© Cengage Learning 2013

Each pathway in Figure 3.14 begins with substances found in the diet. Acetylcholine, for example, is synthesized from choline, which is abundant in milk, eggs, and peanuts. The amino acids phenylalanine and tyrosine, present in proteins, are precursors of dopamine, norepinephrine, and epinephrine. Remember from Chapter 2 that people with phenylketonuria lack the enzyme that converts phenylalanine to tyrosine. They can get tyrosine from their diet, but they need to minimize intake of phenylalanine.

The amino acid *tryptophan*, the precursor to serotonin, crosses the blood–brain barrier by a special transport system that it shares with other large amino acids. The amount of tryptophan in the diet controls the amount of serotonin in the brain (Fadda, 2000), so your serotonin levels rise after you eat foods

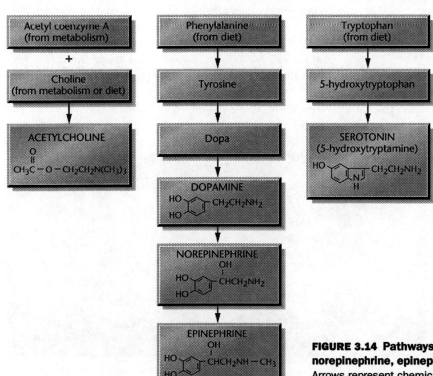

FIGURE 3.14 Pathways in the synthesis of acetylcholine, dopamine, norepinephrine, epinephrine, and serotonin Arrows represent chemical reactions. (© Cengage Learning 2013)

richer in tryptophan, such as soy, and fall after something low in tryptophan, such as maize (American corn). However, tryptophan has to compete with other, more abundant large amino acids, such as phenylalanine, that share the same transport system. One way to increase tryptophan entry to the brain is to decrease consumption of phenylalanine. Another is to eat carbohydrates. Carbohydrates increase the release of the hormone *insulin*, which takes several competing amino acids out of the bloodstream and into body cells, thus decreasing the competition against tryptophan (Wurtman, 1985).

➤ **Stop & Check**

8. Name the three catecholamine neurotransmitters.

ANSWER **8.** Epinephrine, norepinephrine, and dopamine

Storage of Transmitters

Most neurotransmitters are synthesized in the presynaptic terminal, near the point of release. The presynaptic terminal stores high concentrations of neurotransmitter molecules in **vesicles**, tiny nearly spherical packets (Figure 3.15). (Nitric oxide is an exception to this rule. Neurons release nitric oxide as soon as they form it instead of storing it.) The presynaptic terminal also maintains many neurotransmitter molecules outside the vesicles.

It is possible for a neuron to accumulate excess levels of a neurotransmitter. Neurons that release serotonin, dopamine, or norepinephrine contain an enzyme, **MAO (monoamine oxidase)**, that breaks down these transmitters into inactive chemicals. We shall return to MAO in the discussion on depression, because several antidepressant drugs inhibit MAO.

Release and Diffusion of Transmitters

At the end of an axon, the action potential itself does not release the neurotransmitter. Rather, the depolarization opens voltage-dependent calcium gates in the presynaptic terminal. Within 1 or 2 milliseconds (ms) after calcium enters the presynaptic terminal, it causes **exocytosis**—release of neurotransmitter in bursts from the presynaptic neuron into the synaptic cleft that separates one neuron from another. An action potential often fails to release any transmitter, and even when it does, the amount varies (Craig & Boudin, 2001).

After its release from the presynaptic cell, the neurotransmitter diffuses across the synaptic cleft to the postsynaptic membrane, where it attaches to a receptor. The neurotransmitter takes no more than 0.01 ms to diffuse across the cleft, which is only 20 to 30 nanometers (nm) wide. Remember, Sherrington did not believe chemical processes could be fast enough to account for the activity at synapses. He did not imagine such a narrow gap through which chemicals could diffuse so quickly.

Although the brain as a whole uses many neurotransmitters, no single neuron releases them all. For many years, investigators believed that each neuron released just one neurotransmitter, but later researchers found that many, perhaps most, neurons release a combination of two or more transmitters (Hökfelt, Johansson, & Goldstein, 1984). Still later researchers found that at least one kind of neuron releases different transmitters from different branches of its axon: Motor neurons in the spinal cord have one branch to the muscles, where they release acetylcholine, and another branch to other spinal cord neurons, where they release both acetylcholine and glutamate (Nishimaru, Restrepo, Ryge, Yanagawa, & Kiehn, 2005). If one kind of neuron can release different transmitters at different branches, maybe others can, too.

Why does a neuron release a combination of transmitters instead of just one? The combination makes the neuron's message more complex, such as brief excitation followed by slight but prolonged inhibition (P. Jonas, Bischofberger, & Sandkühler, 1998).

Although a neuron releases only a limited number of neurotransmitters, it may receive and respond to many neurotransmitters at different synapses. For example, at various locations on its membrane, it might have receptors for glutamate, serotonin, acetylcholine, and others.

FIGURE 3.15 Anatomy of a synapse
(a) An electron micrograph showing a synapse from the cerebellum of a mouse. The small round structures are vesicles. (b) Electron micrograph showing axon terminals onto the soma of a neuron.

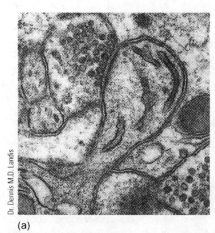
(a)

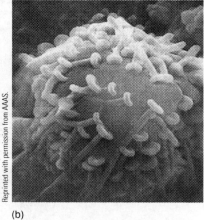
(b)

9. When the action potential reaches the presynaptic terminal, which ion must enter the presynaptic terminal to evoke release of the neurotransmitter?

ANSWER   9. Calcium

Activating Receptors of the Postsynaptic Cell

Sherrington's concept of the synapse was simple: Input produced excitation or inhibition—in other words, on/off. When Eccles recorded from individual cells, he happened to choose cells that produced only brief EPSPs and IPSPs—again, just on/off. The discovery of chemical transmission at synapses didn't change that, at first. Researchers discovered more and more neurotransmitters and wondered, "Why does the nervous system use so many chemicals, if they all produce the same type of message?" Eventually they found that the messages are more complicated and more varied.

The effect of a neurotransmitter depends on its receptor on the postsynaptic cell. When the neurotransmitter attaches to its receptor, the receptor may open a channel—exerting an *ionotropic* effect—or it may produce a slower but longer effect—a *metabotropic* effect.

Ionotropic Effects

At one type of receptor, neurotransmitters exert **ionotropic** effects, corresponding to the brief on/off effects that Sherrington and Eccles studied. Imagine a paper bag that is twisted shut at the top. If you untwist it, the opening grows larger so that something can go into or come out of the bag. An ionotropic receptor is like that. When the neurotransmitter binds to an ionotropic receptor, it twists the receptor enough to open its central channel, which is shaped to let a particular type of ion pass through. In contrast to the sodium and potassium channels along an axon, which are voltage-gated, the channels controlled by a neurotransmitter are **transmitter-gated** or **ligand-gated channels**. (A *ligand* is a chemical that binds to another chemical.) That is, when the neurotransmitter attaches, it opens a channel.

Ionotropic effects begin quickly, sometimes within less than a millisecond after the transmitter attaches (Lisman, Raghavachari, & Tsien, 2007). The effects decay with a half-life of about 5 ms. They are well suited to conveying visual information, auditory information, and anything else that needs to be updated as quickly as possible.

Most of the brain's excitatory ionotropic synapses use the neurotransmitter *glutamate*. In fact, glutamate is the most abundant neurotransmitter

in the nervous system. Most of the inhibitory ionotropic synapses use the neurotransmitter GABA (gamma-amino-butyric acid), which opens chloride gates, enabling chloride ions, with their negative charge, to cross the membrane into the cell more rapidly than usual. Glycine is another common inhibitory transmitter, found mostly in the spinal cord (Moss & Smart, 2001). Acetylcholine, another transmitter at many ionotropic synapses, is excitatory in most cases. Figure 3.16a shows an acetylcholine receptor (hugely magnified, of course), as it would appear if you were looking down at it from within the synaptic cleft. Its outer portion (red) is embedded in the neuron's membrane; its inner portion (purple) surrounds the sodium channel. When the receptor is at rest, the inner portion coils together tightly enough to block sodium passage. When acetylcholine attaches as in Figure 3.16b, the receptor folds outward, widening the sodium channel (Miyazawa, Fujiyoshi, & Unwin, 2003).

Metabotropic Effects and Second Messenger Systems

At other receptors, neurotransmitters exert **metabotropic** effects by initiating a sequence of metabolic reactions that are slower and longer lasting than ionotropic effects (Greengard, 2001). Metabotropic effects emerge 30 ms or more after the release of the transmitter (North, 1989). Typically, they last

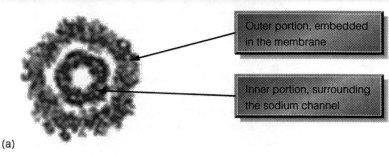

(a)

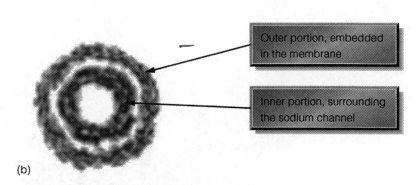

(b)

FIGURE 3.16 The acetylcholine receptor
(a) A cross-section of the receptor at rest, as viewed from the synaptic cleft. The membrane surrounds it. (b) A similar view after acetylcholine has attached to the side of the receptor, opening the central channel wide enough for sodium to pass through. *(Source: From A. Miyazawa, Y. Fujiyoshi, and N. Unwin. "Structure and gating mechanism of the acetylcholine receptor pore," Nature, 423, pp. 949–955)* (© Argosy Publishing Inc.)

up to a few seconds, but sometimes longer. Whereas most ionotropic effects depend on either glutamate or GABA, metabotropic synapses use many neurotransmitters, including dopamine, norepinephrine, and serotonin. . . and sometimes glutamate and GABA too.

Apologies if you find this analogy silly, but it might help clarify metabotropic synapses: Imagine a large room. You are outside the room holding a stick that goes through a hole in the wall and attaches to the hinge of a cage. If you shake the stick, you open that cage and release an angry dog. The dog runs around waking up all the rabbits in the room, which then scurry around causing all kinds of further action. A metabotropic receptor acts a little like that. When a neurotransmitter attaches to a metabotropic receptor, it bends the receptor protein that goes through the membrane of the cell. The other side of that receptor is attached to a **G protein**—that is, a protein coupled to guanosine triphosphate (GTP), an energy-storing molecule. Bending the receptor protein detaches that G protein, which is then free to take its energy elsewhere in the cell, as shown in Figure 3.17 (Levitzki, 1988; O'Dowd, Lefkowitz, & Caron, 1989). The result of that G protein is increased concentration of a second messenger, such as cyclic adenosine monophosphate (cyclic AMP), inside the cell. Just as the "first messenger" (the neurotransmitter) carries information to the postsynaptic cell, the **second messenger** communicates to many areas within the cell. It may open or close ion channels in the membrane or activate a portion of a chromosome. Note the contrast: An ionotropic synapse has effects localized to one point on the membrane, whereas a metabotropic synapse, by way of its second messenger, influences activity in much or all of the cell and over a longer time.

Ionotropic and metabotropic synapses contribute to different aspects of behavior. For vision and hearing, the brain needs rapid, quickly changing information, the kind that ionotropic synapses bring. In contrast, metabotropic synapses are better suited for more enduring effects such as taste (Huang et al.,

2005), smell, and pain (Levine, Fields, & Basbaum, 1993), where the exact timing isn't important anyway. Metabotropic synapses are also important for many aspects of arousal, attention, pleasure, and emotion—again, functions that arise more slowly and last longer than a visual or auditory stimulus.

The brain has a great variety of metabotropic receptors. Even for just serotonin, the brain has at least seven families of receptors, and some of those families include several kinds of receptors. Receptors differ in their chemical properties, responses to drugs, and roles in behavior. Because of this variation in properties, it is possible to devise drugs with specialized effects on behavior. For example, the serotonin receptor type 3 mediates nausea, and the drug *ondansetron* that blocks this receptor helps cancer patients undergo treatment without nausea.

Neuropeptides

Researchers often refer to neuropeptides as **neuromodulators,** because they have several properties that set them apart from other transmitters (Ludwig & Leng, 2006). Whereas the neuron synthesizes most other neurotransmitters in the presynaptic terminal, it synthesizes neuropeptides in the cell body and then slowly transports them to other parts of the cell. Whereas other neurotransmitters are released at the axon terminal, neuropeptides are released mainly by dendrites, and also by the cell body and the sides of the axon. Whereas a single action potential can release other neurotransmitters, neuropeptide release requires repeated stimulation. However, after a few dendrites release a neuropeptide, the released chemical primes other nearby dendrites to release the same neuropeptide also, including dendrites of other cells. That is, neurons containing neuropeptides do not release them often, but when they do, they release substantial amounts. Furthermore, unlike other transmitters that are released immediately adjacent to their receptors, neuropeptides diffuse widely, affecting many neurons in their region of the brain. In that way they resemble hormones. Because many of them exert their effects by altering gene activity, their effects are

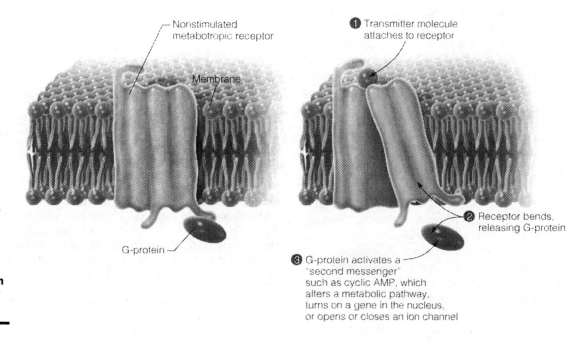

FIGURE 3.17
Sequence of events at a metabotropic synapse, using a second messenger within the postsynaptic neuron
(© Argosy Publishing Inc.)

— Nonstimulated metabotropic receptor

Membrane

G-protein

❶ Transmitter molecule attaches to receptor

❷ Receptor bends, releasing G-protein

❸ G-protein activates a "second messenger" such as cyclic AMP, which alters a metabolic pathway, turns on a gene in the nucleus, or opens or closes an ion channel

TABLE 3.2	Distinctive Features of Neuropeptides	
	Neuropeptides	**Other Neurotransmitters**
Place synthesized	Cell body	Presynaptic terminal
Place released	Mostly from dendrites, also cell body and sides of axon	Axon terminal
Released by	Repeated depolarization	Single action potential
Effect on neighboring cells	They release the neuropeptide too	No effect on neighbors
Spread of effects	Diffuse to wide area	Effect mostly on receptors of the adjacent postsynaptic cell
Duration of effects	Many minutes	Generally less than a second to a few seconds

© Cengage Learning 2013

long-lasting, in the range of 20 minutes or more. Neuropeptides are important for hunger, thirst, intense pain, and other long-term changes in behavior and experience. Table 3.2 summarizes differences between other neurotransmitters and neuropeptides.

For almost any rule about the nervous system, one can find exceptions. One general rule is that a neuron delivers neuropeptides that diffuse to receptors throughout a wide area, but it delivers other transmitters only in small amounts directly adjacent to their receptors. Here is an exception: A **neurogliaform cell**—a kind of neuron that is shaped more like a glia cell—releases huge amounts of GABA all at once, forming a "cloud" that spreads to a large number of neurons in the area, producing widespread inhibition (Oláh et al., 2009).

Stop & Check

10. How do ionotropic and metabotropic synapses differ in speed and duration of effects?

11. What are second messengers, and which type of synapse relies on them?

12. How are neuropeptides special compared to other transmitters?

ANSWERS **10.** Ionotropic synapses act more quickly and more briefly. **11.** At metabotropic synapses, the neurotransmitter attaches to its receptor and thereby releases a chemical (the second messenger) within the postsynaptic cell, which alters metabolism or gene expression of the cell. **12.** Neuropeptides are released only after prolonged stimulation, but when they are released, they are released in large amounts by all parts of the neuron, not just the axon terminal. Neuropeptides diffuse widely, producing long-lasting effects on many neurons.

Hormones

A **hormone** is a chemical that is secreted by cells in one part of the body and conveyed by the blood to influence other cells. A neurotransmitter is like a telephone signal: It

conveys a message from the sender to the intended receiver. Hormones function more like a radio station: They convey a message to any receiver tuned in to the right station. Neuropeptides are intermediate. They are like hormones, except that they diffuse only within the brain, and the blood doesn't carry them to other parts of the body. Figure 3.18 presents the major **endocrine** (hormone-producing) **glands**. Table 3.3 lists some important hormones and their principal effects.

Hormones are particularly useful for coordinating long-lasting changes in multiple parts of the body. For example, birds that are preparing for migration secrete hormones that change their eating and digestion to store extra energy for a long journey. Among the various types of hormones are **protein hormones** and **peptide hormones**, composed of chains of amino acids. (Proteins are longer chains and peptides are shorter.) Protein and peptide hormones attach to membrane receptors, where they activate a second messenger within the cell—exactly like a metabotropic synapse. In fact, many chemicals serve as both neurotransmitters and hormones.

Just as circulating hormones modify brain activity, hormones secreted by the brain control the secretion of many other hormones. The **pituitary gland**, attached to the hypo-

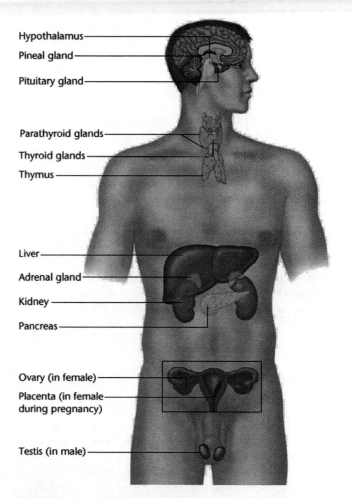

FIGURE 3.18 Location of some major endocrine glands (Source: Starr & Taggart, 1989)

thalamus (Figure 3.19), consists of two distinct glands, the **anterior pituitary** and the **posterior pituitary**, which release different sets of hormones (Table 3.3). The posterior pituitary, composed of neural tissue, can be considered an extension of the hypothalamus. Neurons in the hypothalamus synthesize the hormones **oxytocin** and **vasopressin** (also known as antidiuretic hormone), which migrate down axons to the posterior pituitary, as shown in Figure 3.20. Later, the posterior pituitary releases these hormones into the blood.

The anterior pituitary, composed of glandular tissue, synthesizes six hormones, although the hypothalamus controls their release (Figure 3.20). The hypothalamus secretes **releasing hormones,** which flow through the blood to the anterior pituitary. There they stimulate or inhibit the release of the following hormones:

Adrenocorticotropic hormone (ACTH)	Controls secretions of the adrenal cortex
Thyroid-stimulating hormone (TSH)	Controls secretions of the thyroid gland
Prolactin	Controls secretions of the mammary glands
Somatotropin, also known as growth hormone (GH)	Promotes growth throughout the body
Gonadotropins Follicle-stimulating hormone (FSH) Luteinizing hormone (LH)	Control secretions of the gonads

The hypothalamus maintains fairly constant circulating levels of certain hormones through a negative feedback system. For example, when the level of thyroid hormone is low, the hypothalamus releases *TSH-releasing hormone,* which stimulates the anterior pituitary to release TSH, which in turn causes the thyroid gland to secrete more thyroid hormones (Figure 3.21).

Stop & Check

13. Which part of the pituitary—anterior or posterior—is neural tissue, similar to the hypothalamus? Which part is glandular tissue and produces hormones that control the secretions by other endocrine organs?

14. In what way is a neuropeptide intermediate between other neurotransmitters and hormones?

ANSWERS

13. The posterior pituitary is neural tissue, like the hypothalamus. The anterior pituitary is glandular tissue and produces hormones that control several other endocrine organs. **14.** Most neurotransmitters are released in small amounts close to their receptors. Neuropeptides are released into a brain area in larger amounts or not at all. When released, they diffuse more widely. Hormones are released into the blood for diffuse delivery throughout the body.

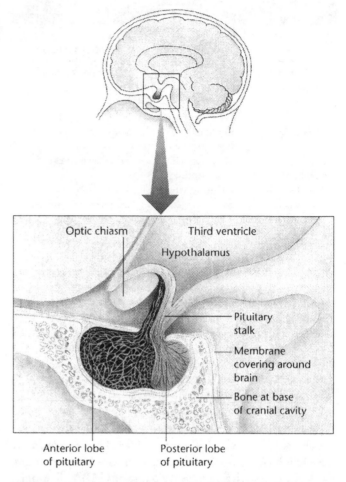

FIGURE 3.19 Location of the hypothalamus and pituitary gland in the human brain *(Source: Starr & Taggart, 1989)*

Inactivation and Reuptake of Neurotransmitters

A neurotransmitter does not linger at the postsynaptic membrane. If it did, it might continue exciting or inhibiting the receptor. Various neurotransmitters are inactivated in different ways.

After acetylcholine activates a receptor, it is broken down by the enzyme **acetylcholinesterase** (a-SEE-til-ko-lih-NES-teh-raze) into two fragments: acetate and choline. The choline diffuses back to the presynaptic neuron, which takes it up and reconnects it with acetate already in the cell to form acetylcholine again. Although this recycling process is highly efficient, it takes time, and the presynaptic neuron does not reabsorb every molecule it releases. A sufficiently rapid series of action potentials at any synapse can deplete the neurotransmitter faster than the presynaptic cell replenishes it, thus slowing or interrupting transmission (G. Liu & Tsien, 1995).

Serotonin and the catecholamines (dopamine, norepinephrine, and epinephrine) do not break down into inactive fragments at the postsynaptic membrane. They simply detach from the receptor. At that point, the next step varies. In

TABLE 3.3	Partial List of Hormone-Releasing Glands	
Organ	**Hormone**	**Hormone Functions**
Hypothalamus	Various releasing hormones	Promote or inhibit release of various hormones by pituitary
Anterior pituitary	Thyroid-stimulating hormone (TSH)	Stimulates thyroid gland
	Luteinizing hormone (LH)	Increases production of progesterone (female), testosterone (male); stimulates ovulation
	Follicle-stimulating hormone (FSH)	Increases production of estrogen and maturation of ovum (female) and sperm production (male)
	ACTH	Increases secretion of steroid hormones by adrenal gland
	Prolactin	Increases milk production
	Growth hormone (GH), also known as somatotropin	Increases body growth, including the growth spurt during puberty
Posterior pituitary	Oxytocin	Controls uterine contractions, milk release, certain aspects of parental behavior, and sexual pleasure
	Vasopressin (also known as antidiuretic hormone)	Constricts blood vessels and raises blood pressure, decreases urine volume
Pineal	Melatonin	Increases sleepiness, influences sleep–wake cycle, also has a role in onset of puberty
Thyroid	Thyroxine / Triiodothyronine	Increases metabolic rate, growth, and maturation
Parathyroid	Parathyroid hormone	Increases blood calcium and decreases potassium
Adrenal cortex	Aldosterone	Reduces secretion of salts by the kidneys
	Cortisol, corticosterone	Stimulates liver to elevate blood sugar, increase metabolism of proteins and fats
Adrenal medulla	Epinephrine, norepinephrine	Similar to effects of sympathetic nervous system
Pancreas	Insulin	Increases entry of glucose to cells and increases storage as fats
	Glucagon	Increases conversion of stored fats to blood glucose
Ovary	Estrogens	Promote female sexual characteristics
	Progesterone	Maintains pregnancy
Testis	Androgens	Promote sperm production, growth of pubic hair, and male sexual characteristics
Liver	Somatomedins	Stimulate growth
Kidney	Renin	Converts a blood protein into angiotensin, which regulates blood pressure and contributes to hypovolemic thirst
Thymus	Thymosin (and others)	Support immune responses
Fat cells	Leptin	Decreases appetite, increases activity, necessary for onset of puberty

© Cengage Learning 2013

certain brain areas, the presynaptic neuron takes up most of the released neurotransmitter molecules intact and reuses them. This process, called **reuptake**, occurs through special membrane proteins called **transporters**. Individuals vary in the activity of certain transporters. Genetic variations in serotonin transporters relate to individual differences in anxiety (Murphy et al., 2008). Transporters also differ in their abundance from one brain area to another. Dopamine transporters in the caudate nucleus are highly efficient, and reuptake accounts for nearly all of the released dopamine. In other brain areas, fewer transporters are present, and reuptake is slower. If dopamine is released rapidly in those areas, it accumulates and an enzyme called **COMT** (catechol-o-methyltransferase) breaks down the excess into inactive chemicals that cannot stimulate the dopamine receptors. Those breakdown products wash away and eventually show up in the blood and urine. In the prefrontal cortex, COMT breaks down about half of the released dopamine (Yavich, Forsberg, Karayiorgou, Gogos, & Männistö, 2007). A consequence is that neurons in that area easily diminish their supply of dopamine, and they cannot release dopamine rapidly for long.

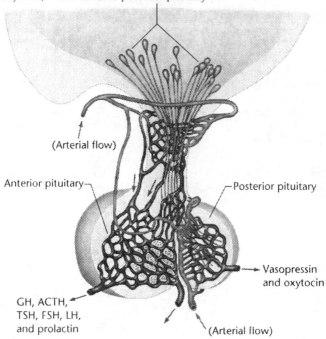

Hypothalamus secretes releasing hormones and inhibiting hormones that control anterior pituitary. Also synthesizes vasopressin and oxytocin, which travel to posterior pituitary.

(Arterial flow)

Anterior pituitary

Posterior pituitary

Vasopressin and oxytocin

GH, ACTH, TSH, FSH, LH, and prolactin

(Arterial flow)

FIGURE 3.20 Pituitary hormones
The hypothalamus produces vasopressin and oxytocin, which travel to the posterior pituitary (really an extension of the hypothalamus). The posterior pituitary releases those hormones in response to neural signals. The hypothalamus also produces releasing hormones and inhibiting hormones, which travel to the anterior pituitary, where they control the release of six hormones synthesized there. (© Cengage Learning 2013)

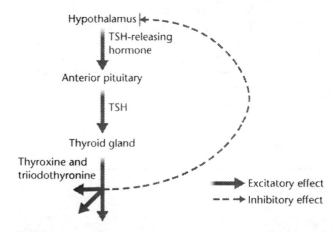

Hypothalamus

TSH-releasing hormone

Anterior pituitary

TSH

Thyroid gland

Thyroxine and triiodothyronine

→ Excitatory effect
--→ Inhibitory effect

FIGURE 3.21 Negative feedback in the control of thyroid hormones
The hypothalamus secretes a releasing hormone that stimulates the anterior pituitary to release TSH, which stimulates the thyroid gland to release its hormones. Those hormones in turn act on the hypothalamus to decrease its secretion of the releasing hormone. (© Cengage Learning 2013)

The neuropeptides are neither inactivated nor reabsorbed. They simply diffuse away. Because these large molecules are resynthesized slowly, a neuron can temporarily exhaust its supply.

Stop & Check

15. What happens to acetylcholine molecules after they stimulate a postsynaptic receptor?

16. What happens to serotonin and catecholamine molecules after they stimulate a postsynaptic receptor?

ANSWERS

15. The enzyme acetylcholinesterase breaks acetylcholine molecules into two smaller molecules, acetate and choline, which are then reabsorbed by the presynaptic terminal. **16.** Most serotonin and catecholamine molecules are reabsorbed by the presynaptic terminal. Some of their molecules are broken down into inactive chemicals, which then diffuse away.

Negative Feedback from the Postsynaptic Cell

Suppose someone often sends you an e-mail message and then, worried that you might not have received it, sends it again and again. To prevent cluttering your inbox, you might add a system that provides an automatic answer, "Yes, I got your message. Don't send it again."

A couple of mechanisms in the nervous system serve that function. First, many presynaptic terminals have receptors sensitive to the same transmitter they release. These receptors are known as **autoreceptors**—receptors that respond to the released transmitter by inhibiting further synthesis and release. That is, they provide negative feedback (Kubista & Boehm. 2006).

Second, some postsynaptic neurons respond to stimulation by releasing special chemicals that travel back to the presynaptic terminal, where they inhibit further release of the transmitter. Nitric oxide is one such transmitter. Two others are *anandamide* and *2-AG* (*sn*-2 arachidonylglycerol). We shall discuss them further in the next module, as we consider drug mechanisms. Here, the point is that postsynaptic neurons have ways to control or limit their own input.

Electrical Synapses

At the start of this module, you learned that Sherrington was wrong to assume that synapses convey messages electrically. Well, he wasn't completely wrong. A few special-purpose synapses operate electrically. Electrical transmission is faster than even the fastest chemical transmission, and electrical synapses have evolved in cases where exact synchrony between two cells is important. For example, some of the cells that control your rhythmic breathing are synchronized by electrical synapses. (It's important to inhale on the left side at the same time as on the right side.)

At an electrical synapse, the membrane of one neuron comes into direct contact with the membrane of another, as shown in Figure 3.22. This contact is called a **gap junction**. Fairly large pores of the membrane of one neuron line up pre-

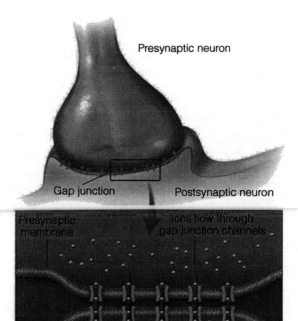

FIGURE 3.22 A gap junction for an electrical synapse
(© Argosy Publishing Inc.)

cisely with similar pores in the membrane of the other cell. These pores are large enough for sodium and other ions to pass readily, and unlike the other membrane channels we have considered, these pores remain open constantly. Therefore, whenever one of the neurons is depolarized, sodium ions from that cell can pass quickly into the other neuron and depolarize it, too. As a result, the two neurons act almost as if they were in fact a single neuron. A major point to note here is that the nervous system has a great variety of types of synapses, serving a similar variety of functions.

MODULE 3.2 ■ IN CLOSING

Neurotransmitters and Behavior

Synapses are the building blocks of behavior. They determine which messages get transmitted, and where, and for how long. One of the guiding assumptions of biological psychology is that much of the difference in behavior between one person and another relates to activity at the synapses. For example, people with greater amounts of dopamine release tend to be more impulsive and more inclined to seek immediate

pleasure (Buckholtz et al., 2010). The drugs that help control Parkinson's disease, anxiety, schizophrenia, and other disorders act at synapses, suggesting that these disorders reflect excesses or deficits of certain transmitters. Perhaps even normal personality differences also depend on variations in synapses. From quantitative variations in synapses come many rich variations in behavior.

SUMMARY

1. The great majority of synapses operate by transmitting a neurotransmitter from the presynaptic cell to the postsynaptic cell. Otto Loewi demonstrated this point by stimulating a frog's heart electrically and then transferring fluids from that heart to another frog's heart.   **59**

2. Many chemicals are used as neurotransmitters. Most are amino acids or chemicals derived from amino acids.   **60**

3. An action potential opens calcium channels in the axon terminal, and the calcium enables release of neurotransmitters.   **62**

4. At ionotropic synapses, a neurotransmitter attaches to a receptor that opens the gates to allow a particular ion, such as sodium, to cross the membrane. Ionotropic effects are fast and brief. At metabotropic synapses, a neurotransmitter activates a second messenger inside the postsynaptic cell, leading to slower but longer lasting changes.   **63**

5. Neuropeptides diffuse widely, affecting many neurons for a period of minutes. Neuropeptides are important for hunger, thirst, and other slow, long-term processes.   **64**

6. Hormones are released into the blood to affect receptors scattered throughout the body. Their mechanism of effect resembles that of a metabotropic synapse.   **65**

7. After a neurotransmitter (other than a neuropeptide) has activated its receptor, many of the transmitter molecules reenter the presynaptic cell through transporter molecules in the membrane. This process, known as reuptake, enables the presynaptic cell to recycle its neurotransmitter.   **66**

8. Postsynaptic neurons have mechanisms to inhibit further release of the neurotransmitter from the presynaptic neuron.   **69**

KEY TERMS

Terms are defined in the module on the page number indicated. They're also presented in alphabetical order with definitions in the book's Subject Index/Glossary, which begins on page 561. Interactive flashcards and crossword puzzles are among the online resources available to help you learn these terms and the concepts they represent.

acetylcholine **60**	ionotropic effects **63**	posterior pituitary **66**
acetylcholinesterase **66**	ligand-gated channels **63**	protein hormones **65**
amino acids **60**	MAO **62**	purines **60**
anterior pituitary **66**	metabotropic effects **63**	releasing hormones **66**
autoreceptors **69**	monoamines **60**	reuptake **67**
catecholamines **61**	neurogliaform cell **65**	second messenger **64**
COMT **67**	neuromodulators **64**	transmitter-gated
endocrine glands **65**	neuropeptides **60**	channels **63**
exocytosis **62**	neurotransmitters **60**	transporters **67**
gap junction **69**	nitric oxide **60**	vasopressin **66**
G protein **64**	oxytocin **66**	vesicles **62**
gases **60**	peptide hormones **65**	
hormone **65**	pituitary gland **65**	

THOUGHT QUESTION

Suppose axon A enters a ganglion (cluster of neurons) and axon B leaves on the other side. An experimenter who stimulates A shortly thereafter records an impulse traveling down B. We want to know whether B is just an extension of axon A or whether A formed an excitatory synapse on some neuron in the ganglion, whose axon is axon B. How could an experimenter determine the answer? You should be able to think of more than one good method. Presume that the anatomy within the ganglion is so complex that you cannot simply trace the course of an axon through it.

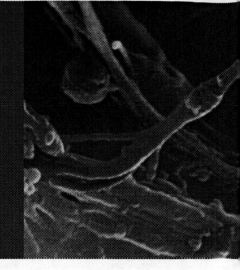

MODULE 3.3

Synapses, Drugs, and Addictions

Did you know that your brain is constantly making chemicals resembling opiates? It also makes its own marijuana-like chemicals, and it has receptors that respond to cocaine and LSD. Nearly every drug with psychological effects acts at the synapses. (The exceptions are Novocain and related anesthetic drugs that block sodium channels in the membrane instead of acting at synapses.) By studying the effects of drugs, we learn more about the drugs and also about synapses. This module deals mainly with abused drugs. Later chapters will consider antidepressants, antipsychotic drugs, and other psychiatric medications.

Most of the commonly abused drugs derive from plants. For example, nicotine comes from tobacco, caffeine from coffee, opiates from poppies, and cocaine from coca. We might wonder why our brains respond to plant chemicals. An explanation is more apparent if we put it the other way: Why do plants produce chemicals that affect our brains? Nearly all neurotransmitters and hormones are the same in humans as in other species (Cravchik & Goldman, 2000). So if a plant evolves a chemical to attract bees, repel caterpillars, or whatever, that chemical is likely to affect humans also.

▌ Drug Mechanisms

Drugs either facilitate or inhibit transmission at synapses. A drug that blocks a neurotransmitter is an **antagonist**, whereas a drug that mimics or increases the effects is an **agonist**. (The term *agonist* is derived from a Greek word meaning "contestant." The term *agony* derives from the same root. An *antagonist* is an "anti-agonist," or member of the opposing team.) A *mixed agonist–antagonist* is an agonist for some effects of the neurotransmitter and an antagonist for others or an agonist at some doses and an antagonist at others.

Drugs influence synaptic activity in many ways. As in Figure 3.23, which illustrates a dopamine synapse, a drug can increase or decrease the synthesis of the neurotransmitter, cause it to leak from its vesicles, increase its release, decrease its reuptake, block its breakdown into inactive chemicals, or act on the postsynaptic receptors.

Investigators say that a drug has an **affinity** for a receptor if it binds to it, like a key into a lock. Affinities vary from strong to weak. A drug's **efficacy** is its tendency to activate the

receptor. A drug that binds to a receptor but fails to stimulate it has a high affinity but low efficacy.

The effectiveness and side effects of drugs vary from one person to another. Why? Most drugs affect several kinds of receptors. People vary in their abundance of each kind of receptor. For example, one person might have a relatively large number of dopamine type D_4 receptors and relatively few D_1 or D_2 receptors, whereas someone else has the reverse (Cravchik & Goldman, 2000).

Stop & Check

17. Is a drug with high affinity and low efficacy an agonist or an antagonist?

ANSWER 17. It is an antagonist because, by occupying the receptor, it blocks out the neurotransmitter.

▌ A Survey of Abused Drugs

Let's consider some commonly abused drugs. In the process, we learn about synapses as well as drugs.

What Abused Drugs Have in Common

Despite many differences among abused drugs, they share certain effects on dopamine and norepinephrine synapses. The story behind the discovery of the brain mechanisms begins with a pair of young psychologists who were trying to answer a different question.

James Olds and Peter Milner (1954) wanted to test whether stimulation of a certain brain area might influence which direction a rat turns. When they implanted their electrode, they missed the intended target and instead hit an area called the septum. To their surprise, when the rat received the brain stimulation, it sat up, looked around, and sniffed, as if reacting to a favorable stimulus. Olds and Milner later placed rats in boxes where they could press a lever to produce electrical **self-stimulation of the brain** (Figure 3.24). With electrodes in the septum and certain other places, rats sometimes pressed as often as 2,000 times per hour (Olds, 1958).

71

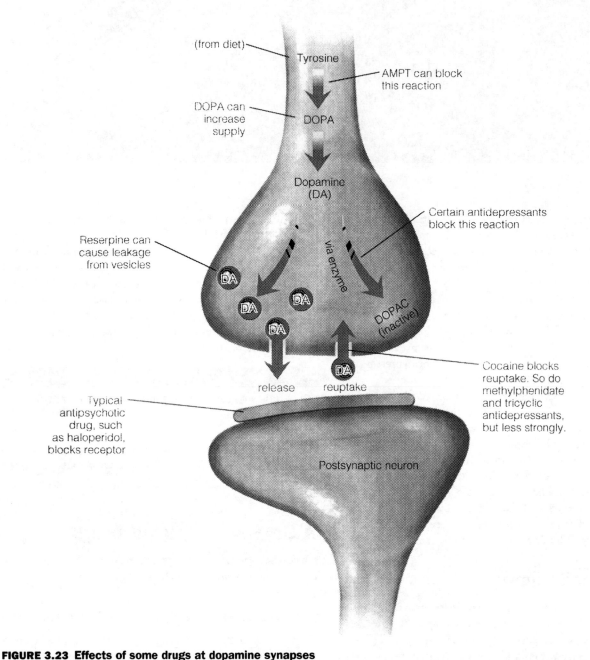

FIGURE 3.23 Effects of some drugs at dopamine synapses
Drugs can alter any stage of synaptic processing, from synthesis of the neurotransmitter through release and reuptake. (© *Argosy Publishing Inc.)*

Later researchers found many brain areas that rats would work to stimulate. All those areas had axons that directly or indirectly increase the release of dopamine or norepinephrine in the **nucleus accumbens**, as illustrated in Figure 3.25 (Wise, 1996).

The nucleus accumbens is central to reinforcing experiences of all types. Sexual excitement also stimulates this area (Damsma, Pfaus, Wenkstern, Philips, & Fibiger, 1992; Lorrain, Riolo, Matuszewich, & Hull, 1999), and so does the taste of sugar (Roitman, Wheeler, Wightman, & Carelli, 2008). If you simply imagine something pleasant, you activate your nucleus accumbens (Costa, Lang, Sabatinelli, Versace, &

Bradley, 2010). Gambling activates this area for habitual gamblers (Breiter, Aharon, Kahneman, Dale, & Shizgal, 2001), and video game playing activates it for habitual video game players (Ko et al., 2009; Koepp et al., 1998). People with major depression show much less than normal response in the nucleus accumbens, corresponding to the fact that they show little motivation and report getting little joy out of life (Pizzagalli et al., 2009).

Reinforcement has two components that psychologists call "wanting" and "liking" (Berridge & Robinson, 1995, 1998). Ordinarily, you want something that you like, but wanting (motivation) is not always the same as liking (pleasure). You might

FIGURE 3.24 A rat pressing a lever for self-stimulation of its brain

want medicine but not enjoy it. You might know you would enjoy an extremely rich, fattening dessert, but you don't want it. If you narrowly miss out on the opportunity for some prize or award, you might work extra hard at the next opportunity to get it, indicating that you *want* it, even if the prize itself doesn't bring you great pleasure (Litt, Khan, & Shiv, 2010). Recordings from individual cells in rats suggest that small parts of the nucleus accumbens respond to pleasure (liking), but larger areas respond to motivation—that is, wanting (Peciña, 2008).

Like sex, food, and other reinforcing experiences, addictive drugs strongly activate the nucleus accumbens by releasing dopamine or norepinephrine (Caine et al., 2007; Weinshenker & Schroeder, 2007). The liking-wanting distinction

is important here, because people addicted to a drug show an overwhelming, all-consuming drive to obtain the drug, even though it no longer provides much pleasure. We shall continue an exploration of addiction later in this module.

18. What do drug use, sex, gambling, and video game playing have in common?

ANSWER

18. They increase the release of dopamine in the nucleus accumbens.

Stimulant Drugs

Stimulant drugs increase excitement, alertness, and activity, while elevating mood and decreasing fatigue. Both **amphetamine** and **cocaine** stimulate dopamine synapses in the nucleus accumbens and elsewhere by increasing the presence of dopamine in the presynaptic terminal. Recall reuptake: The presynaptic terminal ordinarily reabsorbs released dopamine through a protein called the **dopamine transporter**. Amphetamine and cocaine inhibit the transporter, thus decreasing reuptake and prolonging the effects of released dopamine (Beuming et al., 2008; Schmitt & Reith, 2010; Zhao et al., 2010). Amphetamine has similar effects on the serotonin and norepinephrine transporters. Methamphetamine has effects similar to those of amphetamine, but stronger.

Thus, stimulant drugs increase the accumulation of dopamine in the synaptic cleft. However, the excess dopamine in the synapse washes away faster than the presynaptic cell makes more to replace it. A few hours after taking a stimulant

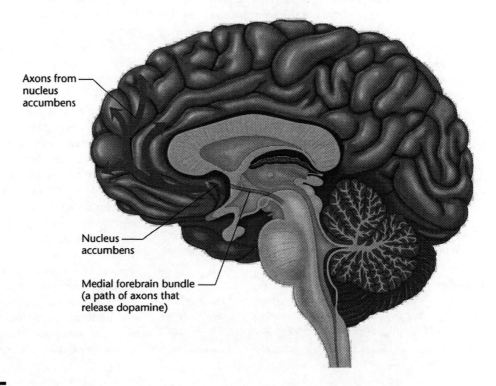

FIGURE 3.25 Location of the nucleus accumbens in the human brain
Nearly all abused drugs, as well as a variety of other highly reinforcing or addictive activities, increase dopamine release in the nucleus accumbens.
(© Cengage Learning 2013)

Axons from nucleus accumbens

Nucleus accumbens

Medial forebrain bundle (a path of axons that release dopamine)

drug, a user has a deficit of the transmitters and enters a withdrawal state, marked by reduced energy, reduced motivation, and mild depression.

Stimulant drugs produce varied behavioral effects. Low doses enhance attention, and low doses of amphetamine are sometimes used as a treatment for attention deficit disorder (ADHD), a condition marked by impulsiveness and poor control of attention. However, higher doses of stimulant drugs impair attention and learning (Stalnaker et al., 2007). A study of pairs of human twins, in which one twin abused cocaine or amphetamine and the other did not, found that the twin abusing stimulant drugs showed attentional problems that lingered for a year after quitting the drugs (Toomey et al., 2003). By altering blood flow, cocaine also increases the risk of stroke and epilepsy (Strickland, Miller, Kowell, & Stein, 1998).

Methylphenidate (Ritalin), another stimulant drug, is also prescribed for people with attention-deficit hyperactivity disorder. Methylphenidate and cocaine block the reuptake of dopamine in the same way at the same brain receptors. The differences between the drugs relate to dose and time course. Cocaine users typically sniff it or inject it to produce a rapid rush of effect on the brain. People taking methylphenidate pills experience a gradual increase in the drug's concentration over an hour or more, followed by a slow decline. Therefore, methylphenidate does not produce the sudden rush of excitement that is common with cocaine. However, someone who injects methylphenidate experiences effects similar to cocaine's, including the risk of addiction.

You might wonder whether the use of methylphenidate in childhood makes people more likely to abuse drugs later. This is not an easy question to investigate. Overall, people with ADHD are more likely than other people to use and abuse tobacco, alcohol, and many other drugs. The needed comparison is between people with ADHD who have taken methylphenidate and those who have not. However, no one can randomly assign people to these two groups. Those receiving methylphenidate probably differ from those not receiving it in several ways. Bearing these difficulties in mind, researchers have conducted a few studies, and have found inconclusive results. Some studies suggest that using methylphenidate increases the risk of later drug abuse, and other studies find that it decreases the risk (Golden, 2009). Evidently the risk does not change enormously, one way or the other.

▶ **Stop & Check**

19. How do amphetamine and cocaine influence dopamine synapses?

20. Why is methylphenidate generally less disruptive to behavior than cocaine is despite the drugs' similar mechanisms?

ANSWERS

19. They interfere with reuptake of released dopamine.
20. The effects of a methylphenidate pill develop and decline in the brain much more slowly than do those of cocaine.

Nicotine

Nicotine, a compound present in tobacco, stimulates a family of acetylcholine receptors, conveniently known as *nicotinic receptors*. Nicotinic receptors are abundant on neurons that release dopamine in the nucleus accumbens, so nicotine increases dopamine release there (Levin & Rose, 1995; Pontieri, Tanda, Orzi, & DiChiara, 1996). Nicotine increases dopamine release in mostly the same cells that cocaine stimulates (Pich et al., 1997). Animals with larger numbers of nicotine receptors show enhanced behavioral responses to rewarding situations and novel stimuli (Fagen, Mitchum, Vezina, & McGehee, 2007). That is, nicotine enhances reward.

One consequence of repeated exposure to nicotine is that receptors in the nucleus accumbens become more sensitive to nicotine (Changeux, 2010). However, they become less responsive than usual to other kinds of reinforcement (Epping-Jordan, Watkins, Koob, & Markou, 1998). The same pattern emerges with cocaine and other addictions: enhanced response to the drug and decreased reward by anything else.

▶ **Stop & Check**

21. How does nicotine affect dopamine synapses?

ANSWER

21. Nicotine excites acetylcholine receptors on neurons that release dopamine and thereby increases dopamine release.

Opiates

Opiate drugs are derived from, or chemically similar to those derived from, the opium poppy. Familiar opiates include morphine, heroin, and methadone. Because heroin enters the brain faster than morphine, it produces a bigger rush of effects and is more strongly addictive. Opiates relax people, decrease their attention to real-world problems, and decrease their sensitivity to pain. Although opiates are frequently addictive, people who take them as painkillers under medical supervision almost never abuse them. Addiction depends on the person, the reasons for taking the drug, the dose, and the social setting.

People used morphine and other opiates for centuries without knowing how the drugs affected the brain. Then Candace Pert and Solomon Snyder found that opiates attach to specific receptors in the brain (Pert & Snyder, 1973). It was a safe guess that vertebrates had not evolved such receptors just to enable us to become drug addicts; the brain must produce its own chemical that attaches to these receptors. Soon investigators found that the brain produces certain neuropeptides now known as *endorphins*—a contraction of *endogenous morphines*. This discovery was important because it indicated that opiates relieve pain by acting on receptors in the brain. This finding also paved the way for the discovery of other neuropeptides that regulate emotions and motivations.

Endorphins indirectly activate dopamine release. Endorphin synapses inhibit neurons that release GABA, a transmitter that inhibits the firing of dopamine neurons

(North, 1992). By inhibiting an inhibitor, the net effect is to increase dopamine release. However, endorphins also have reinforcing effects independent of dopamine. Researchers managed to develop mice with an almost complete lack of dopamine in the nucleus accumbens. These mice show a preference for places in which they received morphine (Hnasko, Sotak, & Palmiter, 2005). Evidently endorphins have rewarding effects on their own, as well as effects that depend on dopamine.

Stop & Check

22. How do opiates influence dopamine synapses?

ANSWER   22. Opiates stimulate endorphin synapses, which inhibit neurons that inhibit release of dopamine. By inhibiting an inhibitor, opiates increase the release of dopamine.

Marijuana

Marijuana leaves contain the chemical Δ^9-tetrahydrocannabinol (Δ^9-THC) and other **cannabinoids** (chemicals related to Δ^9-THC). Cannabinoids have been used medically to relieve pain or nausea, to combat glaucoma (an eye disorder), and to increase appetite. Purified THC (under the name *dronabinol*) has been approved for medical use in the United States, although marijuana itself has not—except in certain states, where state law and federal law conflict.

Common psychological effects of marijuana include an intensification of sensory experience and an illusion that time has slowed down. Studies have reported impairments of memory and cognition, especially in new users and heavy users. (Moderate users develop partial tolerance.) The observed memory impairments in heavy users could mean either that marijuana impairs memory or that people with memory impairments are more likely to use marijuana. However, former users show improved memory after 4 weeks of abstention from the drug (Pope, Gruber, Hudson, Huestis, & Yurgelun-Todd, 2001). That improvement implies that marijuana use had impaired their memory.

Investigators could not explain marijuana's effects until 1988, when researchers finally found the brain's cannabinoid receptors (Devane, Dysarz, Johnson, Melvin, & Howlett, 1988). Cannabinoid receptors are among the most abundant receptors in many areas of the mammalian brain (Herkenham, 1992; Herkenham, Lynn, de Costa, & Richfield, 1991), although they are scarce in the medulla, the area that controls breathing and heartbeat. Consequently, even large doses of marijuana do not stop breathing or heartbeat. In contrast, opiates have strong effects on the medulla, and opiate overdoses are life threatening.

Just as the discovery of opiate receptors in the brain led to finding the brain's endogenous opiates, investigators identified two brain chemicals that bind to cannabinoid receptors—**anandamide** (from the Sanskrit word *ananda*, meaning "bliss") (Calignano, LaRana, Giuffrida, & Piomelli, 1998;

DiMarzo et al., 1994) and the more abundant *sn*-2 arachidonylglycerol, abbreviated **2-AG** (Stella, Schweitzer, & Piomelli, 1997).

Cannabinoid receptors are peculiar in being located on the *presynaptic* neuron. When certain neurons are depolarized, they release anandamide or 2-AG as retrograde transmitters that travel back to the incoming axons and inhibit further release of either glutamate (Kreitzer & Regehr, 2001; R. I. Wilson & Nicoll, 2002) or GABA (Földy, Neu, Jones, & Soltesz, 2006; Oliet, Baimoukhametova, Piet, & Bains, 2007). In effect, anandamide and 2-AG tell the presynaptic cell, "The postsynaptic cell got your message. You don't need to send it again." The cannabinoids in marijuana attach to these same presynaptic receptors, again telling them, "The cell got your message. Stop sending it." The presynaptic cell, unaware that it hadn't sent any message at all, stops sending. In short, the chemicals in marijuana decrease both excitatory and inhibitory messages from many neurons.

Why are marijuana's effects—at least some of them—pleasant or habit forming? Remember that virtually all abused drugs increase the release of dopamine in the nucleus accumbens. Cannabinoids do so indirectly. One place in which they inhibit GABA release is the ventral tegmental area of the midbrain, a major source of axons that release dopamine in the nucleus accumbens. By inhibiting GABA there, cannabinoids decrease inhibition (and therefore increase activity) of the neurons that release dopamine in the nucleus accumbens (Cheer, Wassum, Heien, Phillips, & Wightman, 2004).

Researchers have tried to explain some of marijuana's other effects. Cannabinoids relieve nausea by inhibiting serotonin type 3 synapses ($5-HT_3$), which are known to be important for nausea (Fan, 1995). Cannabinoid receptors are abundant in areas of the hypothalamus and hippocampus that influence feeding, and stimulation of these receptors increases the rewarding value of a meal (Massa et al., 2010).

The report that "time passes more slowly" under marijuana's influences is harder to explain, but whatever the reason, we can demonstrate it in rats as well: Consider a rat that has learned to press a lever for food on a fixed-interval schedule, where only the first press of any 30-second period produces food. With practice, a rat learns to wait after each press before it starts pressing again. Under the influence of marijuana, rats press sooner after each reinforcer. For example, instead of waiting 20 seconds, a rat might wait only 10 or 15. Evidently, the 10 or 15 seconds *felt like* 20 seconds; time was passing more slowly (Han & Robinson, 2001).

Stop & Check

23. What are the effects of cannabinoids on neurons?

ANSWER   23. Cannabinoids released by the postsynaptic neuron attach to receptors on presynaptic neurons, where they inhibit further release of both glutamate and GABA.

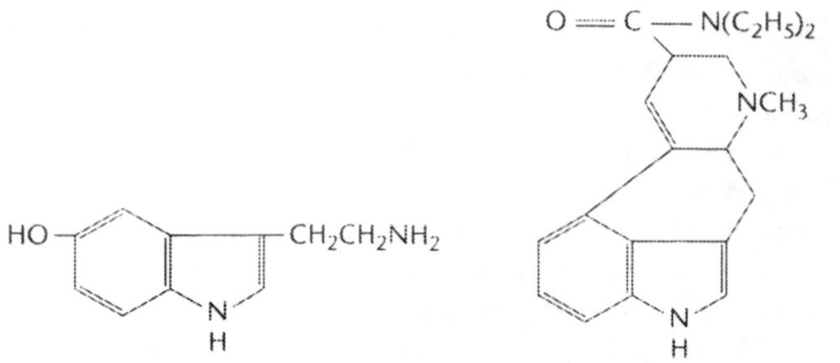

FIGURE 3.26 Resemblance of the neurotransmitter serotonin to LSD, a hallucinogenic drug (© Cengage Learning 2013)

Hallucinogenic Drugs

Drugs that distort perception are called **hallucinogenic drugs**. Many hallucinogenic drugs, such as lysergic acid diethylamide (LSD), chemically resemble serotonin (Figure 3.26). They attach to serotonin type 2A ($5\text{-}HT_{2A}$) receptors and provide stimulation at inappropriate times or for longer than usual durations. (Why and how the inappropriate stimulation of those receptors leads to distorted perceptions is an unanswered question.)

The drug methylenedioxymethamphetamine (MDMA, or "ecstasy") is a stimulant at low doses, increasing the release of dopamine and producing effects similar to amphetamine or cocaine. At higher doses, it also releases serotonin, altering perception and cognition like hallucinogenic drugs. Many people use MDMA at dance parties to increase their energy levels and pleasure. However, after the effects wear off, users experience lethargy and depression. One of the effects is increased body temperature, occasionally to life-threatening levels.

Many studies on rodents and monkeys have found that repeated large injections of MDMA damage neurons that contain serotonin. One reason is that increased body temperature harms neurons. Another reason is that certain metabolites of MDMA are directly toxic to neurons (Capela et al., 2009).

The amount of risk to human users is not entirely clear. Most animal studies use larger doses than what most people take. Still, researchers have found that many repeated users show indications of long-term loss of serotonin receptors, persisting depression, anxiety, and impaired learning and memory (Capela et al., 2009). Gradual recovery occurs over a period of months. Those deficits may or may not be effects of MDMA itself, as most people who use MDMA also use a variety of other drugs (Hanson & Luciana, 2010).

Table 3.4 summarizes the effects of some commonly abused drugs.

> **Stop & Check**

24. If incoming serotonin axons were destroyed, LSD would still have its full effects. However, if incoming dopamine axons were destroyed, amphetamine and cocaine would lose their effects. Explain the difference.

ANSWER

24. Amphetamine and cocaine act by increasing the net release of dopamine and other transmitters. If those neurons were damaged, amphetamine and cocaine would be ineffective. In contrast, LSD directly stimulates the receptor on the postsynaptic membrane.

TABLE 3.4   Summary of Some Drugs and Their Effects

Drugs	Main Behavioral Effects	Main Synaptic Effects
Amphetamine	Excitement, alertness, elevated mood, decreased fatigue	Blocks reuptake of dopamine and several other transmitters
Cocaine	Excitement, alertness, elevated mood, decreased fatigue	Blocks reuptake of dopamine and several other transmitters
Methylphenidate (Ritalin)	Increased concentration	Blocks reuptake of dopamine and others, but gradually
MDMA ("ecstasy")	Low dose: stimulant Higher dose: sensory distortions	Releases dopamine Releases serotonin, damages axons containing serotonin
Nicotine	Mostly stimulant effects	Stimulates nicotinic-type acetylcholine receptor, which (among other effects) increases dopamine release in nucleus accumbens
Opiates (e.g., heroin, morphine)	Relaxation, withdrawal, decreased pain	Stimulates endorphin receptors
Cannabinoids (marijuana)	Altered sensory experiences, decreased pain and nausea, increased appetite	Excites negative-feedback receptors on presynaptic cells; those receptors ordinarily respond to anandamide and 2AG
Hallucinogens (e.g., LSD)	Distorted sensations	Stimulates serotonin type 2A receptors ($5\text{-}HT_{2A}$)

Alcohol and Alcoholism

We treat alcohol separately because alcohol is the most common of the abused drugs and the research on it is extensive. People in most of the world have used alcohol throughout history. In moderate amounts, it relaxes people and decreases anxiety (Gilman, Ramchandani, Davis, Bjork, & Hommer, 2008), although people who quit alcohol often experience an increase in anxiety (Pandey et al., 2008). In larger amounts, alcohol causes health problems, impairs judgment, and ruins lives. **Alcoholism** or **alcohol dependence** is the habitual use of alcohol despite medical or social harm.

Alcohol affects neurons in several ways. It facilitates response at the GABA$_A$ receptor, the brain's main inhibitory site. It also blocks activity at the glutamate receptors, the brain's main excitatory site (Tsai et al., 1998). Both the GABA effect and the glutamate effect lead to a decrease in brain activity. From a behavioral standpoint, people sometimes describe alcohol as a stimulant, but that is only because alcohol decreases activity in brain areas responsible for inhibiting risky behaviors (Tu et al., 2007). Alcohol also increases stimulation at dopamine receptors in the nucleus accumbens (Chaudhri, Sahuque, & Janak, 2009).

Genetics

Studies of twins and adoptees confirm a strong influence of genetics on vulnerability to alcoholism (Ducci & Goldman, 2008). Heredity has a stronger role in some cases of alcoholism than others. Researchers distinguish two types of alcoholism, although not everyone fits neatly into one type or the other. People with **Type I** (or **Type A**) **alcoholism** develop alcohol problems gradually, usually after age 25, and may or may not have relatives with alcohol abuse. Those with **Type II** (or **Type B**) **alcoholism** have more rapid onset, usually before age 25. Most are men, and most have close relatives with alcohol problems (J. Brown, Babor, Litt, & Kranzler, 1994; Devor, Abell, Hoffman, Tabakoff, & Cloninger, 1994).

Genes influence the likelihood of alcoholism in various ways, most of which are not specific to alcohol. For example, many genes that affect alcohol have similar effects on nicotine intake (Lè et al., 2006). One identified gene controls variations in the dopamine type 4 receptor, one of the five known types of dopamine receptor. The type 4 receptor has two common forms, *short* and *long*. The long form is less sensitive, and people with the long form report stronger than average cravings for additional alcohol after having one drink (Hutchison, McGeary, Smolen, & Bryan, 2002). Researchers believe that people with less sensitive receptors seek more alcohol to compensate for receiving less than normal reinforcement.

Another key gene controls COMT, an enzyme that breaks down dopamine after its release. Some people have a less active form of this enzyme and others have a more active form. The more active form breaks down more dopamine and therefore tends to decrease reinforcement. People with that gene tend, on average, to be more impulsive—to choose immediate rewards instead of bigger rewards later. This gene is common

among people with the impulsive form of alcoholism (Boettiger et al., 2007). Other genes influence alcohol use by their effects on risk-taking behavior (Fils-Aime et al., 1996; Virkkunen et al., 1994), responses to stress (Choi et al., 2004; Kreek, Nielsen, Butelman, & LaForge, 2005), and reactions to anxiety-provoking situations (Pandey et al., 2008).

Prenatal environment also contributes to the risk for alcoholism. A mother who drinks alcohol during pregnancy increases the probability that her child will develop alcoholism later, independently of how much she drinks as the child is growing up (Baer, Sampson, Barr, Connor, & Streissguth, 2003). Experiments with rats have also shown that prenatal exposure to alcohol increases alcohol consumption after birth (March, Abate, Spear, & Molina, 2009). All of these biological forces interact, of course, with stressful experiences, opportunities for alcohol use, and other environmental factors.

➤ **Stop & Check**

25. Which type of alcoholism—Type I or Type II—has a stronger genetic basis? Which type has earlier onset?

26. Name at least two ways a gene could influence alcoholism.

ANSWERS 25. Type II has a stronger genetic basis and earlier onset. 26. Genes can influence alcoholism by producing less sensitive dopamine receptors, faster breakdown of dopamine by the enzyme COMT, greater risk-taking behavior, and altered responses to stress. Of course, other possibilities not mentioned in this section also exist.

Risk Factors

Are some people more likely than others to develop an alcohol problem? If we can identify those people, perhaps psychologists could intervene early to prevent alcoholism. We don't know whether early intervention would help, but it is worth a try.

To identify people at risk, one strategy is to study huge numbers of people for years: Measure as many factors as possible for a group of children or adolescents, years later determine which of them developed alcohol problems, and then see which early factors predicted the onset of alcoholism. Such studies find that alcoholism is more likely among those who were described in childhood as impulsive, risk-taking, easily bored, sensation-seeking, and outgoing (Dick, Johnson, Viken, & Rose, 2000; Legrand, Iacono, & McGue, 2005).

Other research follows this design: First, identify young men who are not yet problem drinkers. Compare those whose fathers were alcoholics to those who have no close relative with an alcohol problem. Because of the strong familial tendency toward alcoholism, researchers expect that many of the sons of alcoholics are future alcoholics themselves. (Researchers focus on men instead of women because almost all Type II alcoholics are men. They study sons of fathers with alcoholism instead of mothers to increase the chance of seeing genetic instead of prenatal influences.) The idea is that any behavior more common in the sons of alcoholics is probably a predictor of future alcoholism (Figure 3.27).

Here are the findings:

- Sons of alcoholics show *less* than average intoxication after drinking a moderate amount of alcohol. They report feeling less drunk, show less body sway, and register less change on an EEG (Schuckit & Smith, 1996; Volavka et al., 1996). Presumably, someone who begins to feel tipsy after a drink or two stops, whereas one who "holds his liquor well" continues drinking, perhaps enough to impair his judgment. A follow-up study found that sons of alcoholics who report low intoxication after moderate drinking have a probability greater than 60% of developing alcoholism (Schuckit & Smith, 1997). Low response to alcohol predicts later alcohol abuse, even after controlling for other variables, such as age of first alcoholic drink (Trim, Schuckit, & Smith, 2009). Similar results have been reported for women (Eng, Schuckit, & Smith, 2005).

- Alcohol decreases stress for most people, but it decreases it even more for sons of alcoholics (Levenson, Oyama, & Meek, 1987).

- Sons of alcoholics have some brain peculiarities, including a smaller than normal amygdala in the right hemisphere (Hill et al., 2001). These young men were not yet alcohol abusers, so the brain abnormality represents a predisposition to alcoholism, not a result of it.

 Stop & Check

27. What are two ways sons of alcoholics differ behaviorally, on average, from sons of nonalcoholics?

ANSWER 27. Sons of alcoholics show less intoxication, including less body sway, after drinking a moderate amount of alcohol. They also show greater relief from stress after drinking alcohol.

Addiction

Addiction poses a paradox: Nearly everyone with an addiction recognizes that the habit does more harm than good. As the addiction progresses, the pleasures become weaker while the costs and risks increase. And yet the person remains preoccupied, unable to quit. When we talk about addiction, we think mainly of alcohol and other drugs, but the same principles apply to gambling, overeating, or excessive video game playing. In each case, the person finds it difficult to quit a habit that has become clearly disadvantageous. Why?

Tolerance and Withdrawal

As an addiction develops, many of its effects, especially the enjoyable effects, decrease. That decrease is called **tolerance**. Because of tolerance, heroin users raise their amount and fre-

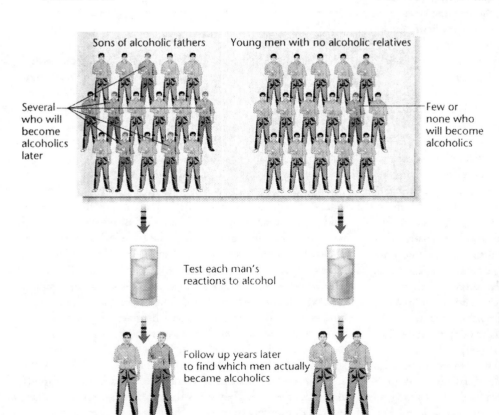

FIGURE 3.27 Design for studies of predisposition to alcoholism
Sons of alcoholic fathers are compared to other young men of the same age and same current drinking habits. Any behavior that is more common in the first group is presumably a predictor of later alcoholism. (© Cengage Learning 2013)

quency of use to greater and greater levels, eventually taking amounts that would kill other people. Drug tolerance, a complex phenomenon, is to a large extent learned. For example, rats that consistently receive opiates or other drugs in a distinctive location show more tolerance in that location than elsewhere (Cepeda-Benito, Davis, Reynoso, & Harraid, 2005; Siegel, 1983). Evidently they learn to suppress their responses when they know what to expect.

As the body comes to expect the drug, at least under certain circumstances, it reacts strongly when the drug is absent. The effects of drug cessation are called **withdrawal**. The withdrawal symptoms after someone quits heroin or other opiates include anxiety, sweating, vomiting, and diarrhea. Symptoms of alcohol withdrawal include irritability, fatigue, shaking, sweating, and nausea. In severe cases, alcohol withdrawal progresses to hallucinations, convulsions, fever, and cardiovascular problems. Nicotine withdrawal leads to irritability, fatigue, insomnia, headache, and difficulty concentrating. Even habitual video game players (those who average more than 4 hours per day) show distress symptoms during a period of abstinence.

One explanation that theorists have advanced to explain addiction is that it is an attempt to avoid withdrawal symptoms. However, that cannot be the whole explanation. Ex-smokers sometimes report strong cravings months or years after quitting.

A modified explanation is that someone with an addiction learns to use the substance to cope with stress. In one study, researchers gave rats an opportunity to press a lever to inject themselves with heroin. Then they withdrew the opportunity for the drug. Midway through the withdrawal period, some of the rats had an opportunity to self-administer heroin again, while others went through withdrawal without heroin. Later, when rats went through withdrawal a second time, all the rats had an opportunity to press a lever to try to get heroin, but this time, the lever was inoperative. Although both groups of rats pressed the lever, those that had self-administered heroin during the previous withdrawal state pressed far more frequently (Hutcheson, Everitt, Robbins, & Dickinson, 2001). Evidently, receiving an addictive drug during a withdrawal period is a powerful experience. In effect, the user—rat or human—learns that the drug relieves the distress caused by drug withdrawal. That learning can generalize to other situations, so that the user craves the drug during other kinds of distress.

Stop & Check

28. Someone who is quitting an addictive substance for the first time is strongly counseled not to try it again. Why?

ANSWER

28. Taking an addictive drug during the withdrawal period is likely to lead to a habit of using the drug to relieve other kinds of distress.

Cravings in Response to Cues

Another hypothesis is that a drug user learns to associate cues with a drug. Later, even after a long period of abstinence, exposure to those cues triggers a renewed craving. Both humans and rats during abstention from a drug show heightened seeking of the drug (i.e., craving) after a reminder of the drug. For example, seeing a lit cigarette triggers a craving in smokers (Hutchison, LaChance, Niaura, Bryan, & Smolen, 2002), a video of cocaine use triggers cravings in cocaine users (Volkow et al., 2006), and the sight of a popular video game triggers a craving in a habitual excessive video game player (Thalemann et al., 2007). A drug-related cue increases activity in the nucleus accumbens and several related areas (Gloria et al., 2009). However, after an instruction to inhibit the craving, people are capable of decreasing this arousal (Volkow et al., 2010).

Brain Reorganization

Although escape from withdrawal symptoms and conditioned responses to cues are important, they seem insufficient to explain the way an addiction completely dominates someone's life. Somehow, the addiction hijacks a person's motivations. It changes the brain so that other kinds of reinforcing experiences become less powerful, less able to compete with the drug.

Recall epigenesis from Chapter 1: Certain events change the expression of genes. Cocaine provides a strong example of that principle. Cocaine increases the activity of certain genes that control changes in dendrites within the nucleus accumbens. The result restructures the nucleus accumbens so that the drug stimulates more dendrites, and other events stimulate fewer (Mameli et al., 2009; Maze et al., 2010). Even sexual stimulation becomes less rewarding. A similar process happens with heroin. In one study, rats had opportunities each day to press levers for heroin and for self-stimulation of the brain. Over 23 days, they took larger amounts of heroin, and became less responsive to the rewarding brain stimulation (Kenny, Chen, Kitamura, Markou, & Koob, 2006).

Furthermore, cocaine induces changes that impair extinction. Ordinarily, if an animal or person learns a response for a reinforcer, and then reinforcement ceases, responding declines through the process called extinction. You can think of extinction as learning to withhold the response. Repeated drug use impairs extinction of the drug-seeking response, so that even if the drug becomes much less reinforcing, the responding persists (Noonan, Bulin, Fuller, & Eisch, 2010).

Stop & Check

29. When addiction develops, how does the nucleus accumbens change its response to the addictive activity and to other reinforcements?

ANSWER

29. The nucleus accumbens becomes selectively sensitized, increasing its response to the addictive activity and decreasing its response to other reinforcing activities.

Medications to Combat Substance Abuse

Many people who wish to overcome substance abuse join Alcoholics Anonymous, Narcotics Anonymous, or similar organizations, and others see psychotherapists. For those who do not respond well to those approaches, several medications are available.

Medications to Combat Alcohol Abuse

After someone drinks ethyl alcohol, enzymes in the liver metabolize it to *acetaldehyde*, a poisonous substance. An enzyme, acetaldehyde dehydrogenase, then converts acetaldehyde to *acetic acid*, a chemical that the body uses for energy:

$$\text{Ethyl alcohol} \xrightarrow{\text{Acetaldehyde dehydrogenase}} \text{Acetaldehyde} \longrightarrow \text{Acetic acid}$$

People with a weaker gene for acetaldehyde dehydrogenase metabolize acetaldehyde more slowly. If they drink much alcohol, they accumulate acetaldehyde, which produces flushing of the face, increased heart rate, nausea, headache, abdominal pain, impaired breathing, and tissue damage. More than a third of the people in China and Japan have a gene that slows acetaldehyde metabolism. Probably for that reason, alcohol abuse has historically been uncommon in those countries (Luczak, Glatt, & Wall, 2006) (Figure 3.28).

The drug *disulfiram*, which goes by the trade name **Antabuse**, antagonizes the effects of acetaldehyde dehydrogenase by binding to its copper ion. Its effects were discovered by accident. The workers in one rubber-manufacturing plant found that when they got disulfiram on their skin, they developed a rash (L. Schwartz & Tulipan, 1933). If they inhaled it, they couldn't drink alcohol without getting sick. Soon therapists tried using disulfiram as a drug, hoping that alcoholics would associate alcohol with illness and stop drinking.

Most studies find that Antabuse is moderately effective (Hughes & Cook, 1997). When it works, it supplements the

alcoholic's own commitment to stop drinking. By taking a daily pill and imagining the illness that could follow a drink of alcohol, the person reaffirms a decision to abstain. In that case, it doesn't matter whether the pill really contains Antabuse or not, because someone who never drinks does not experience the illness (Fuller & Roth, 1979). Those who drink in spite of taking the pill become ill, but often they quit taking the pill instead of quitting alcohol. Antabuse treatment is more effective if friends make sure the person takes the pill daily (Azrin, Sisson, Meyers, & Godley, 1982). A related idea is to have people drink alcohol and then take a drug that produces nausea, thereby forming a learned aversion to the taste of the alcohol. That procedure has been quick and highly effective in the occasions when people have tried it, although its use has never become popular (Revusky, 2009).

Another medication is naloxone (trade name Revia), which blocks opiate receptors and thereby decreases the pleasure from alcohol. Like Antabuse, naloxone is moderately effective. It works best with people who are strongly motivated to quit, and it is more effective for Type II alcoholics (with a family history of alcoholism) than Type I alcoholics (Krishnan-Sarin, Krystal, Shi, Pittman, & O'Malley, 2007).

Stop & Check

30. Who would be likely to drink more alcohol—someone who metabolizes acetaldehyde to acetic acid rapidly or one who metabolizes it slowly?

31. How does Antabuse work?

ANSWERS

30. People who metabolize it rapidly would be more likely to drink alcohol because they suffer fewer unpleasant effects. **31.** Antabuse blocks the enzyme that converts acetaldehyde to acetic acid and therefore makes people sick if they drink alcohol. Potentially, it could teach people an aversion to alcohol, but more often, it works as a way for the person to make a daily recommitment to abstain from drinking.

Medications to Combat Opiate Abuse

Heroin is an artificial substance invented in the 1800s as a supposedly safer alternative for people who were trying to quit morphine. Some physicians at the time recommended that people using alcohol switch to heroin (S. Siegel, 1987). They abandoned this idea when they discovered how addictive heroin is.

Still, the idea has persisted that people who can't quit opiates might switch to a less harmful drug. **Methadone** (METH-uh-don) is similar to heroin and morphine but has the advantage that it can be taken orally. (If heroin or morphine is taken orally, stomach acids break down most of it.) Methadone taken orally gradually enters the blood and then the brain, so its effects rise slowly, avoiding the "rush" experience. Because it is metabolized slowly, the withdrawal symptoms are also gradual. Furthermore, the user avoids the risk of an injection with a possibly infected needle.

FIGURE 3.28 Robin Kalat (the author's teenage daughter) finds an alcohol vending machine in Tokyo in 1998

Buprenorphine and levomethadyl acetate (LAAM), similar to methadone, are also used to treat opiate addiction. LAAM has the advantage of producing a long-lasting effect so that the person visits a clinic three times a week instead of daily. People using any of these drugs live longer and healthier, on average, than heroin or morphine users, and they are far more likely to hold a job (Vocci, Acri, & Elkashef, 2005). However, these drugs do not end the addiction. They merely satisfy the craving in a less dangerous way.

> **Stop & Check**

32. Methadone users who try taking heroin experience little effect from it. Why?

ANSWER

32. Because methadone is already occupying the endorphin receptors, heroin cannot add much stimulation to them.

MODULE 3.3 ■ IN CLOSING

Drugs and Behavior

In studying the effects of drugs, researchers have gained clues that may help combat drug abuse. They have also learned much about synapses. For example, the research on cocaine called attention to the importance of reuptake transporters, and the research on cannabinoids led to increased understanding of the retrograde signaling from postsynaptic cells to presynaptic cells.

However, from the standpoint of understanding the physiology of behavior, much remains to be learned. For example, research has identified dopamine activity in the nucleus accumbens as central to reinforcement and addiction, but ... well, *why* is dopamine activity in that location reinforcing? Stimulation of 5-HT_{2A} receptors produces hallucinations, but again we ask, "Why?" In neuroscience or biological psychology, answering one question leads to new ones, and the deepest questions are usually the most difficult.

SUMMARY

1. A drug that increases activity at a synapse is an agonist; one that decreases activity is an antagonist. Drugs act in many ways, varying in their affinity (tendency to bind to a receptor) and efficacy (tendency to activate it). **71**

2. Reinforcing brain stimulation, reinforcing experiences, and self-administered drugs increase the activity of axons that release dopamine in the nucleus accumbens. **72**

3. Activity in the nucleus accumbens probably contributes more to "wanting" than to "liking," although it has a role in both. Addiction is based heavily on "wanting," as the amount of pleasure declines during addiction. **72**

4. Amphetamine, cocaine, and methylphenidate act by blocking the reuptake transporters and therefore decreasing the reuptake of dopamine and serotonin after their release. **73**

5. Nicotine excites acetylcholine receptors, including the ones on axon terminals that release dopamine in the nucleus accumbens. **74**

6. Opiate drugs stimulate endorphin receptors, which inhibit the release of GABA, which would otherwise inhibit the release of dopamine. Thus, the net effect of opiates is increased dopamine release. **74**

7. At certain synapses in many brain areas, after glutamate excites the postsynaptic cell, the cell responds by releasing endocannabinoids that inhibit further release of both glutamate and GABA by nearby neurons. Chemicals in marijuana mimic the effects of these endocannabinoids. **75**

8. Hallucinogens act by stimulating certain kinds of serotonin receptors. **76**

9. Compared to Type I alcoholism, Type II alcoholism starts faster and sooner, is usually more severe, and affects more men than women. Genes influence alcoholism in several ways, including effects on impulsiveness, responses to stress, and overall calmness. **77**

10. Risk factors for alcoholism, in addition to a family history, include feeling low intoxication after moderate drinking and experiencing much relief from stress after drinking. **77**

11. People with an addiction learn to use an addictive habit to cope with stress. **79**

12. Addiction is associated with sensitization of the nucleus accumbens so that it responds more strongly to the addictive activity and less to other kinds of reinforcement. **79**

13. Ethyl alcohol is metabolized to acetaldehyde, which is then metabolized to acetic acid. People who, for genetic reasons, are deficient in that second reaction tend to become ill after drinking and therefore are unlikely to drink heavily. **80**

14. Antabuse, a drug sometimes used to treat alcohol abuse, blocks the conversion of acetaldehyde to acetic acid. **80**

15. Methadone and similar drugs are sometimes offered as a substitute for opiate drugs. The substitutes have the advantage that if taken orally, they satisfy the cravings without severely interrupting the person's ability to carry on with life. **80**

KEY TERMS

Terms are defined in the module on the page number indicated. They're also presented in alphabetical order with definitions in the book's Subject Index/Glossary, which begins on page 561. Interactive flashcards and crossword puzzles are among the online resources available to help you learn these terms and the concepts they represent.

affinity 71

agonist 71

alcoholism (alcohol
   dependence) 77

amphetamine 73

anandamide 75

Antabuse 80

antagonist 71

cannabinoids 75

cocaine 73

Δ^9-tetrahydrocannabinol
   (Δ^9-THC) 75

dopamine transporter 73

efficacy 71

hallucinogenic drugs 76

methadone 80

methylphenidate 74

nicotine 74

nucleus accumbens 72

opiate drugs 74

self-stimulation of the
   brain 71

stimulant drugs 73

2-AG 75

tolerance 78

Type I (Type A)
   alcoholism 77

Type II (Type B)
   alcoholism 77

withdrawal 79

THOUGHT QUESTIONS

1. People who take methylphenidate (Ritalin) for control of attention-deficit disorder often report that, although the drug increases their arousal for a while, they feel a decrease in alertness and arousal a few hours later. Explain.

2. The research on sensitization of the nucleus accumbens has dealt with addictive drugs, mainly cocaine. Would you expect a gambling addiction to have similar effects? How could someone test this possibility?

CHAPTER 3 Interactive Exploration and Study

The **Psychology CourseMate** for this text brings chapter topics to life with interactive learning, study, and exam preparation tools, including quizzes and flashcards for the Key Concepts that appear throughout each module, as well as an interactive media-rich eBook version of the text that is fully searchable and includes highlighting and note taking capabilities and interactive versions of the book's **Stop & Check** quizzes and **Try It Yourself Online** activities. The site also features **Virtual Biological Psychology Labs, videos,** and **animations** to help you better understand concepts—logon and learn more at **www.cengagebrain.com**, which is your gateway to all of this text's complimentary and premium resources, including the following:

Virtual Biological Psychology Labs

Explore the experiments that led to modern-day understanding of biopsychology with the Virtual Biological Psychology Labs, featuring a realistic lab environment that allows you to conduct experiments and evaluate data to better understand how scientists came to the conclusions presented in your text. The labs cover a range of topics, including perception, motivation, cognition, and more. You may purchase access at **www.cengagebrain.com**, or login at **login.cengagebrain.com** if an access card was included with your text.

Videos

Understanding Addiction

Animations

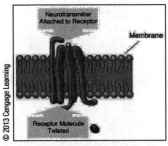

Metabotropic Demonstration

Also available—

- Post-synaptic Potentials
- Synaptic Activation
- Transmitter Release Demo
- Release of Neurotransmitter
- Cholinergic Synapse
- Acetylcholinesterase Inhibits Acetylcholine
- Opiates

Suggestions for Further Exploration

Books

McKim, W. A. (2007). *Drugs and behavior* (6th ed.). Upper Saddle River, NJ: Prentice Hall. Concise, informative text on drugs and drug abuse.

Websites

The Psychology CourseMate for this text provides regularly updated links to relevant online resources for this chapter, such as **The Endocrine Society** and **Nucleus Accumbens.**

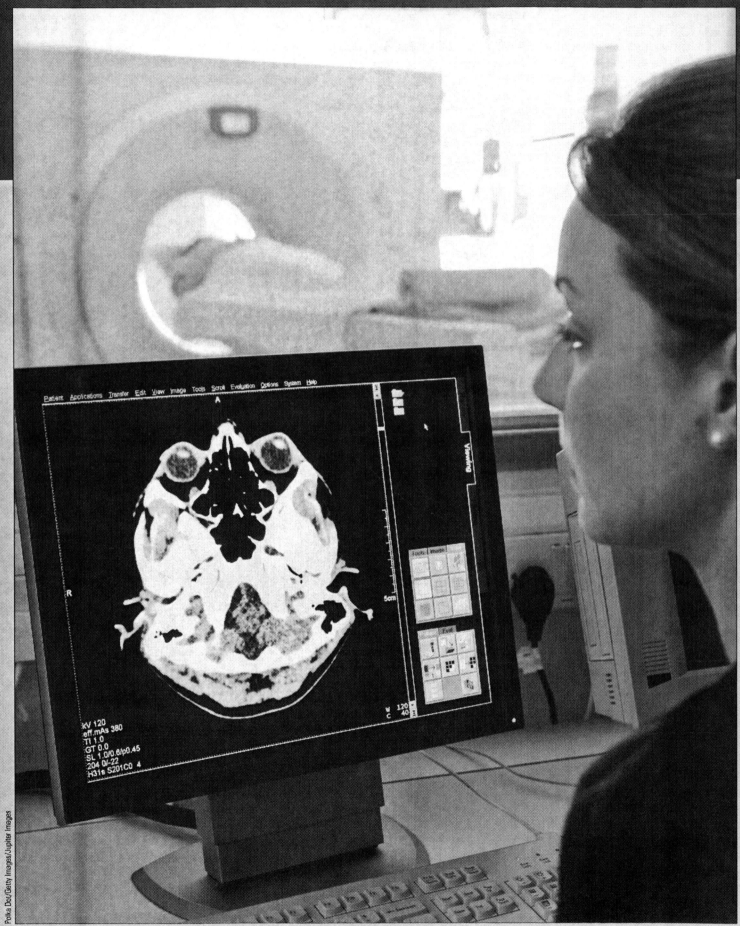

Anatomy of the Nervous System

4

CHAPTER OUTLINE

OPPOSITE: New methods allow researchers to examine living brains.

MAIN IDEAS

1. Each part of the nervous system has specialized functions. Damage to different areas results in different behavioral deficits.

2. The cerebral cortex, the largest structure in the mammalian brain, elaborately processes sensory information and provides fine control of movement.

3. As research has identified the different functions of different brain areas, a new question has arisen: How do the areas work together to produce unified experience and behavior?

4. It is difficult to conduct research on the functions of the nervous system. Conclusions come from multiple methods and careful behavioral measurements.

Trying to learn **neuroanatomy** (the anatomy of the nervous system) from a book is like trying to learn geography from a road map. A map can tell you that Mystic, Georgia, is about 40 km north of Enigma, Georgia. Similarly, a book can tell you that the habenula is about 4.6 mm from the interpeduncular nucleus in a rat's brain (proportionately farther in a human brain). But these little gems of information will seem both mysterious and enigmatic unless you are concerned with that part of Georgia or that area of the brain.

This chapter does not provide a detailed road map of the nervous system. It is more like a world globe, describing the large, basic structures (analogous to the continents) and some distinctive features of each.

The first module introduces key neuroanatomical terms and outlines overall structures of the nervous system. In the second module, we concentrate on the structures and functions of the cerebral cortex, the largest part of the mammalian central nervous system. The third module deals with the main methods that researchers use to discover the behavioral functions of brain areas.

Be prepared: This chapter contains a huge number of new terms. You should not expect to memorize all of them at once, and you should review this chapter repeatedly.

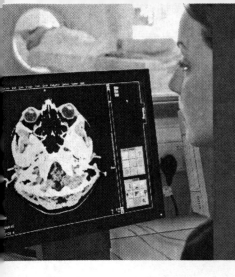

Structure of the Vertebrate Nervous System

Your nervous system consists of many substructures, a huge number of neurons, and an even huger number of synapses. How do all the parts work together to make one behaving unit? Does each neuron have an independent function? Or does the brain operate as an undifferentiated whole?

The answer is, "something between those extremes." Consider an analogy to human society: Each individual has a special role, such as teacher, farmer, or nurse, but no one performs any function without the cooperation of many other people. Similarly, each brain area and each neuron has a specialized role, but they also depend on the cooperation of other areas.

Terminology to Describe the Nervous System

For vertebrates, we distinguish the central nervous system from the peripheral nervous system (Figure 4.1). The **central nervous system (CNS)** is the brain and the spinal cord. The **peripheral nervous system (PNS)** connects the brain and spinal cord to the rest of the body. Part of

the PNS is the **somatic nervous system**, which consists of the axons conveying messages from the sense organs to the CNS and from the CNS to the muscles. The axons to the

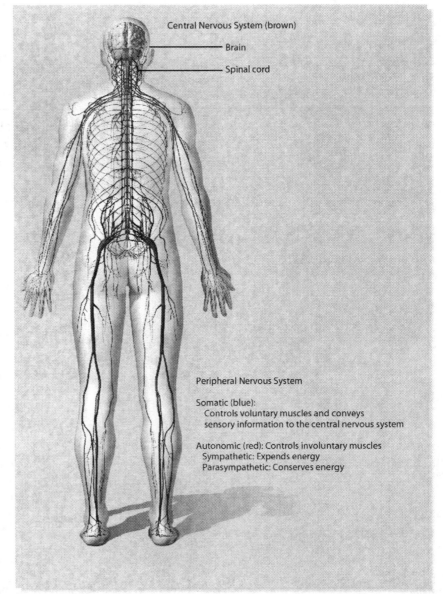

Central Nervous System (brown)
— Brain
— Spinal cord

Peripheral Nervous System

Somatic (blue):
  Controls voluntary muscles and conveys
  sensory information to the central nervous system

Autonomic (red): Controls involuntary muscles
  Sympathetic: Expends energy
  Parasympathetic: Conserves energy

FIGURE 4.1 The human nervous system
The central nervous system consists of the brain and spinal cord. The peripheral nervous system is the nerves outside the brain and spinal cord. (© Argosy Publishing Inc.)

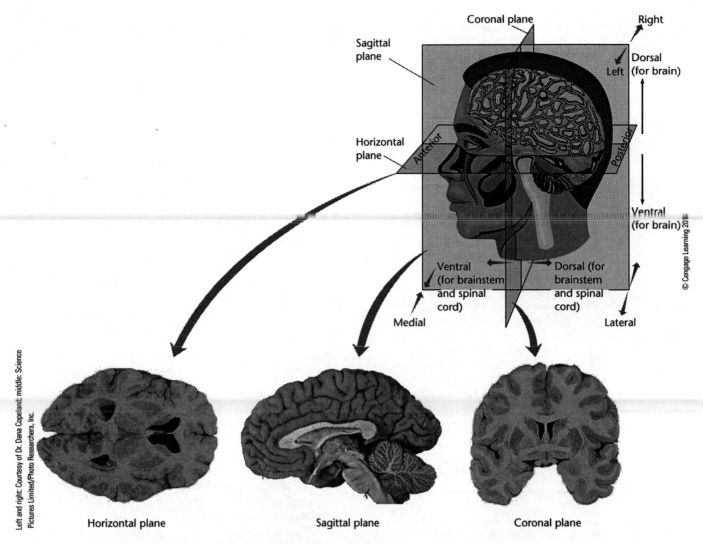

FIGURE 4.2 Terms for anatomical directions in the nervous system
In four-legged animals, dorsal and ventral point in the same direction for the head as they do for the rest of the body. However, humans' upright posture has tilted the head, so the dorsal and ventral directions of the head are not parallel to those of the spinal cord.

muscles are an extension from cell bodies in the spinal cord, so part of each cell is in the CNS and part is in the PNS. Another part of the PNS, the **autonomic nervous system**, controls the heart, intestines, and other organs. The autonomic nervous system has some of its cell bodies within the brain or spinal cord and some in clusters along the sides of the spinal cord.

To follow a map, you must understand *north, south, east,* and *west.* Because the nervous system is three-dimensional, we need more terms to describe it. As Figure 4.2 and Table 4.1 indicate, **dorsal** means toward the back and **ventral** means toward the stomach. (One way to remember these terms is that a *ventri*loquist is literally a "stomach talker.") In a four-legged animal, the top of the brain is dorsal (on the same side as the animal's back), and the bottom of the brain

is ventral (on the stomach side). The same would be true for you if you got down on your knees and crawled. However, when humans evolved upright posture, the position of the head changed relative to the spinal cord. For convenience, we still apply the terms *dorsal* and *ventral* to the same parts of the human brain as other vertebrate brains. Consequently, the dorsal–ventral axis of the human brain is at a right angle to the dorsal–ventral axis of the spinal cord. Figure 4.2 also illustrates the three ways of taking a plane through the brain, known as horizontal, sagittal, and coronal (or frontal).

Table 4.2 introduces additional terms that are worth learning. Tables 4.1 and 4.2 require careful study and review. After you think you have mastered the terms, check yourself with the following.

TABLE 4.1	Anatomical Terms Referring to Directions
Term	**Definition**
Dorsal	Toward the back, away from the ventral (stomach) side. The top of the brain is considered dorsal because it has that position in four-legged animals.
Ventral	Toward the stomach, away from the dorsal (back) side
Anterior	Toward the front end
Posterior	Toward the rear end
Superior	Above another part
Inferior	Below another part
Lateral	Toward the side, away from the midline
Medial	Toward the midline, away from the side
Proximal	Located close (approximate) to the point of origin or attachment
Distal	Located more distant from the point of origin or attachment
Ipsilateral	On the same side of the body (e.g., two parts on the left or two on the right)
Contralateral	On the opposite side of the body (one on the left and one on the right)
Coronal plane	A plane that shows brain structures as seen from the front (or frontal plane)
Sagittal plane	A plane that shows brain structures as seen from the side
Horizontal plane	A plane that shows brain structures as seen from above (or transverse plane)

© Cengage Learning 2013

TABLE 4.2	Terms Referring to Parts of the Nervous System
Term	**Definition**
Lamina	A row or layer of cell bodies separated from other cell bodies by a layer of axons and dendrites
Column	A set of cells perpendicular to the surface of the cortex, with similar properties
Tract	A set of axons within the CNS, also known as a projection. If axons extend from cell bodies in structure A to synapses onto B, we say that the fibers "project" from A onto B.
Nerve	A set of axons in the periphery, either from the CNS to a muscle or gland or from a sensory organ to the CNS
Nucleus	A cluster of neuron cell bodies within the CNS
Ganglion	A cluster of neuron cell bodies, usually outside the CNS (as in the sympathetic nervous system)
Gyrus (pl.: gyri)	A protuberance on the surface of the brain
Sulcus (pl.: sulci)	A fold or groove that separates one gyrus from another
Fissure	A long, deep sulcus

© Cengage Learning 2013

 **Stop & Check**

1. What does *dorsal* mean, and what is its opposite?

2. What term means *toward the side, away from the midline*, and what is its opposite?

3. If two structures are both on the left side of the body, they are _____ to each other. If one is on the left and the other is on the right, they are _____ to each other.

4. The bulges in the cerebral cortex are called _____ . The grooves between them are called _____ .

ANSWERS 1. Dorsal means toward the back, away from the stomach side. Its opposite is ventral. 2. lateral; medial 3. ipsilateral; contralateral 4. gyri; sulci. If you have trouble remembering sulcus, think of the word sulk, meaning "to pout" (and therefore lie low).

The Spinal Cord

The **spinal cord** is the part of the CNS within the spinal column. The spinal cord communicates with all the sense organs and muscles except those of the head. It is a segmented structure, and each segment has on each side a sensory nerve and a motor nerve, as Figure 4.3 shows. According to the **Bell-Magendie law**, which was one of the first discoveries about the functions of the nervous system, the entering dorsal roots (axon bundles) carry sensory information, and the exiting ventral roots carry motor information. The axons to and from the skin and muscles are the peripheral nervous system. The cell bodies of the sensory neurons are in clusters of neurons outside the spinal cord, called the **dorsal root ganglia**. (*Ganglia* is the plural of *ganglion*, a cluster of neurons. In most cases, a neuron cluster outside the CNS is called a ganglion, and a cluster inside the CNS is called a nucleus.) Cell bodies of the motor neurons are inside the spinal cord.

In the cross-section through the spinal cord shown in Figures 4.4 and 4.5, the H-shaped **gray matter** in the center of the cord is densely packed with cell bodies and dendrites. Many neurons of the spinal cord send axons from the gray matter to the brain or other parts of the spinal cord through the **white matter**, which consists mostly of myelinated axons.

Each segment of the spinal cord sends sensory information to the brain and receives motor commands from the brain. All that information passes through tracts of axons in the spinal cord. If the spinal cord is cut at a given segment, the brain loses sensation from that segment and below. The brain also loses motor control over all parts of the body served by that segment and the lower ones.

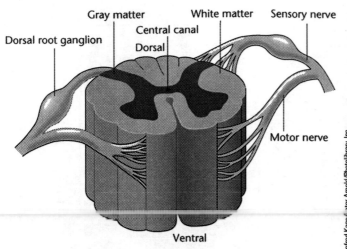

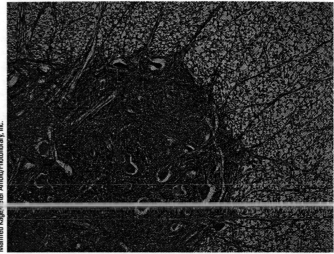

FIGURE 4.3 Diagram of a cross-section through the spinal cord
The dorsal root on each side conveys sensory information to the spinal cord; the ventral root conveys motor commands to the muscles. *(© Cengage Learning 2013)*

FIGURE 4.5 A section of gray matter of the spinal cord (lower left) and white matter surrounding it
Cell bodies and dendrites reside entirely in the gray matter. Axons travel from one area of gray matter to another in the white matter.

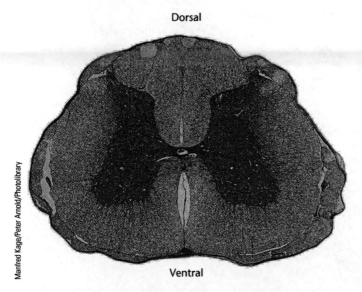

FIGURE 4.4 Photo of a cross-section through the spinal cord
The H-shaped structure in the center is gray matter, composed largely of cell bodies. The surrounding white matter consists of axons. The axons are organized in tracts; some carry information from the brain and higher levels of the spinal cord downward, while others carry information from lower levels upward.

▌The Autonomic Nervous System

The autonomic nervous system consists of neurons that receive information from and send commands to the heart, intestines, and other organs. It has two parts: the sympathetic and parasympathetic nervous systems (Figure 4.6). The **sympathetic nervous system**, a network of nerves that prepare the organs for vigorous activity, consists of chains of ganglia just to the left and right of the spinal cord's central regions (the thoracic and lumbar areas). These ganglia are connected by axons to the spinal cord. Sympathetic axons prepare the organs for "fight or flight"—increasing breathing and heart rate and decreasing digestive activity. Because the sympathetic ganglia are closely linked, they often act as a single system "in sympathy" with one another, although various events activate some parts more than others. The sweat glands, the adrenal glands, the muscles that constrict blood vessels, and the muscles that erect the hairs of the skin have only sympathetic, not parasympathetic, input.

The **parasympathetic nervous system** facilitates vegetative, nonemergency responses. The term *para* means "beside" or "related to," and parasympathetic activities are related to, and generally the opposite of, sympathetic activities. For example, the sympathetic nervous system increases heart rate, but the parasympathetic nervous system decreases it. The parasympathetic nervous system increases digestive activity, whereas the sympathetic nervous system decreases it. Although the sympathetic and parasympathetic systems produce contrary effects, both are constantly active to varying degrees, and many stimuli arouse parts of both systems.

The parasympathetic nervous system is also known as the craniosacral system because it consists of the cranial nerves and nerves from the sacral spinal cord (Figure 4.6). Unlike the ganglia in the sympathetic system, the parasympathetic ganglia are not arranged in a chain near the spinal cord. Rather, long *preganglionic* axons extend from the spinal cord to parasympathetic ganglia close to each internal organ. Shorter *postganglionic* fibers then extend from the parasympathetic ganglia into the organs themselves. Because the parasympathetic ganglia are not linked to one another, they act more independently than the sympathetic ganglia do. Parasympathetic activity decreases heart rate, increases digestive rate, and, in general, conserves energy.

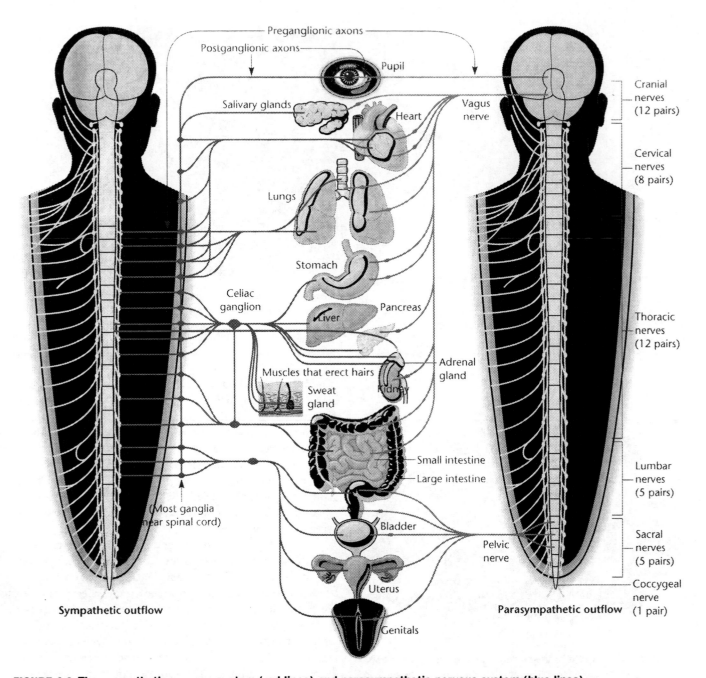

FIGURE 4.6 The sympathetic nervous system (red lines) and parasympathetic nervous system (blue lines)
Note that the adrenal glands and hair erector muscles receive sympathetic input only. *(Starr & Taggart, 1989)*

The parasympathetic nervous system's postganglionic axons release the neurotransmitter acetylcholine. Most of the postganglionic synapses of the sympathetic nervous system use norepinephrine, although a few, such as those that control the sweat glands, use acetylcholine. Because the two systems use different transmitters, certain drugs excite or inhibit one system or the other. For example, over-the-counter cold remedies exert most of their effects by blocking parasympathetic activity or increasing sympathetic activity. Because the flow of sinus fluids is a parasympathetic response, drugs that block the parasympathetic system inhibit sinus flow. The side effects of cold remedies stem from their pro-sympathetic, anti-parasympathetic activities: They increase heart rate and inhibit salivation and digestion.

Stop & Check

5. Sensory nerves enter which side of the spinal cord, dorsal or ventral?

6. Which functions are controlled by the sympathetic nervous system? Which are controlled by the parasympathetic nervous system?

ANSWERS

5. Dorsal 6. The sympathetic nervous system prepares the organs for vigorous fight-or-flight activity. The parasympathetic system increases vegetative responses such as digestion.

Goose Bumps

Erection of the hairs, known as "goose bumps" or "goose flesh," occurs when we are cold. What does it have to do with the fight-or-flight functions associated with the sympathetic nervous system? Part of the answer is that we also get goose bumps when we are frightened. You have heard the expression, "I was so frightened my hairs stood on end." You may also have seen a frightened cat erect its fur. Human body hairs are so short that erecting them accomplishes nothing, but a cat with erect fur looks bigger. A frightened porcupine erects its quills, which are just modified hairs (Richter & Langworthy, 1933). The behavior that makes the quills so useful—their erection in response to fear—evolved before the quills themselves did. ∎

▌The Hindbrain

The brain has three major divisions: the hindbrain, the midbrain, and the forebrain (Figure 4.7 and Table 4.3). Some neuroscientists prefer these terms with Greek roots: rhombencephalon (hindbrain), mesencephalon (midbrain), and prosencephalon (forebrain). You may encounter these terms in other reading.

The **hindbrain**, the posterior part of the brain, consists of the medulla, the pons, and the cerebellum. The medulla and pons, the midbrain, and certain central structures of the forebrain constitute the **brainstem** (Figure 4.8).

The **medulla**, or medulla oblongata, is just above the spinal cord and can be regarded as an enlarged extension of the spinal cord into the skull. The medulla controls vital reflexes—including breathing, heart rate, vomiting, salivation, coughing, and sneezing—through the **cranial nerves**, which control sensations from the head, muscle movements in the head, and much of the parasympathetic output to the or-

TABLE 4.3	Major Divisions of the Vertebrate Brain	
Area	**Also Known as**	**Major Structures**
Forebrain	Prosencephalon ("forward-brain")	
	Diencephalon ("between-brain")	Thalamus, hypothalamus
	Telencephalon ("end-brain")	Cerebral cortex, hippocampus, basal ganglia
Midbrain	Mesencephalon ("middle-brain")	Tectum, tegmentum, superior colliculus, inferior colliculus, substantia nigra inferior colliculus, substantia nigra
Hindbrain	Rhombencephalon (literally, "parallelogram-brain")	Medulla, pons, cerebellum
	Metencephalon ("afterbrain")	Pons, cerebellum
	Myelencephalon ("marrow-brain")	Medulla

© Cengage Learning 2013

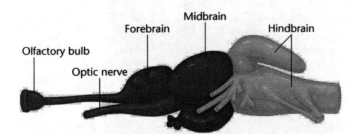

FIGURE 4.7 Three major divisions of the vertebrate brain
In a fish brain, as shown here, the forebrain, midbrain, and hindbrain are clearly visible as separate bulges. In adult mammals, the forebrain grows and surrounds the entire midbrain and part of the hindbrain. (© Cengage Learning 2013)

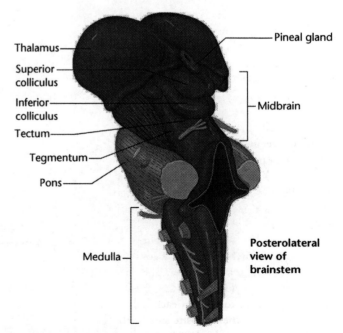

FIGURE 4.8 The human brainstem
This composite structure extends from the top of the spinal cord into the center of the forebrain. The pons, pineal gland, and colliculi are ordinarily surrounded by the cerebral cortex. (© Cengage Learning 2013)

TABLE 4.4 The Cranial Nerves

Number and Name	Major Functions
I. Olfactory	Smell
II. Optic	Vision
III. Oculomotor	Control of eye movements; pupil constriction
IV. Trochlear	Control of eye movement
V. Trigeminal	Skin sensations from most of the face; control of jaw muscles for chewing and swallowing
VI. Abducens	Control of eye movements
VII. Facial	Taste from the anterior two thirds of the tongue; control of facial expressions, crying, salivation, and dilation of the head's blood vessels
VIII. Statoacoustic	Hearing; equilibrium
IX. Glossopharyngeal	Taste and other sensations from throat and posterior third of the tongue; control of swallowing, salivation, throat movements during speech
X. Vagus	Sensations from neck and thorax; control of throat, esophagus, and larynx; parasympathetic nerves to stomach, intestines, and other organs
XI. Accessory	Control of neck and shoulder movements
XII. Hypoglossal	Control of muscles of the tongue

Cranial nerves III, IV, and VI are coded in red to highlight their similarity: control of eye movements. Cranial nerves VII, IX, and XII are coded in green to highlight their similarity: taste and control of tongue and throat movements. Cranial nerve VII has other important functions as well. Nerve X (not highlighted) also contributes to throat movements, although it is primarily known for other functions.
© Cengage Learning 2013

gans. Some of the cranial nerves include both sensory and motor components, whereas others have just one or the other. Damage to the medulla is frequently fatal, and large doses of opiates are life-threatening because they suppress activity of the medulla.

Just as the lower parts of the body are connected to the spinal cord via sensory and motor nerves, the receptors and muscles of the head and organs connect to the brain by 12 pairs of cranial nerves (one of each pair on the right side and one on the left), as shown in Table 4.4. Each cranial nerve originates in a *nucleus* (cluster of neurons) that integrates the sensory information, regulates the motor output, or both. The cranial nerve nuclei for nerves V through XII are in the medulla and pons. Those for cranial nerves I through IV are in the midbrain and forebrain (Figure 4.9).

The **pons** lies anterior and ventral to the medulla. Like the medulla, it contains nuclei for several cranial nerves. The term *pons* is Latin for "bridge," reflecting the fact that in the pons, axons from each half of the brain cross to the opposite side of the spinal cord so that the left hemisphere controls the muscles of the right side of the body and the right hemisphere controls the left side.

The medulla and pons also contain the reticular formation and the raphe sys-

tem. The **reticular formation** has descending and ascending portions. The descending portion is one of several brain areas

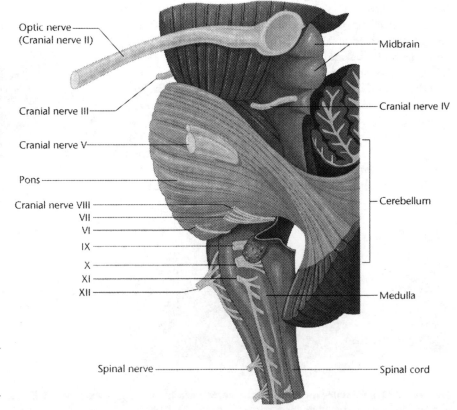

FIGURE 4.9 Cranial nerves II through XII
Cranial nerve I, the olfactory nerve, connects directly to the olfactory bulbs of the forebrain. *(Based on Braus, 1960)*

that control the motor areas of the spinal cord. The ascending portion sends output to much of the cerebral cortex, selectively increasing arousal and attention in one area or another (Guillery, Feig, & Lozsádi, 1998). The **raphe system** also sends axons to much of the forebrain, modifying the brain's readiness to respond to stimuli (Mesulam, 1995).

The **cerebellum** is a large hindbrain structure with many deep folds. It has long been known for its contributions to the control of movement (Chapter 8), and many older textbooks describe the cerebellum as important for "balance and coordination." True, people with cerebellar damage are clumsy and lose their balance, but the functions of the cerebellum extend far beyond balance and coordination. People with damage to the cerebellum have trouble shifting their attention back and forth between auditory and visual stimuli (Courchesne et al., 1994). They have much difficulty with timing, including sensory timing. For example, they are poor at judging whether one rhythm is faster than another.

▮ The Midbrain

As the name implies, the **midbrain** is in the middle of the brain, although in adult mammals it is dwarfed and surrounded by the forebrain. The midbrain is more prominent in

birds, reptiles, amphibians, and fish. The roof of the midbrain is called the **tectum**. (*Tectum* is the Latin word for "roof." The same root occurs in the geological term *plate tectonics*.) The swellings on each side of the tectum are the **superior colliculus** and the **inferior colliculus** (Figures 4.8 and 4.10). Both are important for sensory processing—the inferior colliculus for hearing and the superior colliculus for vision.

Under the tectum lies the **tegmentum**, the intermediate level of the midbrain. (In Latin, *tegmentum* means a "covering," such as a rug on the floor. The tegmentum covers several other midbrain structures, although it is covered by the tectum.) The tegmentum includes the nuclei for the third and fourth cranial nerves, parts of the reticular formation, and extensions of the pathways between the forebrain and the spinal cord or hindbrain. Another midbrain structure, the **substantia nigra**, gives rise to a dopamine-containing pathway that facilitates readiness for movement (Chapter 8).

▮ The Forebrain

The **forebrain** is the most prominent part of the mammalian brain. It consists of two cerebral hemispheres, one on the left and one on the right (Figure 4.11). Each hemisphere is organized to receive sensory information, mostly from the contralateral (opposite) side of the body, and to control muscles,

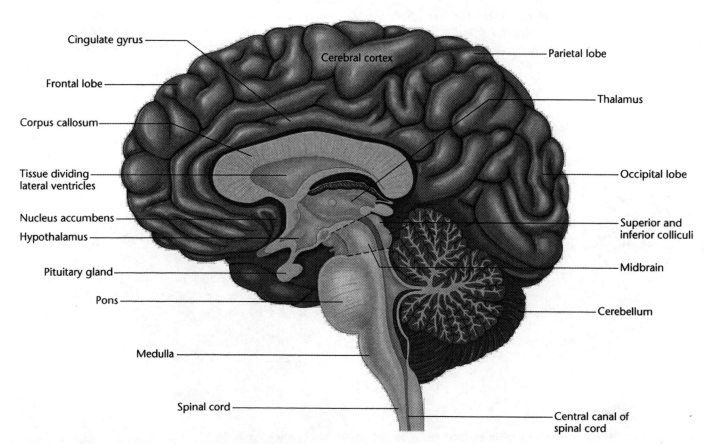

FIGURE 4.10 A sagittal section through the human brain
(After Nieuwenhuys, Voogd, & vanHuijzen, 1988)

mostly on the contralateral side, by way of axons to the spinal cord and the cranial nerve nuclei.

The outer portion is the cerebral cortex. (*Cerebrum* is a Latin word meaning "brain." *Cortex* is a Latin word for "bark" or "shell.") Under the cerebral cortex are other structures, including the thalamus, which is the main source of input to the cerebral cortex. The basal ganglia are a set of structures important for certain aspects of movement. A number of other interlinked structures, known as the **limbic system**, form a border (or *limbus*, the Latin word for "border") around the brainstem. These structures are particularly important for motivations and emotions, such as eating, drinking, sexual activity, anxiety, and aggression. The limbic system includes the olfactory bulb, hypothalamus, hippocampus, amygdala, and cingulate gyrus of the cerebral cortex. Figure 4.12 shows the positions of these structures in three-dimensional perspective. Figures 4.10 and 4.13 show coronal (from the front) and sagittal (from the side) sections through the human brain. Figure 4.13 also includes a view of the ventral surface of the brain.

In describing the forebrain, we begin with the subcortical areas. The next module focuses on the cerebral cortex. In later chapters, we return to each of these areas as they become relevant.

Thalamus

The thalamus and hypothalamus form the *diencephalon*, a section distinct from the *telencephalon*, which is the rest of the forebrain. The **thalamus** is a pair of structures (left and right) in the center of the forebrain. The term derives from a Greek word meaning "anteroom," "inner chamber," or "bridal bed." It resembles two avocados joined side by side, one in the left hemisphere and one in the right. Most sensory information goes first to the thalamus, which processes it and sends output to the cerebral cortex. An exception to this rule is olfactory information, which progresses from the olfactory receptors to the olfactory bulbs and then directly to the cerebral cortex.

Many nuclei of the thalamus receive their input from a sensory system, such as vision, and transmit information to a single area of the cerebral cortex, as in Figure 4.14. The cerebral cortex sends information back to the thalamus, prolonging and magnifying certain kinds of input at the expense of others, thereby focusing attention on particular stimuli (Komura et al., 2001).

Hypothalamus

The **hypothalamus** is a small area near the base of the brain just ventral to the thalamus (Figures 4.10 and 4.12). It has widespread connections with the rest of the forebrain and the midbrain. The hypothalamus contains a number of distinct nuclei, which we examine in Chapters 10 and 11. Partly through nerves and partly through hypothalamic hormones, the hypothalamus conveys messages to the pituitary gland, altering its release of hormones. Damage to any hypothalamic nucleus leads to abnormalities in motivated behaviors, such as feeding, drinking, temperature regulation, sexual behavior, fighting, or activity level. Because of these important behavioral effects, the small hypothalamus attracts much research attention.

Anterior

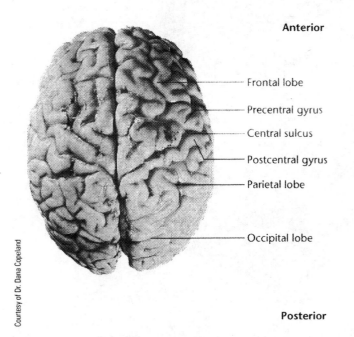

Frontal lobe

Precentral gyrus

Central sulcus

Postcentral gyrus

Parietal lobe

Occipital lobe

Courtesy of Dr. Dana Copeland

Posterior

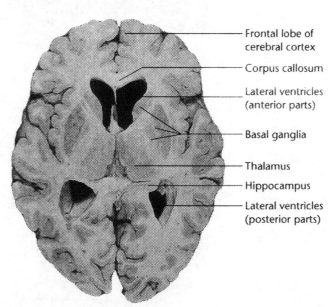

Frontal lobe of cerebral cortex

Corpus callosum

Lateral ventricles (anterior parts)

Basal ganglia

Thalamus

Hippocampus

Lateral ventricles (posterior parts)

FIGURE 4.11 **Dorsal view of the brain surface and a horizontal section through the brain**

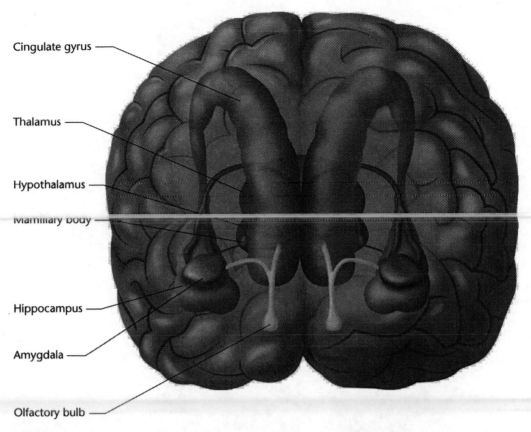

Cingulate gyrus

Thalamus

Hypothalamus

Mamillary body

Hippocampus

Amygdala

Olfactory bulb

FIGURE 4.12 The limbic system is a set of subcortical structures that form a border (or limbus) around the brainstem
(© Cengage Learning 2013)

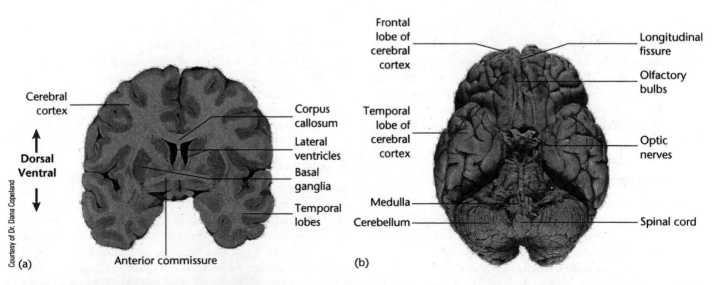

Cerebral cortex

Dorsal

Ventral

Corpus callosum

Lateral ventricles

Basal ganglia

Temporal lobes

Anterior commissure

(a)

Courtesy of Dr. Dana Copeland

Frontal lobe of cerebral cortex

Temporal lobe of cerebral cortex

Medulla

Cerebellum

Longitudinal fissure

Olfactory bulbs

Optic nerves

Spinal cord

(b)

FIGURE 4.13 Two views of the human brain
(a) A coronal section. Note how the corpus callosum and anterior commissure provide communication between the left and right hemispheres. **(b)** The ventral surface. The optic nerves (cut here) extend from the eyes to the brain.

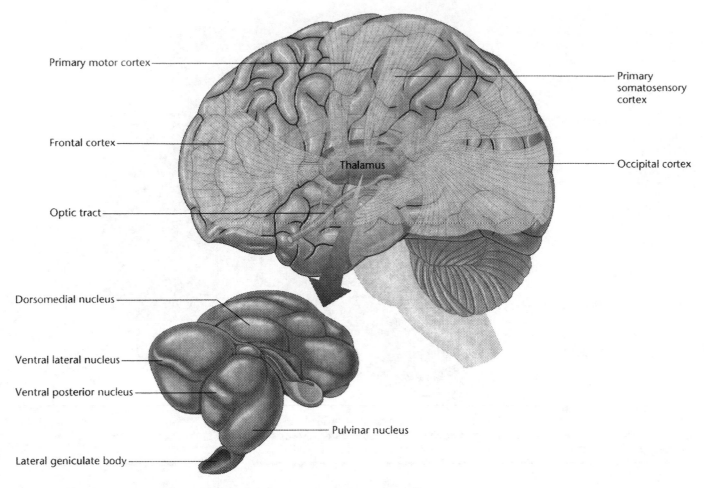

Primary motor cortex

Frontal cortex

Optic tract

Thalamus

Primary somatosensory cortex

Occipital cortex

Dorsomedial nucleus

Ventral lateral nucleus

Ventral posterior nucleus

Pulvinar nucleus

Lateral geniculate body

FIGURE 4.14 Routes of information from the thalamus to the cerebral cortex
Each thalamic nucleus projects its axons to a different location in the cortex. *(After Nieuwenhuys, Voogd, & vanHuijzen, 1988)*

Pituitary Gland

The **pituitary gland** is an endocrine (hormone-producing) gland attached to the base of the hypothalamus by a stalk that contains neurons, blood vessels, and connective tissue (Figure 4.10). In response to messages from the hypothalamus, the pituitary synthesizes hormones that the blood carries to organs throughout the body.

Basal Ganglia

The **basal ganglia**, a group of subcortical structures lateral to the thalamus, include three major structures: the caudate nucleus, the putamen, and the globus pallidus (Figure 4.15). Some authorities include other structures as well.

The basal ganglia have subdivisions that exchange information with different parts of the cerebral cortex. It has long been known that damage to the basal ganglia impairs movement, as in conditions such as Parkinson's disease and Huntington's disease. However, the role of the basal ganglia extends beyond movement. The basal ganglia are critical for learning and remembering how to do something (as opposed to learning factual information or remembering specific events). They are also important for attention, language, planning, and other cognitive functions (Stocco, Lebiere, & Anderson, 2010).

Basal Forebrain

Several structures lie on the ventral surface of the forebrain, including the **nucleus basalis**, which receives input from the hypothalamus and basal ganglia and sends axons that release acetylcholine to widespread areas in the cerebral cortex (Figure 4.16). The nucleus basalis is a key part of the brain's system for arousal, wakefulness, and attention, as we consider in Chapter 9. Patients with Parkinson's disease and Alzheimer's disease have impairments of attention and intellect because of inactivity or deterioration of their nucleus basalis.

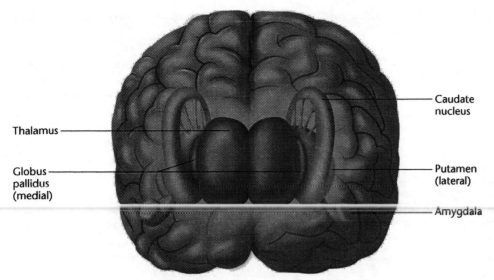

Thalamus

Globus pallidus (medial)

Caudate nucleus

Putamen (lateral)

Amygdala

FIGURE 4.15 The basal ganglia The thalamus is in the center, the basal ganglia are lateral to it, and the cerebral cortex is on the outside. *(After Nieuwenhuys, Voogd, & vanHuijzen, 1988)*

Hippocampus

The **hippocampus** (from the Latin word meaning "seahorse," a shape suggested by the hippocampus) is a large structure between the thalamus and the cerebral cortex, mostly toward the posterior of the forebrain, as shown in Figure 4.12. We consider the hippocampus in more detail in Chapter 12. The gist of that discussion is that the hippocampus is critical for storing certain kinds of memories, especially memories for individual events. People with hippocampal damage have trouble storing new memories, but they do not lose all the memories they had before the damage occurred.

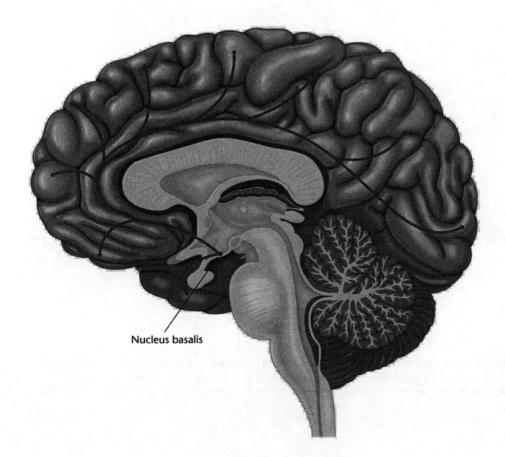

Nucleus basalis

FIGURE 4.16 The basal forebrain The nucleus basalis and other structures in this area send axons throughout the cortex, increasing its arousal and wakefulness through release of the neurotransmitter acetylcholine. *(After Woolf, 1991)*

Stop & Check

7. Of the following, which are in the hindbrain, which in the midbrain, and which in the forebrain: basal ganglia, cerebellum, hippocampus, hypothalamus, medulla, pituitary gland, pons, substantia nigra, superior and inferior colliculi, tectum, tegmentum, thalamus?

8. Which area is the main source of input to the cerebral cortex?

ANSWERS

8. Thalamus

7. Hindbrain: cerebellum, medulla, and pons. Midbrain: substantia nigra, superior and inferior colliculi, tectum, and tegmentum. Forebrain: basal ganglia, hippocampus, hypothalamus, pituitary, and thalamus.

▌The Ventricles

The nervous system begins its development as a tube surrounding a fluid canal. The canal persists into adulthood as the **central canal**, a fluid-filled channel in the center of the spinal cord, and as the **ventricles**, four fluid-filled cavities within the brain. Each hemisphere contains one of the two large lateral ventricles (Figure 4.17). Toward their posterior, they connect to the third ventricle, positioned at the midline, separating the left thalamus from the right thalamus. The third ventricle connects to the fourth ventricle in the center of the medulla.

Cells called the *choroid plexus* inside the four ventricles produce **cerebrospinal fluid (CSF)**, a clear fluid similar to blood plasma. CSF fills the ventricles, flowing from the lateral ventricles to the third and fourth ventricles. From the fourth ventricle, some of it flows into the central canal of the spinal cord, but more goes into the narrow spaces between the brain and the thin **meninges**, membranes that surround the brain and spinal cord. In one of those narrow spaces, the subarachnoid space, the blood gradually reabsorbs the CSF. Although the brain has no pain receptors, the meninges do, and meningitis—inflammation of the meninges—is painful. Swollen blood vessels in the meninges are responsible for the pain of a migraine headache (Hargreaves, 2007).

Cerebrospinal fluid cushions the brain against mechanical shock when the head moves. It also provides buoyancy. Just as a person weighs less in water than on land, cerebrospinal fluid helps support the weight of the brain. It also provides a reservoir of hormones and nutrition for the brain and spinal cord.

If the flow of CSF is obstructed, it accumulates within the ventricles or in the subarachnoid space, increasing pressure on the brain. When this occurs in infants, the skull bones spread, causing an overgrown head. This condition, known as *hydrocephalus* (HI-dro-SEFF-ah-luss), is usually associated with mental retardation.

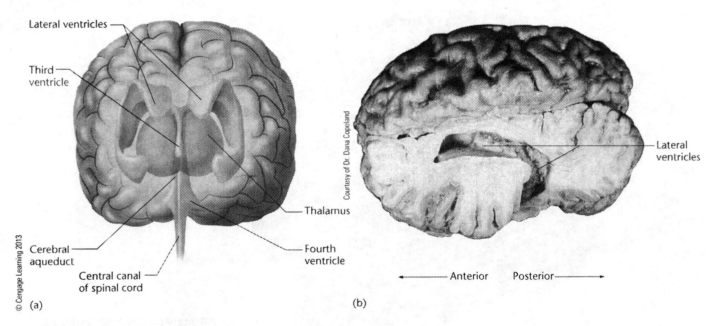

Courtesy of Dr. Dana Copeland

© Cengage Learning 2013

(a) (b)

FIGURE 4.17 The cerebral ventricles
(a) Diagram showing positions of the four ventricles. **(b)** Photo of a human brain, viewed from above, with a horizontal cut through one hemisphere to show the position of the lateral ventricles. Note that the two parts of this figure are seen from different angles.

MODULE 4.1 ■ IN CLOSING

Learning Neuroanatomy

The brain is a complex structure. This module has introduced a great many terms and facts. Do not be discouraged if you have trouble remembering them. It will help to return to this module to review anatomy as you encounter structures again in later chapters. Gradually, the material will become more familiar.

It helps to see the brain from different angles and perspectives. Check this fantastic website, The Whole Brain Atlas, which includes detailed photos of both normal and abnormal human brains: **http://www.med.harvard.edu/AANLIB/home.html**

SUMMARY

1. The vertebrate nervous system has two main divisions, the central nervous system and the peripheral nervous system. 86

2. Each segment of the spinal cord has a sensory nerve and a motor nerve on both the left and right sides. Spinal pathways convey information to the brain. 88

3. The sympathetic nervous system (one of the two divisions of the autonomic nervous system) activates the body's internal organs for vigorous activities. The parasympathetic system (the other division) promotes digestion and other nonemergency processes. 89

4. The central nervous system consists of the spinal cord, the hindbrain, the midbrain, and the forebrain. 91

5. The hindbrain consists of the medulla, pons, and cerebellum. The medulla and pons control breathing, heart rate, and other vital functions through the cranial nerves. The cerebellum contributes to movement and timing short intervals. 91

6. The cerebral cortex receives its sensory information (except for olfaction) from the thalamus. 94

7. The subcortical areas of the forebrain include the thalamus, hypothalamus, pituitary gland, basal ganglia, and hippocampus. 94

8. The cerebral ventricles contain fluid that provides buoyancy and cushioning for the brain. 98

KEY TERMS

Terms are defined in the module on the page number indicated. They're also presented in alphabetical order with definitions in the book's Subject Index/Glossary, which begins on page 561. Interactive flashcards and crossword puzzles are among the online resources available to help you learn these terms and the concepts they represent.

autonomic nervous system 87
basal ganglia 96
Bell-Magendie law 88
brainstem 91
central canal 98
central nervous system (CNS) 86
cerebellum 93
cerebrospinal fluid (CSF) 98
cranial nerves 91
dorsal 87
dorsal root ganglia 88
forebrain 93
gray matter 88

hindbrain 91
hippocampus 97
hypothalamus 94
inferior colliculus 93
limbic system 94
medulla 91
meninges 98
midbrain 93
neuroanatomy 85
nucleus basalis 96
parasympathetic nervous system 89
peripheral nervous system (PNS) 86
pituitary gland 96
pons 92

raphe system 93
reticular formation 93
somatic nervous system 86
spinal cord 88
substantia nigra 93
superior colliculus 93
sympathetic nervous system 89
tectum 93
tegmentum 93
thalamus 94
ventral 87
ventricles 98
white matter 88

THOUGHT QUESTION

The drug phenylephrine is sometimes prescribed for people suffering from a sudden loss of blood pressure or other medical disorders. It acts by stimulating norepinephrine synapses, including those that constrict blood vessels. One common side effect of this drug is goose bumps. Explain why. What other side effects might be likely?

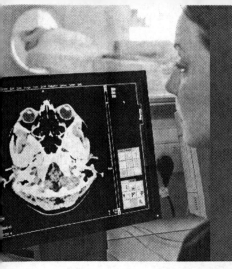

MODULE 4.2

The Cerebral Cortex

The most prominent part of the mammalian brain is the **cerebral cortex**, consisting of the cellular layers on the outer surface of the cerebral hemispheres. The cells of the cerebral cortex are gray matter, and their axons extending inward are white matter (Figure 4.13). Neurons in each hemisphere communicate with neurons in the corresponding part of the other hemisphere through two bundles of axons, the **corpus callosum** (Figures 4.10, 4.11, and 4.13) and the smaller **anterior commissure** (Figure 4.13). Several other commissures (pathways across the midline) link subcortical structures.

If we compare mammalian species, we see differences in the size of the cerebral cortex and the degree of folding (Figure 4.18). The cerebral cortex constitutes a higher percentage of the brain in **primates**—monkeys, apes, and humans—than in other species of comparable size. Figure 4.19 shows the size of the cerebral cortex in comparison to the rest of the brain for insectivores and two suborders of primates (Barton & Harvey, 2000). Figure 4.20 compares species in another way (D. A. Clark, Mitra, & Wang, 2001). The investigators arranged the insectivores and primates from left to right in terms of what percentage of their brain was devoted to the forebrain, which includes the cerebral cortex. They also inserted tree shrews, a species often considered intermediate. Note that as the proportion devoted to the forebrain increases, the relative sizes of

the midbrain and medulla decrease. Curiously, the cerebellum occupies a remarkably constant percentage—approximately 13% of any mammalian brain (D. A. Clark et al., 2001). That is, the cerebellum maintains an almost constant proportion to the whole brain. (Why? No one knows.)

Organization of the Cerebral Cortex

The microscopic structure of the cells of the cerebral cortex varies from one cortical area to another and correlates with differences in function. Much research has been directed toward understanding the relationship between structure and function.

In humans and most other mammals, the cerebral cortex contains up to six distinct **laminae**, layers of cell bodies that are parallel to the surface of the cortex and separated from each other by layers of fibers (Figure 4.21). The laminae vary in thickness and prominence from one part of the cortex to another, and a given lamina may be absent from certain areas. Lamina V, which sends long axons to the spinal cord and other distant areas, is thickest in the motor cortex, which has the greatest control of the muscles. Lamina IV, which receives axons from the various sensory nuclei of the thalamus, is

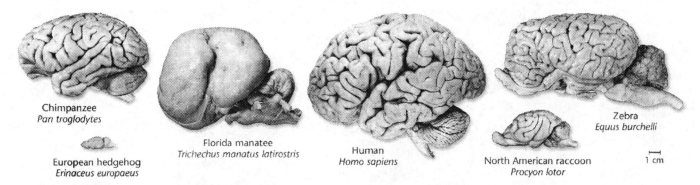

Chimpanzee
Pan troglodytes

European hedgehog
Erinaceus europaeus

Florida manatee
Trichechus manatus latirostris

Human
Homo sapiens

North American raccoon
Procyon lotor

Zebra
Equus burchelli

1 cm

FIGURE 4.18 Comparison of mammalian brains
The human brain is the largest of those shown, although whales, dolphins, and elephants have still larger brains. All mammals have the same brain subareas in the same locations. *(From the University of Wisconsin—Madison Comparative Mammalian Brain Collection, Wally Welker, Curator. Project supported by the Natural Science Foundation.)*

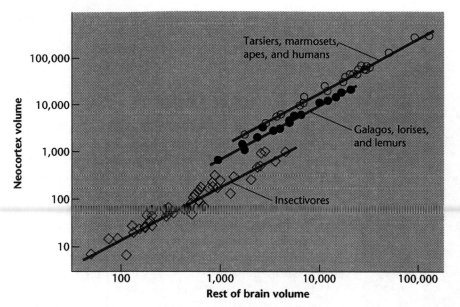

FIGURE 4.19 Relationship between volume of the cortex and volume of the rest of the brain
For each of the three groups, cortical volume increases quite predictably as a function of the volume of the rest of the brain. However, the lines for the two primate groups are displaced upward. *(Fig. 1, p. 1055 in R. A. Barton & R. H. Harvey, "Mosaic evolution of brain structure in mammals." Nature, 405, p. 1055–1058. Reprinted with permission from Nature. Copyright © 2000 Macmillan Magazine Limited.)*

prominent in all the primary sensory areas (visual, auditory, and somatosensory) but absent from the motor cortex.

The cells of the cortex are also organized into **columns** of cells perpendicular to the laminae. Figure 4.22 illustrates the idea of columns, although in nature they are not so straight. The cells within a given column have similar properties to one another. For example, if one cell in a column responds to touch on the palm of the left hand, then the other cells in that column do, too. If one cell responds to a horizontal pattern of light at a particular location, then other cells in the column respond to the same pattern in nearby locations.

We now turn to some specific parts of the cortex. Researchers make fine distinctions among areas of the cerebral cortex based on the structure and function of cells. For convenience, we group these areas into four *lobes* named for the skull bones that lie over them: occipital, parietal, temporal, and frontal.

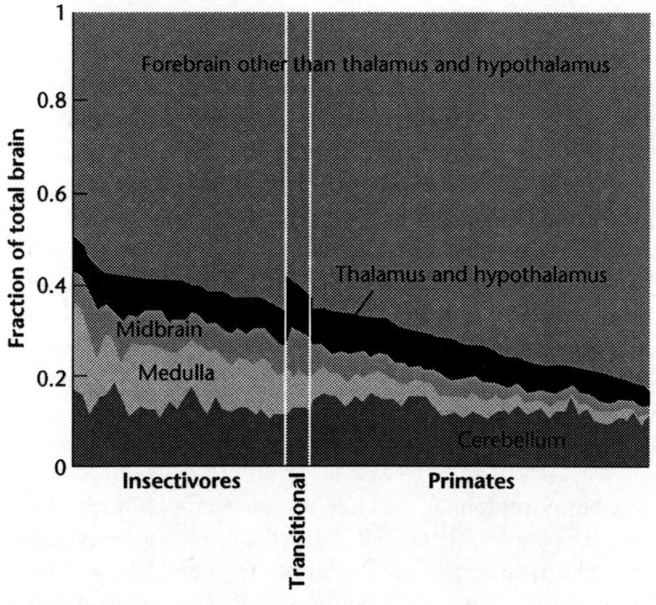

FIGURE 4.20 Relative sizes of five brain components in insectivores and primates
The forebrain composes a larger percentage of primate than insectivore brains. Note also the near constant fraction devoted to the cerebellum. *(Fig. 1, p. 189 in D. A. Clark, P. P. Mitra, & S. S-H. Wong, "Scalable architecture in mammalian brains." Nature, 411, pp. 189–193. Reprinted with permission from Nature. Copyright © 2001 Macmillan Magazine Limited.)*

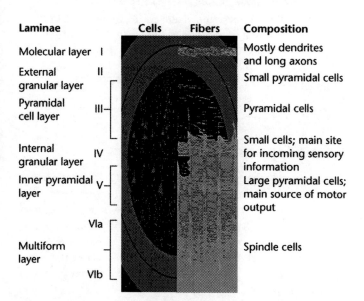

FIGURE 4.21 The six laminae of the human cerebral cortex
(From S. W. Ranson & S. L. Clark, The Anatomy of the Nervous System, 1959. Copyright © 1959 W. B. Saunders Co. Reprinted by permission.)

Surface of cortex

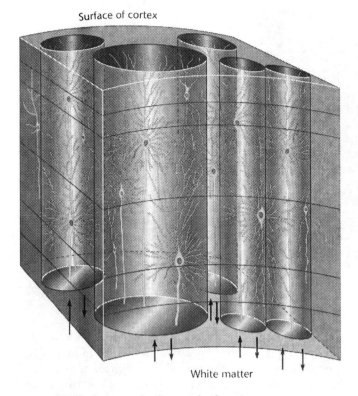

White matter

FIGURE 4.22 Columns in the cerebral cortex
Each column extends through several laminae. Neurons within a given column have similar properties. For example, in the somatosensory cortex, all the neurons within a given column respond to stimulation of the same area of skin. (© Cengage Learning 2013)

Stop & Check

9. If several neurons of the visual cortex all respond best when the retina is exposed to horizontal lines of light, then those neurons are probably in the same _____ .

ANSWER   9. column

The Occipital Lobe

The **occipital lobe**, at the posterior (caudal) end of the cortex (Figure 4.23), is the main target for visual information. The posterior pole of the occipital lobe is known as the *primary visual cortex*, or *striate cortex*, because of its striped appearance in cross-section. Destruction of any part of the striate cortex causes *cortical blindness* in the related part of the visual field. For example, extensive damage to the striate cortex of the right hemisphere causes blindness in the left visual field (that is, the left side of the world from the viewer's perspective). A person with cortical blindness has normal eyes and pupillary reflexes, but no conscious visual perception and no visual imagery (not even in dreams). People who suffer eye damage become blind, but if they have an intact occipital

cortex and previous visual experience, they can still imagine visual scenes and can still have visual dreams (Sabo & Kirtley, 1982). In short, the eyes provide the stimulus and the visual cortex provides the experience.

The Parietal Lobe

The **parietal lobe** lies between the occipital lobe and the **central sulcus**, one of the deepest grooves in the surface of the cortex (Figure 4.23). The area just posterior to the central sulcus, the **postcentral gyrus**, or *primary somatosensory cortex*, receives sensations from touch receptors, muscle-stretch receptors, and joint receptors. Brain surgeons sometimes use only local anesthesia (anesthetizing the scalp but leaving the brain awake). If during this process they lightly stimulate the postcentral gyrus, people report tingling sensations on the opposite side of the body.

The postcentral gyrus includes four bands of cells parallel to the central sulcus. Separate areas along each band receive simultaneous information from different parts of the body, as shown in Figure 4.24a (Nicolelis et al., 1998). Two of the bands receive mostly light-touch information, one receives deep-pressure information, and one receives a combination of both (Kaas, Nelson, Sur, Lin, & Merzenich, 1979). In effect, the postcentral gyrus represents the body four times.

Information about touch and body location is important not only for its own sake but also for interpreting visual and auditory information. For example, if you see something in the upper-left portion of the visual field, your brain needs to know which direction your eyes are turned, the position of your head, and the tilt of your body before it can determine the location of whatever you see. The parietal lobe monitors all the information about eye, head, and body positions and passes it on to brain areas that control movement (Gross & Graziano, 1995). The parietal lobe is essential not only for spatial information but also numerical information (Hubbard, Piazza, Pinel, & Dehaene, 2005). That overlap makes sense when you consider all the ways in which numbers relate to space—including the fact that we initially use our fingers to count.

The Temporal Lobe

The **temporal lobe** is the lateral portion of each hemisphere, near the temples (Figure 4.23). It is the primary cortical target for auditory information. The human temporal lobe—in most cases, the left temporal lobe—is essential for understanding spoken language. The temporal lobe also contributes to complex aspects of vision, including perception of movement and recognition of faces. A tumor in the temporal lobe may give rise to elaborate auditory or visual hallucinations, whereas a tumor in the occipital lobe ordinarily evokes only simple sensations, such as flashes of light. When psychiatric patients report hallucinations, brain scans detect extensive activity in the temporal lobes (Dierks et al., 1999).

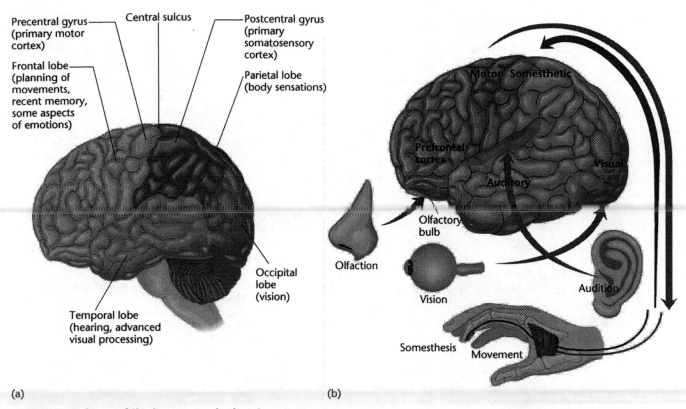

FIGURE 4.23 Areas of the human cerebral cortex
(a) The four lobes: occipital, parietal, temporal, and frontal. **(b)** The primary sensory cortex for vision, hearing, and body sensations; the primary motor cortex; and the olfactory bulb, a noncortical area responsible for the sense of smell. *(Part b: T. W. Deacon, 1990)*

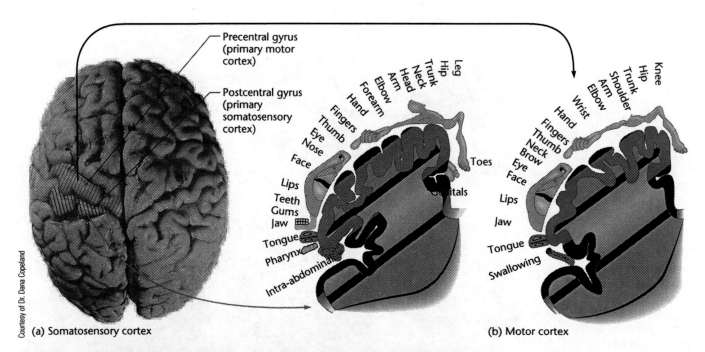

FIGURE 4.24 Approximate representation of sensory and motor information in the cortex
(a) Each location in the somatosensory cortex represents sensation from a different body part. **(b)** Each location in the motor cortex regulates movement of a different body part. *(After Penfield & Rasmussen, 1950)*

The temporal lobes are also important for emotional and motivational behaviors. Temporal lobe damage can lead to a set of behaviors known as the **Klüver-Bucy syndrome** (named for the investigators who first described it). Previously wild and aggressive monkeys fail to display normal fears and anxieties after temporal lobe damage (Klüver & Bucy, 1939). They put almost anything they find into their mouths and attempt to pick up snakes and lighted matches (which intact monkeys consistently avoid). Interpreting this behavior is difficult. For example, a monkey might handle a snake because it is no longer afraid (an emotional change) or because it no longer recognizes what a snake is (a cognitive change). We explore these issues in Chapter 12.

▌ The Frontal Lobe

The **frontal lobe**, containing the primary motor cortex and the prefrontal cortex, extends from the central sulcus to the anterior limit of the brain (Figure 4.23). The posterior portion of the frontal lobe just anterior to the central sulcus, the **precentral gyrus**, is specialized for the control of fine movements, such as moving one finger at a time. Separate areas are responsible for different parts of the body, mostly on the contralateral (opposite) side but also with slight control of the ipsilateral (same) side. Figure 4.24b shows the traditional map of the precentral gyrus, also known as the *primary motor cortex*. However, the map is only an approximation. For example, within the arm area, there is no one-to-one relationship between brain location and specific muscles (Graziano, Taylor, & Moore, 2002).

The most anterior portion of the frontal lobe is the **prefrontal cortex**. In general, the larger a species' cerebral cortex, the higher the percentage of the prefrontal cortex it occupies (Figure 4.25). For example, it forms a larger portion of the cortex in humans and the great apes than in other species (Semendeferi, Lu, Schenker, & Damasio, 2002). The dendrites in the prefrontal cortex have up to 16 times as many dendritic spines (Figure 2.7) as neurons in other cortical areas (Elston, 2000). As a result, the prefrontal cortex integrates an enormous amount of information.

▶ **Stop & Check**

10. Which lobe of the cerebral cortex includes the primary auditory cortex?

11. Which lobe of the cerebral cortex includes the primary somatosensory cortex?

12. Which lobe of the cerebral cortex includes the primary visual cortex?

13. Which lobe of the cerebral cortex includes the primary motor cortex?

ANSWERS

10. Temporal lobe **11.** Parietal lobe **12.** Occipital lobe **13.** Frontal lobe

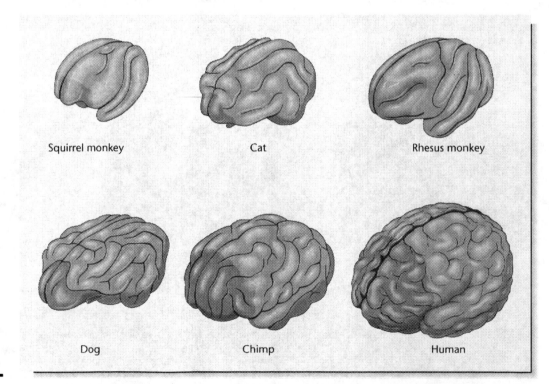

Squirrel monkey

Cat

Rhesus monkey

Dog

Chimp

Human

FIGURE 4.25 Species differences in prefrontal cortex
Note that the prefrontal cortex (blue area) constitutes a larger proportion of the human brain than of these other species. *(After Fuster, 1989)*

The Rise and Fall of Prefrontal Lobotomies

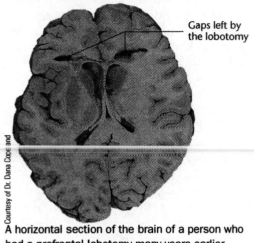

Courtesy of Dr. Dana Cope and

Gaps left by
the lobotomy

A horizontal section of the brain of a person who
had a prefrontal lobotomy many years earlier.
The two holes in the frontal cortex are the visible
results of the operation.

You may have heard of the infamous procedure known as
prefrontal lobotomy—surgical disconnection of the prefrontal cortex from the rest of the brain. The surgery con-
sisted of damaging the prefrontal cortex or cutting its connections to the rest of the cortex. Lobotomy began with a
report that damaging the prefrontal cortex of laboratory primates made them tamer without noticeably impairing their
sensations or coordination. A few physicians reasoned
loosely that the same operation might help people who suffered from severe, untreatable psychiatric disorders.

In the late 1940s and early 1950s, about 40,000 prefrontal lobotomies were performed in the United States
(Shutts, 1982), many of them by Walter Freeman, a medical
doctor untrained in surgery. His techniques were crude, even
by the standards of the time, using such instruments as an
electric drill and a metal pick. He performed many operations
in his office or other nonhospital sites. (Freeman carried his
equipment in his car, which he called his "lobotomobile.")

At first, Freeman and others limited the technique to
people with severe schizophrenia, for which no effective
treatment was available at the time. Later, Freeman lo-
botomized people with less serious disorders, including
some whom we would consider normal by today's standards. After drug therapies became available in the mid-
1950s, lobotomies quickly dropped out of favor.

Among the common consequences of prefrontal lobotomy were apathy, a loss of the ability to plan and
take initiative, memory disorders, distractibility, and a
loss of emotional expressions (Stuss & Benson, 1984).
People with prefrontal damage lost their social inhibitions, ignoring the rules of polite, civilized conduct. They
often acted impulsively because they failed to calculate
adequately the probable outcomes of their behaviors.

Modern View of the Prefrontal Cortex

The prefrontal cortex is a complex structure. Different parts of it,
even a few millimeters apart from one another, perform significantly different functions (Gilbert, Henson, & Simons, 2010).
One major function is working memory, the ability to remember
recent events, such as where you parked your car or what you
were talking about before being interrupted (Goldman-Rakic,
1988). People with damage to the prefrontal cortex have trouble
on the **delayed-response task**, in which they see or hear something, and then have to respond to it after a delay.

The prefrontal cortex is also important for making decisions and planning movements, especially for behaviors that
depend on the context (E. Miller, 2000). For example, if the
phone rings, do you answer it? It depends: You would in your
own home, but probably not in someone else's. If you see a
good friend from a distance, do you shout out a greeting? Yes
in a public park, but not in a library. People with prefrontal
cortex damage often fail to adjust to their context, so they behave inappropriately or impulsively.

> **Stop & Check**

14. What are the functions of the prefrontal cortex?

ANSWER

14. The prefrontal cortex is especially important
for working memory (memory for what is currently
happening) and for planning actions based on the
context.

How Do the Parts Work Together?

How do various brain areas combine to produce integrated
behavior and the experience of a single self? Consider the
sensory areas of the cerebral cortex. The visual area, auditory
area, and somatosensory area are in different locations, only
weakly connected with one another. When you hold your radio or iPod, how does your brain know that the object you see
is also what you feel and what you hear?

The question of how various brain areas produce a perception of a single object is known as the **binding problem**, or
large-scale integration problem. In an earlier era, researchers
thought that various kinds of sensory information converged
onto what they called the association areas of the cortex (Figure 4.26). Their guess was that those areas "associate" vision
with hearing, hearing with touch, or current sensations with
memories of previous experiences. Later research found that
the association areas perform advanced processing on a particular sensory system, such as vision or hearing, but few cells
combine one sense with another. Discarding the idea that
various senses converge in the association areas called attention to the binding problem. If different sensory paths don't
converge, then how do we know that something we see is also
what we hear or feel?

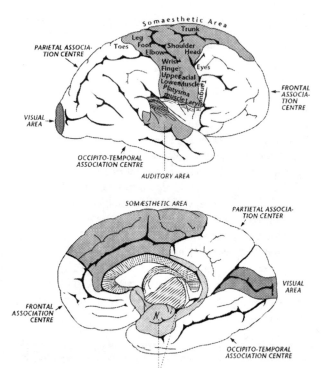

FIGURE 4.26 An old, somewhat misleading view of the cortex
Note the designation "association centre" in this illustration of the cortex from an old introductory psychology textbook *(Hunter, 1923)*. Today's researchers are more likely to regard those areas as "additional sensory areas."

Although we cannot fully explain binding, we know what is necessary for it to occur: It occurs if you perceive two sensations as happening at the same time and in the same place. For example, when a skilled ventriloquist makes the dummy's mouth move at the same time as his or her own speech, in nearly the same place, you perceive the sound as coming from the dummy. As part of this illusion, the visual stimulus alters the response of the auditory cortex, so that the sound really does seem to come from the same location as the dummy's mouth (Bonath et al., 2007). In contrast, when you watch a foreign-language film that was poorly dubbed and the lips do not move at the same time as the speech, you perceive that the words did *not* come from those lips.

Applying these principles, researchers arranged a camera to video someone's back and sent the pictures to a three-dimensional display mounted to the person's head. The person viewed his or her own back, apparently 2 meters in front. Then someone stroked the participant's back, so that the person simultaneously felt the touch and saw the action, apparently 2 meters in front. After a while, the person had what you might call an "out of body" experience, perceiving the body as being 2 meters in front of its real position. When asked, "please return to your seat," the person walked to a spot displaced from the

actual seat, as if he or she had actually been moved forward (Lenggenhager, Tadi, Metzinger, & Blanke, 2007).

Here is a demonstration you can try: If you see a light flash once while you hear two beeps, you will sometimes think you saw the light flash twice. If the tone is soft, you may experience the opposite: The tone beeps twice during one flash of light, and you think you heard only one beep. If you saw three flashes of light, you might think you heard three beeps (Andersen, Tiippana, & Sams, 2004). The near simultaneity of lights and sounds causes you to bind them and perceive an illusion. You can experience this phenomenon with the Online Try It Yourself activity "Illustration of Binding."

ONLINE

Here is another great demonstration to try (I. H. Robertson, 2005). Position yourself parallel to a large mirror, as in Figure 4.27, so that you see your right hand and its reflection in the mirror. Keep your left hand out of sight. Now repeatedly clench and unclench both hands in unison. Wiggle your fingers, touch your thumb to each finger, and so forth, in each case doing the same thing with both hands at the same time. At each moment you will feel your left hand doing the same thing you see the hand in the mirror doing, which (being the mirror image of your right hand) looks like your left hand. After 2 or 3 minutes, you may start to feel that the hand in the mirror is your own left hand. Some people feel that they have three hands—the right hand, the real left hand, and the apparent left hand in the mirror!

TRY IT
YOURSELF

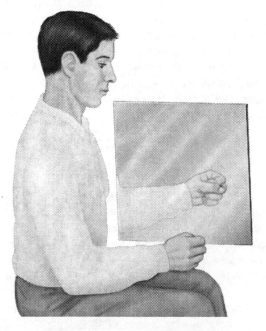

FIGURE 4.27 An illusion to demonstrate binding
Clench and unclench both hands while looking at your right hand and its reflection in the mirror. Keep your left hand out of sight. After a couple of minutes, you may start to experience the hand in the mirror as being your own left hand.
(© Cengage Learning 2013)

So binding depends on perceiving two or more aspects of a stimulus as coming from approximately the same location. People with damage to the parietal cortex have trouble locating objects in space—that is, they are not sure where anything is—and they often fail to bind objects. For example, if they see a display such as

they might report seeing a green triangle and a red square instead of a red triangle and a green square (L. Robertson, Treisman, Friedman-Hill, & Grabowecky, 1997; Treisman, 1999; R. Ward, Danziger, Owen, & Rafal, 2002; Wheeler & Treisman, 2002).

Even people with intact brains sometimes make mistakes of this kind if the displays are flashed very briefly or while they are distracted (Holcombe & Cavanagh, 2001; Lehky, 2000). You can experience this failure of binding with the Online Try It Yourself activity "Failure of Binding."

ONLINE

Stop & Check

15. What is meant by the binding problem, and what is necessary for binding to occur?

ANSWER

15. The binding problem is the question of how the brain combines activity in different brain areas to produce unified perception and coordinated behavior. Binding requires identifying the location of an object and perceiving sight, sound, and other aspects of a stimulus as being simultaneous. When the sight and sound appear to come from the same location at the same time, we bind them as a single experience.

Functions of the Cerebral Cortex

The human cerebral cortex is so large that we easily slip into thinking of it as "the" brain. In fact, only mammals have a true cerebral cortex, and many animals produce impressive and complex behaviors without a cerebral cortex.

What, then, is the function of the cerebral cortex? The primary function seems to be one of elaborating sensory material.

Even fish, which have no cerebral cortex, can see, hear, and so forth, but they do not recognize and remember all the complex aspects of sensory stimuli that mammals do. The cerebral cortex takes information and analyzes it in great detail.

SUMMARY

1. Although brain size varies among mammalian species, the overall organization is similar. **100**

2. The cerebral cortex has six laminae (layers) of neurons. A given lamina may be absent from certain parts of the cortex. For example, the lamina responsible for sensory input is absent from the motor cortex. The cortex is organized into columns of cells arranged perpendicular to the laminae. **100**

3. The occipital lobe of the cortex is primarily responsible for vision. Damage to part of the occipital lobe leads to blindness in part of the visual field. **102**

4. The parietal lobe processes body sensations. The postcentral gyrus contains four separate representations of the body. **102**

5. The temporal lobe contributes to hearing, complex aspects of vision, and processing of emotional information. **102**

6. The frontal lobe includes the precentral gyrus, which controls fine movements. It also includes the prefrontal cortex, which contributes to memories of recent stimuli and planning of movements. **104**

7. The prefrontal cortex is important for working memory and for planning actions that depend on the context. **105**

8. The binding problem is the question of how we connect activities in different brain areas, such as sights and sounds. The various brain areas do not all send their information to a single central processor. **105**

9. Binding requires perceiving that two aspects of a stimulus (such as sight and sound) occurred at the same place at the same time. **106**

KEY TERMS

Terms are defined in the module on the page number indicated. They're also presented in alphabetical order with definitions in the book's Subject Index/Glossary, which begins on page 561. Interactive flashcards and crossword puzzles are among the online resources available to help you learn these terms and the concepts they represent.

anterior commissure **100**	delayed-response task **105**	postcentral gyrus **104**
binding problem **105**	frontal lobe **104**	prefrontal cortex **104**
central sulcus **102**	Klüver-Bucy syndrome **104**	prefrontal lobotomy **105**
cerebral cortex **100**	laminae **100**	primates **100**
columns **101**	occipital lobe **102**	temporal lobe **102**
corpus callosum **100**	parietal lobe **102**	

THOUGHT QUESTION

When monkeys with Klüver-Bucy syndrome pick up lighted matches and snakes, we do not know whether they are displaying an emotional deficit or an inability to identify the object. What kind of research method might help answer this question?

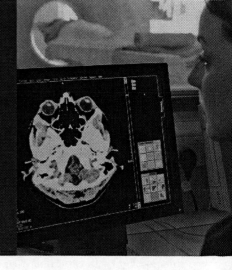

Research Methods

Imagine yourself trying to understand a large, complex machine. You could begin by describing the appearance and location of the machine's parts. That task could be formidable, but it is easy compared to discovering what each part does.

Similarly, describing the structure of the brain is difficult enough, but the real challenge is to discover how it works. Throughout the text, we shall consider many research methods as they become relevant. However, most methods fall into a few categories. This module provides an overview of those categories and the logic behind them:

1. *Examine the effects of brain damage.* After damage or temporary inactivation, what aspects of behavior are impaired?

2. *Examine the effects of stimulating a brain area.* Ideally, if damaging some area impairs a behavior, stimulating that area should enhance the behavior.

3. *Record brain activity during behavior.* We might record changes in brain activity during fighting, sleeping, finding food, solving a problem, or any other behavior.

4. *Correlate brain anatomy with behavior.* Do people with some unusual behavior also have unusual brains? If so, in what way?

Effects of Brain Damage

In 1861, French neurologist Paul Broca found that a patient who had lost the ability to speak had damage in part of his left frontal cortex. Additional patients with loss of speech also showed damage in and around that area, now known as *Broca's area.* This discovery revolutionized neurology, as many other physicians at the time doubted that different brain areas had different functions at all.

Since then, researchers have made countless reports of behavioral impairments after brain damage. Brain damage can produce an inability to recognize faces, an inability to perceive motion, a shift of attention to the right side of the body and world, increased or decreased hunger, changes in emotional responses, memory impairments, and a host of other highly specialized effects.

Some of the most interesting results come from humans with brain damage, but human studies have their limitations. Few people have damage confined to just one brain area, and no two people have exactly the same damage. Therefore researchers often turn to producing carefully localized damage in laboratory animals. An **ablation** is a removal of a brain area, generally with a surgical knife. However, surgical removal is difficult for tiny structures far below the surface of the brain. In that case, researchers make a **lesion**, meaning damage. To damage a structure in the interior of the brain, researchers use a **stereotaxic instrument**, a device for the precise placement of electrodes in the brain (Figure 4.28). By consulting a stereotaxic atlas (map) of some species' brain, a researcher aims an electrode at the desired position relative to certain landmarks on the skull. Then the researcher anesthetizes an animal, drills a small hole in the skull, inserts the electrode (which is insulated except at the tip), lowers it to the target, and passes an

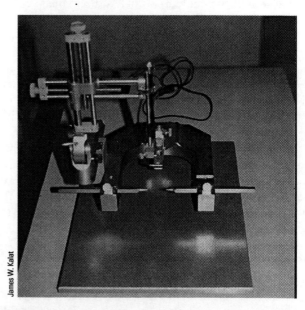

James W. Kalat

FIGURE 4.28 A stereotaxic instrument for locating brain areas in small animals
Using this device, researchers can insert an electrode to stimulate, record from, or damage any point in the brain.

electrical current just sufficient to damage that area. For example, researchers have made lesions in parts of the hypothalamus to explore their contributions to eating and drinking. After the death of the animal, someone takes slices of its brain, applies stains, and verifies the actual location of the damage.

Suppose a researcher makes a lesion and reports some behavioral deficit. You might ask, "How do we know the deficit wasn't caused by anesthetizing the animal, drilling a hole in its skull, and lowering an electrode to this target?" (Good question.) To test this possibility, an experimenter produces a *sham lesion* in a control group, performing all the same procedures except for passing the electrical current. Any behavioral difference between the two groups must result from the lesion and not the other procedures.

Besides lesions, several other procedures can inactivate various brain structures or systems. In the *gene-knockout approach*, researchers use biochemical methods to direct a mutation to a particular gene that is important for certain types of cells, transmitters, or receptors (Joyner & Guillemot, 1994).

Transcranial magnetic stimulation, the application of an intense magnetic field to a portion of the scalp, temporarily inactivates neurons below the magnet (Walsh & Cowey, 2000). This procedure enables researchers to study a given individual's behavior with the brain area active, then inactive, and then active again. Figure 4.29 shows the apparatus. For example, one study found that when transcranial magnetic stimulation temporarily silenced people's visual cortex, they had no conscious perception of visual stimuli, but could nevertheless direct their eye movements toward a light. This result suggests that the visual cortex is necessary for conscious perception, but not for all visually guided movements (Ro, Shelton, Lee, & Chang, 2004).

After any kind of brain damage or inactivation, the problem for psychologists is to specify the exact behavioral deficit. By analogy, suppose you cut a wire in a television and the picture disappeared. You would know that this wire is necessary for the picture, but you would not know why. Similarly, if you damaged a brain area and the animal stopped eating, you wouldn't know why. Did it lose its hunger? Its ability to taste food? Its ability to find the food? Its ability to move at all? You would need many further behavioral tests to narrow down the possibilities.

> **Stop & Check**

16. What is the difference between a lesion and an ablation?

ANSWER

16. A lesion is damage to a structure. An ablation is removal of the structure. For example, a blood clot might produce a lesion, whereas surgery could produce an ablation.

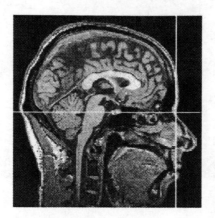

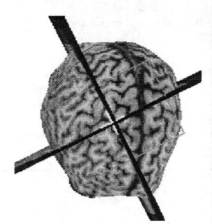
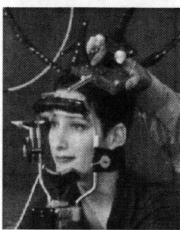

FIGURE 4.29 Apparatus for magnetic stimulation of a human brain Procedure is known as transcranial magnetic stimulation, or TMS. *(Reprinted from "Brain Mapping: The Methods," 2e, 2002, Toga et al., pp. 691–705, 2002, with permission from Elsevier.)*

Effects of Brain Stimulation

If brain damage impairs some behavior, stimulation should increase it. Researchers can insert electrodes to stimulate brain areas in laboratory animals. A new technique, *optogenetics*, enables researchers to turn on activity in targeted neurons by a device that shines a laser light within the brain (Buchen, 2010).

With humans, the choices are more limited. Occasionally researchers insert electrodes into the brain of someone who already has the brain exposed in preparation for brain surgery. In other cases, they use a less invasive (and less precise) method, applying a magnetic field to the scalp to stimulate the brain areas beneath it (Fitzgerald, Brown, & Daskalakis, 2002). Whereas intense transcranial magnetic stimulation inactivates the underlying area, a brief, mild application stimulates it.

A limitation of any stimulation study is that complex behaviors and experiences depend on a temporal pattern of activity across many brain areas, not just a general increase of activity in one, so an artificial stimulation produces artificial responses. For example, electrically or magnetically stimulating the visual cortex produces reports of flashing points of light, not the sight of any recognizable object. It is easier to discover which brain area is responsible for vision (or movement or whatever) than to discover how it produces a meaningful pattern.

Stop & Check

17. How do the effects of brief, mild magnetic stimulation differ from those of longer, more intense stimulation?

18. Why does electrical or magnetic stimulation of the brain seldom produce complex, meaningful sensations or movements?

ANSWERS
17. Brief, mild magnetic stimulation on the scalp increases activity in the underlying brain areas, whereas longer, more intense stimulation blocks it. **18.** Meaningful sensations and movements require a pattern of precisely timed activity in a great many cells, not just a burst of overall activity diffusely in one area.

Recording Brain Activity

Suppose damage to some brain area impairs a behavior (eating, for example) and stimulation of that area increases the behavior. We can further confirm the connection if we demonstrate that the activity of that area increases during occurrences of the behavior. With laboratory animals, researchers insert electrodes to record brain activity, or they use more recent methods that record the activity of many individual neurons at the same time (Kerr & Denk, 2008).

Studies of human brains almost always use noninvasive methods—that is, methods that record from outside the skull without inserting anything. A device called the **electroencephalograph (EEG)** records electrical activity of the brain through electrodes—ranging from just a few to more than a hundred—attached to the scalp (Figure 4.30). Electrodes glued to the scalp measure the average activity at any moment for the population of cells under the electrode. The output is then amplified and recorded. This device can record spontaneous brain activity or activity in response to a stimulus, in which case we call the results **evoked potentials** or **evoked responses**. In one study, researchers recorded evoked potentials from young adults as they watched pictures of nudes of both sexes. Men reported high arousal by the female nudes, while women reported neutral feelings to both the males and females, but both men's and women's brains showed strong evoked potentials to the opposite-sex nudes (Costa, Braun, & Birbaumer, 2003). That is, evoked potentials sometimes reveal information that self-reports do not.

A **magnetoencephalograph (MEG)** is similar, but instead of measuring electrical activity, it measures the faint magnetic fields generated by brain activity (Hari, 1994). Like an EEG, an MEG recording identifies the approximate location of activity to within about a centimeter. However, an

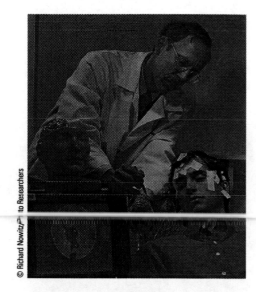

FIGURE 4.30 Electroencephalography
An electroencephalograph records the overall activity of neurons under various electrodes attached to the scalp.

MEG has excellent temporal resolution, showing changes from 1 millisecond to the next.

Figure 4.31 shows an MEG record of brain responses to a brief tone heard in the right ear. The diagram represents a human head as viewed from above, with the nose at the top (Hari, 1994). Researchers using an MEG can identify the times at which various brain areas respond and thereby trace a wave of brain activity from its point of origin to all the other areas that process it (Salmelin, Hari, Lounasmaa, & Sams, 1994).

Another method, **positron-emission tomography (PET)**, provides a high-resolution image of activity in a living brain by recording the emission of radioactivity from injected chemicals. First, the person receives an injection of glucose or some other chemical containing radioactive atoms. When a radioactive atom decays, it releases a positron that immediately collides with a nearby electron, emitting two gamma rays in exactly opposite directions. The person's head is surrounded by a set of gamma ray detectors (Figure 4.32). When two detectors record gamma rays at the same time, they identify a spot halfway between those detectors as the point of origin of the gamma rays. A computer uses this information to determine how many gamma rays are coming from each spot in the brain and therefore how much of the radioactive chemical is located in each area (Phelps & Mazziotta, 1985). The areas showing the most radioactivity are the ones with the most blood flow and, therefore, presumably, the most brain activity. For an example of a PET study, we shall see in Chapter 9 how PET identified the brain areas that become active during a certain stage of sleep.

Ordinarily, PET scans use radioactive chemicals with a short half-life, made in a device called a cyclotron. Because cyclotrons are large and expensive, PET scans are available only at research hospitals. Furthermore, PET requires ex-

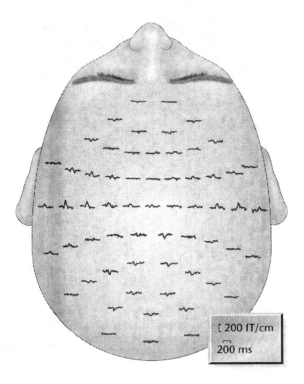

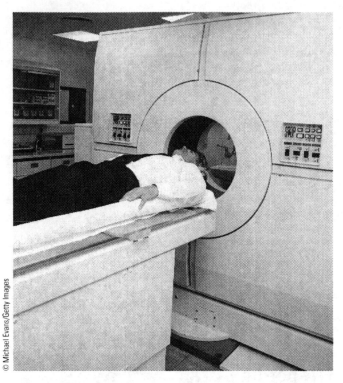

FIGURE 4.31 A result of magnetoencephalography, showing responses to a tone in the right ear
The nose is shown at the top. For each spot on the diagram, the display shows the changing response over a few hundred ms following the tone. (Note calibration at lower right.) The tone evoked responses in many areas, with the largest responses in the temporal cortex, especially on the left side. *(Reprinted from Neuroscience: From the Molecular to the Cognitive, by R. Hari, 1994, p. 165, with kind permission from Elsevier Science—NL, Sara Burgerhartstraat 25, 1055 KV Amsterdam, The Netherlands.)*

FIGURE 4.32 A PET scanner
A person engages in a cognitive task while attached to this apparatus that records which areas of the brain become more active and by how much.

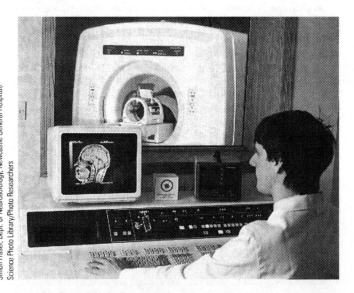

FIGURE 4.33 An fMRI scan of a human brain
An fMRI produces fairly detailed photos at rates up to about one per second. *(Wagner et al., 1998)*

posing the brain to radioactivity. For most purposes, PET scans have been replaced by **functional magnetic resonance imaging (fMRI)**, which is less expensive and less risky. Standard MRI scans record the energy released by water molecules after removal of a magnetic field. (The text provides more details about this method later.) An fMRI is a modified version of MRI based on hemoglobin (the blood protein that binds oxygen) instead of water (Detre & Floyd, 2001). Hemoglobin with oxygen reacts to a magnetic field differently than hemoglobin without oxygen. Researchers set the fMRI scanner to detect hemoglobin with and without oxygen (Viswanathan & Freeman, 2007). When a brain area becomes more active, two relevant changes occur: First, blood vessels dilate to allow more blood flow to the area. Second, as the brain area uses oxygen, the percentage of hemoglobin without oxygen increases. An fMRI scan records both of these processes (Sirotin, Hillman, Bordier, & Das, 2009). An fMRI image has a spatial resolution of 1 or 2 mm (almost as good as standard MRI) and temporal resolution of about a second (Figure 4.33).

An fMRI while you were, for example, reading would mean nothing without a comparison to something else. Researchers would record your brain activity while you were reading and during a comparison task and then subtract the brain activity during the comparison task to determine which areas are more active during reading. As a comparison task, for example, researchers might ask you to look at a page written in a language you do not understand. That task would activate visual areas just as the reading task did, but it presumably would not activate the language areas of your brain. Figure 4.34 illustrates the idea.

Here is one example of an fMRI study: Researchers asked which brain areas become more active when your "mind wanders." Several brain areas, including the posterior cingulate cortex, consistently show increased activity during times when people have no particular task (M. F. Mason et al., 2007). Later, when researchers watched people's performance on a task requiring constant attention, they saw performance decline whenever activity increased in these mind-wandering areas (Weissman, Roberts, Visscher, & Woldorff, 2006). Evidently, the non-task-related activity interferes with the brain processes necessary for vigilance.

Interpreting fMRI results is a complex task. Suppose researchers find that some area becomes more active while people process emotional information. Later, during some other activity, that area again becomes active. Can we therefore assume that the person is undergoing an emotional experience? Not necessarily. A given area may have many functions, and we have to be cautious about equating one area with one function.

The best way to test our understanding is this: If we think we know what a given fMRI pattern means, we should be able to use that pattern to identify what someone is doing or thinking. In other words, we should be able to use it to read someone's mind, to a limited degree. In one study, researchers used fMRI to record activity in the visual cortex as people looked at 1,750 photographs. Then they showed 120 new photographs similar to one or more of the original ones, and analyzed the fMRI results with a computer. In most cases they were able to use the fMRI results to guess which of the new photographs the person was seeing. Accuracy was high if they recorded the fMRI response several times to each photo, but even with a single trial, they usually identified either the correct photo or something similar (Kay, Naselaris, Prenger, & Gallant, 2008).

In another study, researchers used fMRI to monitor people's intentions. In each trial, a participant was to decide freely whether to "add" or "subtract," without telling anyone. After a delay, a pair of numbers appeared on the screen (to be added or subtracted, depending on the person's decision), and then an array of four numbers. At that point the person was to point to the correct answer as quickly as possible. In the example shown in Figure 4.35, if the person had decided to add, the correct answer would be 89 (upper right) and if the decision was to subtract, the answer would be 23 (lower left). A key point is that the numbers and their positions were unpredictable. During the delay, the person could think "add" or "subtract" but could not choose a particular position of response. The fMRI recordings from the prefrontal cortex enabled researchers to predict people's behaviors with 71% accuracy (Haynes et al., 2007).

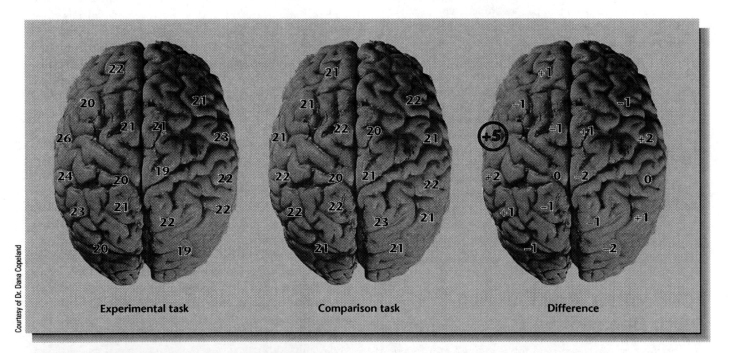

FIGURE 4.34 Subtraction for a brain scan procedure
Numbers on the brain at the left show hypothetical levels of arousal during some task, measured in arbitrary units. The brain at the center shows activity during the same brain areas during a comparison task. The brain at the right shows the differences. The highlighted area shows the largest difference. In actual data, the largest increases in activity would be one or two tenths of a percent.

Courtesy of Dr. Dana Copeland

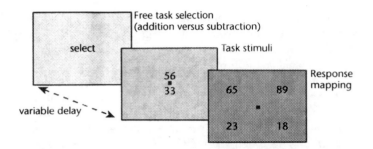

FIGURE 4.35 Procedure for monitoring people's intentions
People decided silently whether to add or subtract. After a delay, they saw two numbers. After applying either addition or subtraction, they chose the correct answer among four choices. An fMRI during the delay could predict whether the person was about to add or subtract. *(From Haynes, J.-D., Katsuyuki, S., Rees, G., Gilbert, S., Frith, C., & Passingham, R. E. (2007). Reading hidden intentions in the human brain.* Current Biology, 17, *323-328.)*

How far can this procedure go? At this point we can read people's minds in only this very limited way. It would be hazardous to guess how far the procedure might or might not develop in the future. The main point is that trying to read people's minds (in a limited way) tests how well we understand what the brain recordings mean.

Stop & Check

19. What does fMRI measure?

20. Suppose someone demonstrates that a particular brain area becomes active when people are listening to music. When that area becomes active later, what, if anything, can we conclude?

ANSWERS

19. It measures changes in blood flow to the brain. It detects an increase in blood flow to a brain area immediately after an increase in brain activity, and it also detects a slightly slower increase in the percentage of hemoglobin lacking oxygen. **20.** Without further evidence, we should not draw any conclusion. Perhaps the person is listening to music again, but this area may perform functions other than listening to music. A good test of how well we understand the area would be to find out whether we can use fMRI recordings to guess which type of music someone is hearing (or whether they are listening at all).

Correlating Brain Anatomy with Behavior

One of the first ways ever used for studying brain function sounds easy: Find someone with unusual behavior and then look for unusual features of the brain. In the 1800s, Franz

Gall observed some people with excellent verbal memories who had protruding eyes. He inferred that verbal memory depended on brain areas behind the eyes that had pushed the eyes forward. Gall then examined the skulls of people with other talents or personalities. He assumed that bulges and depressions on their skull corresponded to the brain areas below them. His process of relating skull anatomy to behavior is known as **phrenology**. One of his followers made the phrenological map in Figure 4.36.

One problem with phrenologists was their uncritical use of data. In some cases, they examined just one person with a behavioral quirk to define a brain area presumably responsible for it. Another problem was that skull shape has little relationship to brain anatomy. The skull is thicker in some places than others and thicker in some people than others.

Today, researchers examine detailed brain anatomy in detail in living people. One method is **computerized axial tomography**, better known as a **CT** or **CAT scan** (Andreasen, 1988). A physician injects a dye into the blood (to increase contrast in the image) and then places the person's head into a CT scanner like the one shown in Figure 4.37a. X-rays are passed through the head and recorded by detectors on the opposite side. The CT scanner is rotated slowly until a measurement has been taken at each angle over 180 degrees. From the measurements, a computer constructs images of the brain. Figure 4.37b is an example. CT scans help detect tumors and other structural abnormalities.

Another method is **magnetic resonance imaging (MRI)** (Warach, 1995), based on the fact that any atom with an odd-numbered atomic weight, such as hydrogen, has an axis of rotation. An MRI device applies a powerful magnetic field (about 25,000 times the magnetic field of the earth) to align all the axes of rotation and then tilts them with a brief radio frequency field. When the radio frequency field is turned off, the atomic nuclei release electromagnetic energy as they relax and return to their original axis. By measuring that energy, MRI devices form an image of the brain, such as the one in Figure 4.38. MRI shows anatomical details smaller than a millimeter in diameter. One drawback is that the person must lie motionless in a confining, noisy apparatus. The procedure is usually not suitable for children or anyone who fears enclosed places.

Researchers using these methods sometimes find that a particular brain area is enlarged in people who have special skills. For example, *Heschl's gyrus,* part of the temporal cortex in the left hemisphere, is known to be important for hearing, especially as it relates to language. This area is larger than average in people who are especially good at learning to identify foreign-language sounds that are not part of their own language (Golestani, Molko, Dehaene, LeBihan, & Pallier, 2006; Wong et al., 2007).

Table 4.5 summarizes various methods of studying brain-behavior relationships.

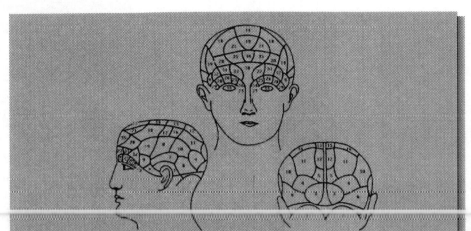

Affective Faculties		Intellectual Faculties	
Propensities	**Sentiments**	**Perceptive**	**Reflective**
? Desire to live	10 Cautiousness	22 Individuality	34 Comparison
• Alimentiveness	11 Approbativeness	23 Configuration	35 Causality
1 Destructiveness	12 Self-esteem	24 Size	
2 Amativeness	13 Benevolence	25 Weight and resistance	
3 Philoprogenitiveness	14 Reverence	26 Coloring	
4 Adhesiveness	15 Firmness	27 Locality	
5 Inhabitiveness	16 Conscientiousness	28 Order	
6 Combativeness	17 Hope	29 Calculation	
7 Secretiveness	18 Marvelousness	30 Eventuality	
8 Acquisitiveness	19 Ideality	31 Time	
9 Constructiveness	20 Mirthfulness	32 Tune	
	21 Imitation	33 Language	

FIGURE 4.36 A phrenologist's map of the brain
Neuroscientists today also try to localize functions in the brain, but they use more careful methods and they study such functions as vision and hearing, not "secretiveness" and "marvelousness." *(From Spurzheim, 1908)*

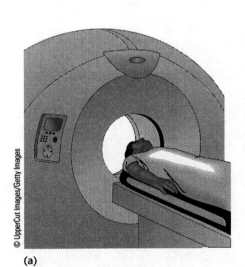

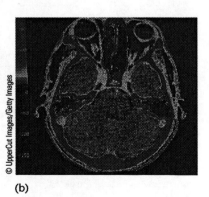

(a)   (b)

FIGURE 4.37 CT scanner
(a) A person's head is placed into the device and then a rapidly rotating source sends X-rays through the head while detectors on the opposite side make photographs. A computer then constructs an image of the brain. **(b)** A view of a normal human brain generated by computerized axial tomography (CT scanning).

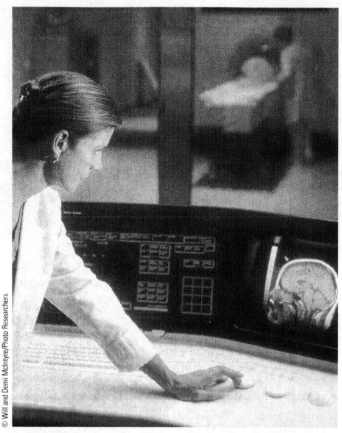

FIGURE 4.38 A view of a living brain generated by magnetic resonance imaging
Any atom with an odd-numbered atomic weight, such as hydrogen, has an inherent rotation. An outside magnetic field can align the axes of rotation. A radio frequency field can then make all these atoms move like tiny gyros. When the radio frequency field is turned off, the atomic nuclei release electromagnetic energy as they relax. By measuring that energy, we can obtain an image of a structure such as the brain without damaging it.

© Will and Demi McIntyre/Photo Researchers

TABLE 4.5

Examine Effects of Brain Damage

Study victims of stroke, etc.	Used with humans; each person has different damage
Lesion	Controlled damage in laboratory animals
Ablation	Removal of a brain area
Gene-knockout	Effects wherever that gene is active (e.g., a receptor)
Transcranial magnetic stimulation	Intense application temporarily inactivates a brain area

Examine Effects of Stimulating a Brain Area

Stimulating electrodes	Invasive; used with laboratory animals, seldom with humans
Transcranial magnetic stimulation	Brief, mild application activates underlying brain area

Record Brain Activity During Behavior

Record from electrodes in brain	Invasive; used with laboratory animals, seldom humans
Electroencephalograph (EEG)	Records from scalp; measures changes by ms, but with low resolution of location of the signal
Evoked potentials	Similar to EEG but in response to stimuli
Magnetoencephalograph (MEG)	Similar to EEG but measures magnetic fields
Positron emission tomography (PET)	Measures changes over both time and location but requires exposing brain to radiation
Functional magnetic resonance imaging (fMRI)	Measures changes over about 1 second, identifies location within 1–2 mm, no use of radiation

Correlate Brain Anatomy with Behavior

Computerized axial tomography (CAT)	Maps brain areas, but requires exposure to X-rays
Magnetic resonance imaging (MRI)	Maps brain areas in detail, using magnetic fields

21. Researchers today sometimes relate differences in people's behavior to differences in their brain anatomy. How does their approach differ from that of phrenologists?

ANSWER   ˙llnʞs ǝɥʇ ʇou 'ɟlǝsʇı uıɐɹq ǝɥʇ ǝuıɯɐxǝ sɹǝɥɔɹɐǝsǝɹ s,ʎɐpoʇ 'osl∀ ˙ʎllɐɔıʇsıʇɐʇs sdnoɹƃ ǝɹɐdɯoɔ sɹǝɥɔɹɐǝsǝɹ s,ʎɐpo┴ ˙ɹoıʌɐɥǝq ɟo ʎʇıppo ǝɯos ɥʇıʍ ǝldoǝd ʍǝɟ ɐ ɹo ǝuo ʇsnɾ uo pǝsɐq suoısnlɔuoɔ ʍǝɹp sʇsıƃolouǝɹɥԀ **˙Ɩ2**

Brain Size and Intelligence

Let's consider in more detail a specific example of correlating brain structure with behavior: What is the relationship between brain size and intelligence? It seems natural to assume that bigger brains are better, but maybe it's not that simple.

In the 1800s and early 1900s, several societies arose whose members agreed to donate their brains after death for research into whether the brains of eminent people were unusual in any way. No conclusion resulted. The brains of the eminent varied considerably, as did those of less eminent people. If brain anatomy was related to intellect in any way, the relation wasn't obvious (Burrell, 2004). Still, the idea lingers: Even if brain size isn't strongly related to intelligence, shouldn't it have *some* relationship?

Comparisons Across Species

All mammalian brains have the same organization, but they differ greatly in size. You can examine a variety of mammalian brains at the Comparative Mammalian Brain Collections website: **http://www.brainmuseum.org/sections/index.html**

Do variations in brain size relate to animal intelligence? We humans like to think of ourselves as the most intelligent animals—after all, we get to define what intelligence means! However, humans do not have the largest brains. Sperm whales' brains are eight times larger than ours, and elephants' are four times larger. Perhaps, many people suggest, intelli-

gence depends on brain-to-body ratio. Figure 4.39 illustrates the relationship between logarithm of body mass and logarithm of brain mass for various vertebrates (Jerison, 1985). Note that the species we regard as most intelligent—such as, ahem, ourselves—have larger brains in proportion to body size than do the species we consider less impressive, such as frogs.

However, brain-to-body ratio has problems also: Chihuahuas have the highest brain-to-body ratio of all dog breeds, not because they were bred for intelligence but because they were bred for small bodies (Deacon, 1997). Squirrel monkeys, which are also very thin, have a higher brain-to-body ratio than humans. (And with the increasing prevalence of human obesity, our brain-to-body ratio is declining!) The elephant nose fish (Figure 4.40), which you might keep in an aquarium, has a 3% brain-to-body ratio compared to 2% for humans (Nilsson, 1999). So neither total brain mass nor brain-to-body ratio puts humans in first place.

A further problem is that we lack a clear definition of animal intelligence (Macphail, 1985). No test could fairly compare elephants, chimpanzees, and dolphins; each species is intelligent in its own way. Given that studies of brain and behavior in nonhumans are not helping, let's abandon that effort and turn to humans.

FIGURE 4.40 An elephant-nose fish
The brain of this odd-looking fish weighs 0.3 g (0.01 ounce), which is 3% of the weight of the whole fish—a vastly higher percentage than most other fish and higher even than humans. What this fish does with so much brain, we don't know, but it may relate to the fish's unusual ability to detect electrical fields.

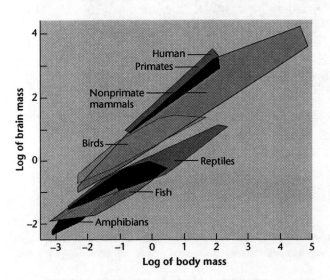

FIGURE 4.39 Relationship of brain mass to body mass across species
Each species is one point within one of the polygons. In general, log of body mass is a good predictor of log of brain mass. Note that primates in general and humans in particular have a large brain mass in proportion to body mass. *(Adapted from Jerison, 1985)*

Stop & Check

22. Why are both brain size and brain-to-body ratio unsatisfactory ways of estimating animal intelligence?

ANSWER cannot determine what correlates with it.
brain size. Furthermore, animal intelligence is undefined, so we
ratio depends on selection for thinness as well as selection for
est brains nor the highest brain-to-body ratios. Brain-to-body
we are confronted with the fact that we have neither the larg-
22. If we consider ourselves to be the most intelligent species,

---

Comparisons Among Humans

For many years, studies of human brain size and intelligence found correlations barely above zero. However, a low correlation between two variables can mean either that they are unrelated or that they were measured poorly. Most early studies measured skull size instead of brain size. Today, using more accurate measurements based on MRI scans, most studies find a moderate positive correlation between brain size and IQ, typically around .3 (McDaniel, 2005).

Presumably certain brain areas are more important than others for intelligence. Several researchers have looked for particular brain areas that might be larger in people who score higher on intelligence tests. Many areas emerged as important, but the areas identified were not exactly the same from one study to the next (Colom et al., 2009; Frangou, Chitins, & Williams, 2004; Haier et al., 2009; Karama et al., 2009). In one case, investigators used MRI to measure the size of gray matter and white matter areas throughout the brains of 23 young adults from one university campus and 24 middle-aged or older adults from another campus. In Figure 4.41, the areas highlighted in red showed a statistically significant correlation with IQ, and those highlighted in yellow showed an even stronger correlation. Note the differences between the two samples, even though the procedures were the same for both (Haier, Jung, Yeo, Head, & Alkire, 2004).

The discrepancies point out some of the problems with this type of research: If we record from all brain areas during some task, it is like testing hundreds of hypotheses at the same time. The evidence will confirm some of them, just by chance. (The protection against this kind of error is to try to replicate the results, but if results vary across experiments, we need to beware.) Also, a given task may activate different areas in different people simply because they approached the task in different ways. That is, a given task—even an intelligence test—may be in fact a different task for different people.

Stop & Check

23. Why do recent studies show a stronger relationship between brain size and IQ than older studies did?

ANSWER the skull.
of brain size, in comparison to measurements based on
23. The use of MRI greatly improves the measurement

Comparisons of Men and Women

Now for the most confusing part: If we examine intelligence test scores and brain size for just men, or for just women, we find a moderate positive correlation. If we combine results for men and women, the correlation declines. Men on average have larger brains than women but equal IQs (Gilmore et al., 2007; Willerman, Schultz, Rutledge, & Bigler, 1991; Witelson, Beresh, & Kigar, 2006). Even if we take into account differences in height, men's brains remain larger (Ankney, 1992).

Although male and female brains differ, on average, behavioral differences, when carefully measured, are smaller than most people expect (Hyde, 2005). For example, vastly more men than women become grand masters in chess. Does that fact indicate a difference in abilities? No. Boys and girls start at an equal level in playing chess and progress at equal rates. Apparently the only reason more men reach the highest level is that vastly more boys

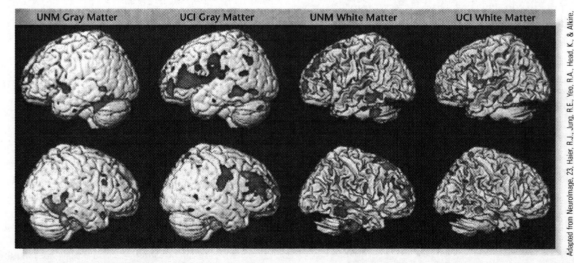

FIGURE 4.41 Cortical areas whose size correlated with IQ
The top row shows the left hemisphere; the bottom row shows the right. UNM and UCI columns show the results for two universities (University of New Mexico and University of California at Irvine). Areas whose size was significantly associated with IQ are shown in red; areas with the strongest relationship are shown in yellow.

Adapted from NeuroImage, 23, Haier, R.J., Jung, R.E., Yeo, R.A., Head, K., & Alkire, M.T., Structural brain variation and general intelligence, pp. 425-433, Copyright 2004 with permission from Elsevier.

than girls *start* playing chess (Chabris & Glickman, 2006). The difference pertains to interests, not abilities.

Many people believe that men tend to be better than women at mathematics. That may have been true in the past, and it still is true today in countries where men have much greater status than women, but in countries where men and women have roughly equal opportunities, their performance on math tests is about equal (Guiso, Monte, Sapienza, & Zingales, 2008). In the United States, girls on average do at least as well as boys in all math courses from elementary school through college, except for certain aspects of geometry, such as the items in Figure 4.42 (Hyde, Lindberg, Linn, Ellis, & Williams, 2008; Spelke, 2005). Even that difference may reflect differences in interests rather than ability. From an early age, most boys spend more time on activities related to angles and distances. In one study, young women who spent 10 hours playing action video games significantly improved on the kind of item shown in Figure 4.42 (Feng, Spence, & Pratt, 2007).

How can we explain why men and women are equal in intellect, but men have larger brains? One potentially relevant factor pertains to relative amounts of gray matter (cell bodies) and white matter (axons). Women average more and deeper sulci on the surface of the cortex, especially in the frontal and parietal areas (Luders et al., 2004). Consequently, the surface area of the cortex is almost equal for men and women. Because the surface is lined with neurons (gray matter), the sexes have about the same number of neurons, despite differences in brain volume (Allen, Damasio, Grabowski, Bruss, & Zhang, 2003). This idea would provide a convincing explanation *if* intelligence depended only on gray matter. However, the research points to important contributions from both gray matter and white matter (Chiang et al., 2009; Narr et al., 2007; van Leeuwen et al., 2009). We are left, then, with the apparent conclusion that women's brains and men's brains differ structurally but accomplish the same thing, presumably because they are organized differently. However, until we can expand on what we mean by "organized differently," it is not very satisfying.

In short, the data do not support any simple summary of the relationship between brain size and intelligence. Progress will

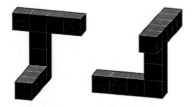

Can the set of blocks on the left be rotated to match the set at the right?

Which of the lines at the left has the same angle as the one at the right?

FIGURE 4.42 Spatial perception tasks
For the first question, the correct answer is *no*.
For the second question, the correct answer is *e*.
On average, men answer more quickly or more accurately than women, but women who spend 10 hours playing video games narrow the gap. (© Cengage Learning 2013)

probably depend on more detailed measurements of specific intellectual abilities and more detailed brain measurements. That is, how do the anatomy, chemistry, and other features of specific brain areas relate to specific aspects of behavior? In the rest of this text, we concentrate on those questions.

Stop & Check

24. In which way do men and women differ most—intellectual performance, total gray matter, or total white matter?

ANSWER
24. Men have more white matter, and therefore larger brains. However, men and women are about equal in gray matter and intellectual performance.

Research Methods and Their Limits

Why do we need so many research methods? It is because few studies conclusively establish one theory or another. Far more often, researchers gradually accumulate evidence that points in a particular direction, until eventually that view becomes dominant. Even in those rare cases when a single study appears to have been decisive, researchers often identify it as decisive only in retrospect, after many additional studies confirmed the finding.

The reason we need so many methods is that almost any study has limitations. Results often depend on what seem like minor details of procedure. Even when several studies using the same method produce similar results, the possibility remains that the method itself has a hidden flaw. Therefore, scientists prefer whenever possible to compare results from widely different methods. The more types of evidence point to a given conclusion, the greater our confidence.

SUMMARY

1. One way to study brain-behavior relationships is to examine the effects of brain damage. If someone suffers a loss after some kind of brain damage, then that area contributes in some way to that behavior. **109**

2. If stimulation of a brain area increases some behavior, presumably that area contributes to the behavior. **110**

3. Researchers try to understand brain-behavior relationships by recording activity in various brain areas during a given behavior. Many methods are available, including EEG, MEG, and fMRI. **111**

4. People who differ with regard to some behavior sometimes also differ with regard to their brain anatomy. MRI is one modern method of imaging a living brain. However, correlations between behavior and anatomy should be evaluated cautiously. **114**

5. Research using modern methods to measure brain size suggests a moderate positive relationship between brain size and intelligence, although many puzzles and uncertainties remain. **117**

6. Men and women are equal in IQ scores, despite men's having larger brains. **118**

KEY TERMS

Terms are defined in the module on the page number indicated. They're also presented in alphabetical order with definitions in the book's Subject Index/Glossary, which begins on page 561. Interactive flashcards and crossword puzzles are among the online resources available to help you learn these terms and the concepts they represent.

ablation **109**

computerized axial tomography (CT or CAT scan) **114**

electroencephalograph (EEG) **111**

evoked potentials or evoked responses **111**

functional magnetic resonance imaging (fMRI) **112**

lesion **109**

magnetic resonance imaging (MRI) **114**

magnetoencephalograph (MEG) **111**

phrenology **114**

positron-emission tomography (PET) **111**

stereotaxic instrument **109**

transcranial magnetic stimulation **110**

THOUGHT QUESTION

Certain unusual aspects of brain structure were observed in the brain of Albert Einstein (M. C. Diamond, Scheibel, Murphy, & Harvey, 1985; Witelson, Kigar, & Harvey, 1999).

One interpretation is that he was born with certain specialized brain features that encouraged his scientific and intellectual abilities. What is an alternative interpretation?

CHAPTER 4 Interactive Exploration and Study

The **Psychology CourseMate** for this text brings chapter topics to life with interactive learning, study, and exam preparation tools, including quizzes and flashcards for the Key Concepts that appear throughout each module, as well as an interactive media-rich eBook version of the text that is fully searchable and includes highlighting and note taking capabilities and interactive versions of the book's **Stop & Check** quizzes and **Try It Yourself Online** activities. The site also features **Virtual Biological Psychology Labs**, **videos**, and **animations** to help you better understand concepts—logon and learn more at **www.cengagebrain.com**, which is your gateway to all of this text's complimentary and premium resources, including the following:

Virtual Biological Psychology Labs

Explore the experiments that led to modern-day understanding of biopsychology with the Virtual Biological Psychology Labs, featuring a realistic lab environment that allows you to conduct experiments and evaluate data to better understand how scientists came to the conclusions presented in your text. The labs cover a range of topics, including perception, motivation, cognition, and more. You may purchase access at **www.cengagebrain.com**, or login at **login.cengagebrain.com** if an access card was included with your text.

Videos

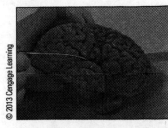

Structures of the Brain, Part 1

Also available—

- Structures of the Brain, Part 2
- Magnetic Stimulation of the Brain
- Research with Brain Scans
- Politics and the Brain
- Visual Mind Reading

Animations

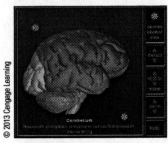

Interactive 3D Brain

Also available—

- Interactive Left Hemisphere Function
- Interactive Sagittal Section: Right Hemisphere #1
- Interactive Sagittal Section: Right Hemisphere #2
- Interactive Sagittal Section: Right Hemisphere #3
- Interactive Brain Puzzle
- Interactive Cortex Puzzle
- Interactive Sensory Cortex
- Structures of the Brain

Suggestions for Further Exploration

Books

Burrell, B. (2004). *Postcards from the brain museum.* New York: Broadway Books. Fascinating history of the attempts to collect brains of successful people and try to relate their brain anatomy to their success.

Klawans, H. L. (1988). *Toscanini's fumble and other tales of clinical neurology.* Chicago: Contemporary Books. Description of illustrative cases of brain damage and their behavioral consequences.

Websites

The Psychology CourseMate for this text provides regularly updated links to relevant online resources for this chapter, such as the **Whole Brain Atlas** and **Comparative Mammalian Brain Collections.**

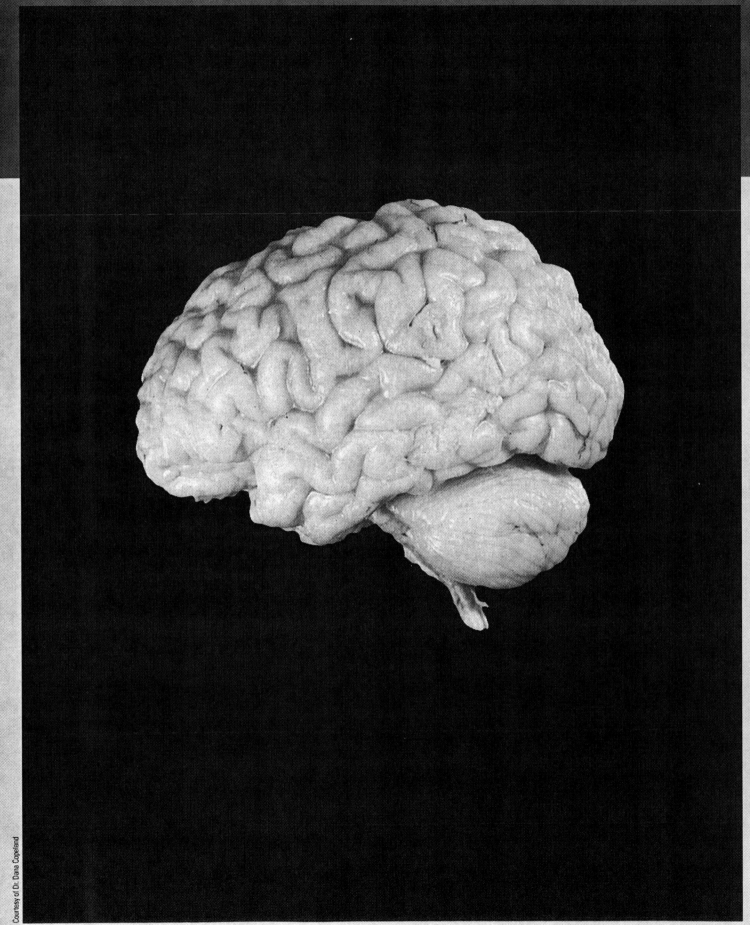

Development and Plasticity of the Brain

5

MAIN IDEAS

1. Neurons begin by migrating to their proper locations and developing axons, which extend to their targets by following chemical pathways.

2. The nervous system forms far more neurons than it needs and then eliminates those that do not establish suitable connections or receive sufficient input. It also forms excess synapses and discards the less active ones.

3. Experiences alter brain anatomy. Plasticity is greatest early in life but continues throughout life.

4. Many mechanisms contribute to recovery from brain damage, including restoration of undamaged neurons to full activity, regrowth of axons, readjustment of surviving synapses, and behavioral adjustments.

"Some assembly required." Have you ever bought a package with those ominous words? Sometimes, all you have to do is attach a few parts, but other times, you face page after page of barely comprehensible instructions.

The human nervous system requires an enormous amount of assembly, and the instructions are different from those for the objects we assemble from a kit. Instead of, "Put this piece here and that piece there," the instructions are, "Put these axons here and those dendrites there, and then wait to see what happens. Keep the connections that work the best and discard the others. Continue making new connections and keeping only the successful ones."

Therefore, we say that the brain's anatomy is *plastic*. It changes rapidly in early development and continues changing throughout life.

OPPOSITE: An enormous amount of brain development has already occurred by the time a person is 1 year old.

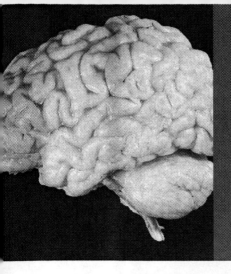

Development of the Brain

Think of all the things you can do that you couldn't have done a few years ago—analyze statistics, read a foreign language, write brilliant critiques of complex issues, and so on. Have you developed these new skills because of brain growth? Many of your dendrites have grown new branches, but your brain as a whole is the same size.

Now think of all the things that 1-year-old children can do that they could not do at birth. Have *they* developed their new skills because of brain growth? To a large extent, yes, although the results depend on experiences as well. Brain development depends on experience in complex ways that blur the distinction between learning and maturation. In this module, we consider how neurons develop, how their axons connect, and how experience modifies development.

Maturation of the Vertebrate Brain

The human central nervous system begins to form when the embryo is about 2 weeks old. The dorsal surface thickens and then long thin lips rise, curl, and merge, forming a neural tube that surrounds a fluid-filled cavity (Figure 5.1). As the tube sinks under the surface of the skin, the forward end enlarges and differentiates into the hindbrain, midbrain, and forebrain (Figure 5.2). The rest becomes the spinal cord. The fluid-filled cavity within the neural tube becomes the central canal of the spinal cord and the four ventricles of the brain, containing the cerebrospinal fluid (CSF). At birth, the average human brain weighs about 350 grams (g). By the end of the first year, it weighs 1,000 g, close to the adult weight of 1,200 to 1,400 g.

Growth and Development of Neurons

Neuroscientists distinguish these processes in the development of neurons: proliferation, migration, differentiation, myelination, and synaptogenesis. **Proliferation** is the production of new cells. Early in development, the cells lining the ventricles of the brain divide. Some cells remain where they are (as *stem cells*), continuing to divide. Others become primitive neurons and glia that begin migrating to other locations. Neuron proliferation is similar among vertebrates, differing mainly in the number of cell divisions. Human brains differ from chimpanzee brains mainly because human neurons continue proliferating longer (Rakic, 1998; Vrba, 1998).

FIGURE 5.1 Early development of the human central nervous system
The brain and spinal cord begin as folding lips surrounding a fluid-filled canal. The stages shown occur at approximately age 2 to 3 weeks. (© Cengage Learning 2013)

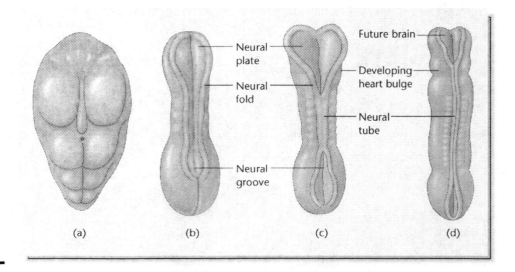

(a) (b) (c) (d)

Neural plate
Neural fold
Neural groove
Future brain
Developing heart bulge
Neural tube

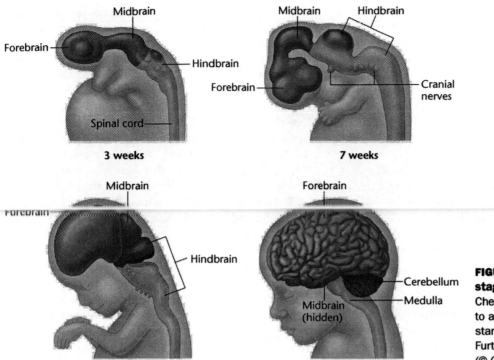

FIGURE 5.2 Human brain at four stages of development
Chemical processes develop the brain to an amazing degree even before the start of any experience with the world. Further changes continue throughout life. (© *Cengage Learning 2013*)

After cells have differentiated as neurons or glia, they **migrate** (move). Some neurons migrate much faster than others, and a few of the slowest don't reach their final destinations until adulthood (Ghashghaei, Lai, & Anton, 2007). Some neurons move radially from the inside of the brain to the outside, some move tangentially along the surface of the brain, and some move tangentially and then radially (Nadarajah & Parnavelas, 2002). Chemicals known as *immunoglobulins* and *chemokines* guide neuron migration. A deficit in these chemicals leads to impaired migration, decreased brain size, decreased axon growth, and mental retardation (Berger-Sweeney & Hohmann, 1997; Crossin & Krushel, 2000; Tran & Miller, 2003). The brain has many kinds of immunoglobulins and chemokines, presumably reflecting the complexity of brain development.

At first, a primitive neuron looks like any other cell. Gradually, the neuron **differentiates**, forming its axon and dendrites. The axon grows first. In many cases, a migrating neuron tows its growing axon along like a tail (Gilmour, Knaut, Maischein, & Nüsslein-Volhard, 2004), allowing its tip to remain at or near its target. In other cases, the axon needs to grow toward its target, finding its way through a jungle of other cells and fibers. After the migrating neuron reaches its destination, its dendrites begin to form.

A later and slower stage of neuronal development is **myelination**, the process by which glia produce the insulating fatty sheaths that accelerate transmission in many vertebrate axons. Myelin forms first in the spinal cord and then in the hindbrain, midbrain, and forebrain. Unlike the rapid prolifer-

ation and migration of neurons, myelination continues gradually for decades (Benes, Turtle, Khan, & Farol, 1994).

The final stage is **synaptogenesis**, or the formation of synapses. Although this process begins before birth, it continues throughout life, as neurons form new synapses and discard old ones. However, the process generally slows in older people, as does the formation of new dendritic branches (Buell & Coleman, 1981; Jacobs & Scheibel, 1993).

Stop & Check

1. Which develops first, a neuron's axon or its dendrites?

ANSWER

1. The axon forms first.

New Neurons Later in Life

Can the adult vertebrate brain generate new neurons? The traditional belief, dating back to Cajal's work in the late 1800s, was that vertebrate brains formed all their neurons in embryological development or early infancy at the latest. Beyond that point, neurons could modify their shape, but the brain could not develop new neurons. Later researchers found exceptions.

The first were the olfactory receptors, which, because they are exposed to the outside world and its toxic chemicals, have a half-life of only 90 days. **Stem cells** in the nose remain immature throughout life. Periodically, they divide, with one cell remaining immature while the other differentiates to replace a dying olfactory receptor. It grows its axon back to the appropriate site in the brain (Gogos, Osborne, Nemes, Mendelsohn, & Axel, 2000; Graziadei & deHan, 1973). Later researchers also found a similar population of stem cells in the interior of the brain. They sometimes divide to form "daughter" cells that migrate to the olfactory bulb and transform into glia cells or neurons (Gage, 2000). The newly formed neurons are necessary for maintaining the olfactory bulb. Any procedure that prevents their formation leads to a gradual shrinkage of the olfactory bulbs, because neurons die without replacement (Imayoshi et al., 2008).

New neurons also form in an area of the songbird brain necessary for singing. This area loses neurons in fall and winter and regains them the next spring (mating season) (Nottebohm, 2002; Wissman & Brenowitz, 2009).

Stem cells also differentiate into new neurons in the adult hippocampus of birds (Smulders, Shiflett, Sperling, & De-Voogd, 2000) and mammals (Song, Stevens, & Gage, 2002; van Praag et al., 2002). The hippocampus is an important area for memory formation. Blocking the formation of new neurons (such as by exposing the hippocampus to X-rays) impairs new memories (Clelland et al., 2009; Meshi et al., 2006).

In general, animals learn most easily when they are young. As they grow older, their neurons become less changeable. Newly formed neurons of the hippocampus go through a stage when they are highly changeable, like those of youth (Ge, Yang, Hsu, Ming, & Song, 2007; Schmidt-Hieber, Jonas, & Bischofberger, 2004). During this period, they integrate into new circuits that represent new memories (Kee, Teixeira, Wang, & Frankland, 2007; Ramirez-Amaya, Marrone, Gage, Worley, & Barnes, 2006). More of the newly formed neurons survive during times of new learning (Tashiro, Makino, & Gage, 2007). A supply of new neurons keeps the hippocampus "young" for learning new tasks. It is also possible that incorporating clusters of new neurons into a single new circuit may be a way of labeling memories that formed at a given time. It might lead to a recollection that certain events happened at the same time (Aimone, Wiles, & Gage, 2006).

Possible formation of new neurons in the mature primate cerebral cortex has been controversial. The best evidence against their formation came from a clever study using a radioactive isotope of carbon, ^{14}C. The concentration of ^{14}C in the atmosphere, compared to other isotopes of carbon, was nearly constant over time until the era of nuclear bomb testing, which released much radioactivity. That era ended with the test ban treaty of 1963. The concentration of ^{14}C peaked in 1963 and has been declining since then. If you examine, for example, tree rings, you will find that a ring that formed in 1963 has the ^{14}C content typical of 1963, a ring that formed in 1990 has the ^{14}C content typical of 1990, and so forth. Researchers examined the carbon in the DNA of various human cells. Every cell keeps its DNA molecules until it dies. When researchers examined people's skin cells, they found a concentration of ^{14}C corresponding to the year in which they did the test. That is, skin cells turn over rapidly, and all of your skin cells are less than a year old. When they examined skeletal muscle cells, they found a ^{14}C concentration corresponding

to 15 years ago, indicating that skeletal muscles are replaced slowly, making the average cell 15 years old. Cells of the heart are, on average, almost as old as the person, indicating that the body replaces no more than 1% of heart cells per year (Bergmann et al., 2009). When researchers examined neurons in the cerebral cortex, they found a ^{14}C concentration corresponding to the year of the person's birth. These results indicate that the mammalian cerebral cortex forms few or no new neurons after birth, at least under normal circumstances (Spalding, Bhardwaj, Buchholz, Druid, & Frisén, 2005).

Are you surprised to learn that your cortex may not have made any new neurons since you were born? Researcher Pasko Rakic (2008, p. 894) commented, "Some people seem to be disappointed by this finding, as if it is a bad thing. I find it fascinating that... during our prolonged lifespan we always use the same cells."

However, the situation may be different after brain damage. After damage to the sensory axons from a monkey's hand, the cerebral cortex on the contralateral side gradually reorganizes, and during this process new neurons do form, as confirmed by chemicals that specifically label newly formed neurons (Vessal & Darian-Smith, 2010). New neurons also form in the cortex after a stroke (Ohira et al., 2010). Most of the newly formed neurons are small ones with inhibitory functions. How long they survive is not yet known.

——————————————————▶ **Stop & Check**

2. In which brain areas do new neurons form in adults?

3. What evidence indicated that new neurons seldom or never form in the adult cerebral cortex?

ANSWERS **2.** Olfactory receptors, neurons in the hippocampus, and neurons in the song-producing areas of certain bird species. **3.** The ^{14}C concentration in the DNA of cerebral cortex neurons corresponds to the level during the year the person was born, indicating that all or nearly all of those neurons are as old as the person is.

Pathfinding by Axons

If you asked someone to run a cable from your desk to another desk across the room, your directions could be simple. But imagine asking someone to run a cable to somewhere on the other side of the country. You would have to give detailed instructions about how to find the right city, building, and desk. The developing nervous system faces a similar challenge because it sends axons over great distances. How do they find their way?

Chemical Pathfinding by Axons

A famous biologist, Paul Weiss (1924), conducted an experiment in which he grafted an extra leg to a salamander and then waited for axons to grow into it. (Unlike mammals, salamanders and other amphibians accept transplants of extra limbs and generate new axon branches to the extra limbs. Much research requires finding the right species to study.) After the axons reached the muscles, the extra leg moved in synchrony with the normal leg next to it.

Weiss dismissed the idea that each axon found its way to exactly the correct muscle in the extra limb. He suggested instead that the nerves attached to muscles at random and then sent a variety of messages, each one tuned to a different muscle. The muscles were like radios tuned to different stations: Each muscle received many signals but responded to only one. (The 1920s were the early days of radio, and it was an appealing analogy to think the nervous system might work like a radio. In the 1600s, Descartes thought the nervous system worked like a hydraulic pump, the most advanced technology of the time. Today many people think the nervous system works like a computer, our own most advanced technology.)

Specificity of Axon Connections

Later evidence supported the interpretation that Weiss had rejected: The salamander's extra leg moved in synchrony with its neighbor because each axon found exactly the correct muscle.

Roger Sperry, a former student of Weiss, performed a classic experiment that showed how sensory axons find their way to their correct targets. The principle is the same as for axons finding their way to muscles. First Sperry cut the optic nerves of some newts. (Note the importance of choosing the right species: A cut optic nerve grows back in newts and other amphibians, but not in mammals or birds.) The damaged optic nerve grew back and connected with the *tectum*, which is amphibians' main visual area (Figure 5.3), thereby reestablishing normal vision.

Courtesy of the Archives, California Institute of Technology]

Roger W. Sperry (1913–1994)

When subjective values have objective consequences... they become part of the content of science.... Science would become the final determinant of what is right and true, the best source and authority available to the human brain for finding ultimate axioms and guideline beliefs to live by, and for reaching an intimate understanding and rapport with the forces that control the universe and created man. (Sperry, 1975, pp. 432–433)

Then Sperry (1943) cut the optic nerve and rotated the eye by 180 degrees. When the axons grew back to the tectum, which area would they contact? The axons from what had originally been the dorsal portion of the retina (which was now ventral) grew back to the area responsible for vision in the dorsal retina. Axons from other parts of the retina also grew back to their original targets. The newt now saw the world upside down and backward, responding to stimuli in the sky as if they were on the ground and to stimuli on the left as if they were on the right (Figure 5.4). Each axon regenerated to the same place where it had originally been, presumably by following a chemical trail.

Chemical Gradients

The next question was: How specific is the axon's aim? The current estimate is that humans have only about 30,000 genes total—far too few to provide a specific target for each

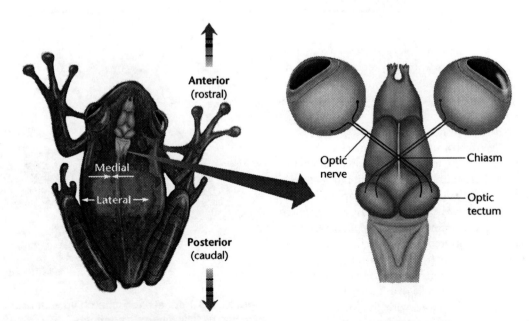

FIGURE 5.3 Connections from eye to brain in a frog
The optic tectum is a large structure in fish, amphibians, reptiles, and birds. Its location corresponds to the midbrain of mammals, but its function is analogous to what the cerebral cortex does in mammals. Note: Connections from eye to brain are different in humans, as described in Chapter 14. *(Source: After Romer, 1962)*

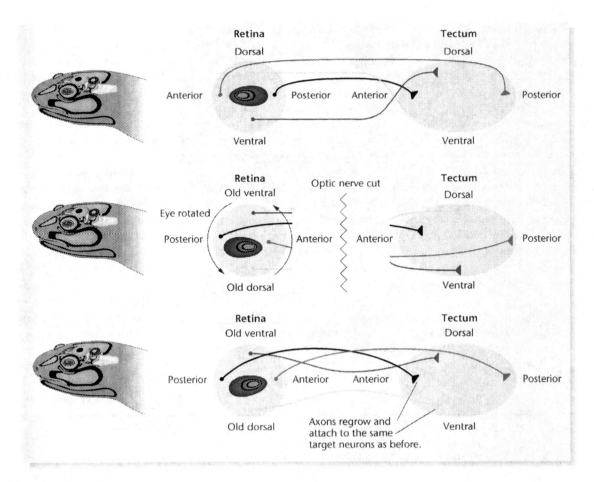

FIGURE 5.4 Sperry's experiment on nerve connections in newts
After he cut the optic nerve and inverted the eye, the axons grew back to their original targets, not to the targets corresponding to the eye's current position. (© Cengage Learning 2013)

of the brain's billions of neurons. Nevertheless, axons find their correct targets with remarkable precision. How do they do it?

A growing axon follows a path of cell–surface molecules, attracted by some chemicals and repelled by others, in a process that steers the axon in the correct direction (Yu & Bargmann, 2001). Eventually, axons sort themselves over the surface of their target area by following a gradient of chemicals. For example, one chemical in the amphibian tectum is a protein known as TOP_{DV} (TOP for *topography*; DV for *dorsoventral*). This protein is 30 times more concentrated in the axons of the dorsal retina than of the ventral retina and 10 times more concentrated in the ventral tectum than in the dorsal tectum. As axons from the retina grow toward the tectum, the retinal axons with the greatest concentration of TOP_{DV} connect to the tectal cells with the highest concentration of that chemical. The axons with the lowest concentration connect to the tectal cells with the lowest concentration. A similar gradient of another protein aligns the axons along the anterior–posterior axis (J. R. Sanes, 1993) (Figure 5.5). By analogy, you could think of men lining up from tallest to shortest, pairing up with women who lined up from tallest to shortest.

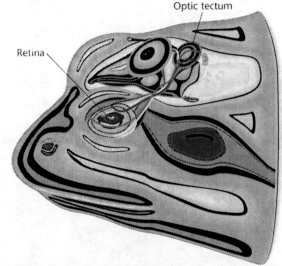

FIGURE 5.5 Retinal axons match up with neurons in the tectum by following two gradients
The protein TOP_{DV} is concentrated mostly in the dorsal retina and the ventral tectum. Axons rich in TOP_{DV} attach to tectal neurons that are also rich in that chemical. A second protein directs axons from the posterior retina to the anterior portion of the tectum (© Cengage Learning 2013)

Stop & Check

4. What was Sperry's evidence that axons grow to a specific target instead of attaching at random?

5. If all cells in an amphibian's tectum produced the same amount of TOP$_{DV}$, what would be the effect on the attachment of axons?

ANSWERS **4.** Sperry found that if he cut a newt's eye and inverted it, axons grew back to their original targets, even though the connections were inappropriate to their new positions on the eye. **5.** Axons would attach haphazardly instead of arranging themselves according to their dorsoventral position on the retina.

Competition Among Axons as a General Principle

When axons initially reach their targets, chemical gradients steer them to approximately their correct location, but it would be hard to imagine that they achieve perfect accuracy. Instead, each axon forms synapses onto many cells in approximately the correct location, and each target cell receives synapses from many axons. Over time, each postsynaptic cell strengthens some synapses—presumably the most appropriate ones—and eliminates others (Hua & Smith, 2004). This adjustment depends on the pattern of input from incoming axons (Catalano & Shatz, 1998). For example, one part of the thalamus receives input from many retinal axons. During embryological development, long before the first exposure to light, repeated waves of spontaneous activity sweep over the retina from one side to the other. Consequently, axons from adjacent areas of the retina send almost simultaneous messages to the thalamus. Each thalamic neuron selects a

group of axons that are simultaneously active. In this way, it finds receptors from adjacent regions of the retina (Meister, Wong, Baylor, & Shatz, 1991). It then rejects synapses from other locations.

These results suggest a general principle, called **neural Darwinism** (Edelman, 1987). In the development of the nervous system, we start with more neurons and synapses than we can keep. Synapses form with only approximate accuracy, and then a selection process keeps some and rejects others. The most successful axons and combinations survive, and the others fail. The principle of competition among axons is an important one, although we should use the analogy with Darwinian evolution cautiously. Mutations in the genes are random events, but neurotrophins steer new axonal branches and synapses in the right direction.

Stop & Check

6. If axons from the retina were prevented from showing spontaneous activity during early development, what would be the probable effect on development of the lateral geniculate?

ANSWER **6.** The axons would attach based on a chemical gradient but could not fine-tune their adjustment based on experience. Therefore, the connections would be less precise.

Determinants of Neuronal Survival

Getting the right number of neurons for each area of the nervous system is more complicated than it might seem. Consider an example. The sympathetic nervous system sends axons to muscles and glands. Each ganglion has enough axons to supply the muscles and glands in its area, with no axons left over. How does the match come out so exact? Long ago, one hypothesis was that the muscles sent chemical messages to tell the sympathetic ganglion how many neurons to form. Rita Levi-Montalcini was largely responsible for disconfirming this hypothesis.

Levi-Montalcini's early life would seem most unfavorable for a scientific career. She was a young Italian Jewish woman

Carla J. Shatz

The functioning of the brain depends upon the precision and patterns of its neural circuits. How is this amazing computational machine assembled and wired during development? The biological answer is so much more wonderful than anticipated! The adult precision is sculpted from an early imprecise pattern by a process in which connections are verified by the functioning of the neurons themselves. Thus, the developing brain is not simply a miniature version of the adult. Moreover, the brain works to wire itself, rather than assembling itself first and then flipping a switch, as might happen in the assembly of a computer. This kind of surprise in scientific discovery opens up new vistas of understanding and possibility and makes the process of doing science infinitely exciting and fascinating. (Shatz, personal communication)

Carla J. Shatz

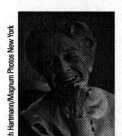

Rita Levi-Montalcini

Many years later, I often asked myself how we could have dedicated ourselves with such enthusiasm to solving this small neuroembryological problem while German armies were advancing throughout Europe, spreading destruction and death wherever they went and threatening the very survival of Western civilization. The answer lies in the desperate and partially unconscious desire of human beings to ignore what is happening in situations where full awareness might lead one to self-destruction.

Erich Hartmann/Magnum Photos New York

during the Nazi era. World War II destroyed the Italian economy, and almost everyone at the time discouraged women from scientific or medical careers. She had to spend several years in hiding during the war, but she spent those years conducting research on development of the nervous system, as she described in her autobiography (Levi-Montalcini, 1988) and a later interview with Moses Chao (2010). She developed a love for research and eventually discovered that the muscles do not determine how many axons *form*; they determine how many *survive*.

Initially, the sympathetic nervous system forms far more neurons than it needs. When one of its neurons forms a synapse onto a muscle, that muscle delivers a protein called **nerve growth factor** (**NGF**) that promotes the survival and growth of the axon (Levi-Montalcini, 1987). An axon that does not receive NGF degenerates, and its cell body dies. That is, each neuron starts life with a "suicide program": If its axon does not make contact with an appropriate postsynaptic cell by a certain age, the neuron kills itself through a process called **apoptosis,**[1] a programmed mechanism of cell death. (Apoptosis is distinct from *necrosis,* which is death caused by an injury or a toxic substance.) NGF cancels the program for apoptosis; it is the postsynaptic cell's way of telling the incoming axon, "I'll be your partner. Don't kill yourself."

The brain's system of overproducing neurons and then applying apoptosis enables the CNS to match the number of incoming axons to the number of receiving cells. When the sympathetic nervous system begins sending axons toward the muscles and glands, it doesn't know the exact size of the muscles or glands. It makes more neurons than necessary and discards the excess. In fact, all areas of the developing nervous system make far more neurons than will survive into adulthood. Each brain area has a period of massive cell death, becoming littered with dead and dying cells (Figure 5.6). This loss of cells is a natural part of development. In fact, loss of cells in a particular brain area often indicates maturation. For example, teenagers lose cells in parts of the prefrontal cortex while showing increased neuronal activity in those areas (Sowell, Thompson, Holmes, Jernigan, & Toga, 1999). Maturation of successful cells is linked to simultaneous loss of less successful ones. Another example is the visual cortex of people born blind. Contrary to what you might guess, the visual cortex is *thicker* than average in people born blind. A likely explanation is that in the absence of visual experience, the visual cortex is unable to prune out the ineffective and inappropriate synapses (Jiang et al., 2009). *food for cells.*

Nerve growth factor is a **neurotrophin**, meaning a chemical that promotes the survival and activity of neurons. (The word *trophin* derives from a Greek word for "nourishment.") In addition to NGF, the nervous system responds to *brain-derived neurotrophic factor* (BDNF) and several other neurotrophins (Airaksinen & Saarma, 2002). Neurotrophins are

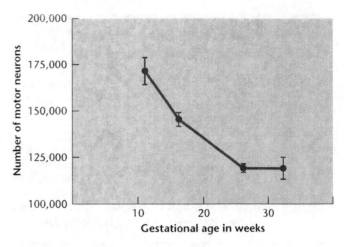

FIGURE 5.6 Cell loss during development of the nervous system
The number of motor neurons in the spinal cord of human fetuses is highest at 11 weeks and drops steadily until about 25 weeks. If an axon fails to make a synapse, its cell dies. (*Source: From N. G. Forger and S. M. Breedlove, Motoneuronal death in the human fetus.* Journal of Comparative Neurology, 264, 1987, 118–122. Copyright © 1987 Alan R. Liss, Inc. Reprinted by permission of N. G. Forger.)

not necessary for survival of brain neurons, but they are essential for growth of axons and dendrites, formation of new synapses, and learning (Alleva & Francia, 2009; Pascual et al., 2008; Rauskolb et al., 2010). Remember the term BDNF, because it becomes important again in Chapter 15 on depression and schizophrenia.

For an immature neuron to avoid apoptosis and survive, it needs to receive neurotrophins not only from its target cells but also from incoming axons. In one study, researchers examined mice with a genetic defect that prevented all release of neurotransmitters. The brains initially assembled normal anatomies, but then neurons started dying rapidly (Verhage et al., 2000). When neurons release neurotransmitters, they also release neurotrophins. Neurons that fail to receive neurotransmitters also fail to receive neurotrophins, and so they die (Poo, 2001).

Stop & Check

7. What process ensures that the spinal cord has the right number of axons to innervate all the muscle cells?

8. What class of chemicals prevents apoptosis?

9. At what age does a person have the greatest number of neurons—before birth, during childhood, during adolescence, or during adulthood?

ANSWERS
7. The nervous system builds far more neurons than it needs and discards those through apoptosis that do not make lasting synapses. 8. Neurotrophins, such as nerve growth factor. 9. The neuron number is greatest before birth.

▌ The Vulnerable Developing Brain

According to Lewis Wolpert (1991), "It is not birth, marriage, or death, but gastrulation, which is truly the most important time of your life." (Gastrulation is one of the early stages of embryological development.) Wolpert's point was that if you mess up in early development, you have problems from then on. Actually, if you mess up during gastrulation, your life is over.

The early stages of brain development are critical. A mutation in one identified gene leads to any of a wide variety of defects in brain development (Bilgüvar et al., 2010). The developing brain is also highly vulnerable to malnutrition, toxic chemicals, and infections that would produce only mild problems at later ages. For example, impaired thyroid function produces lethargy in adults but mental retardation in infants. (Thyroid deficiency was common in the past because of iodine deficiency. It is rare today because table salt is fortified with iodine.) A fever is a mere annoyance to an adult, but it impairs neuron proliferation in a fetus (Laburn, 1996). Low blood glucose decreases an adult's pep, but before birth, it impairs brain development (C. A. Nelson et al., 2000).

The infant brain is highly vulnerable to damage by alcohol. Children of mothers who drink heavily during pregnancy are born with **fetal alcohol syndrome**, a condition marked by hyperactivity, impulsiveness, difficulty maintaining attention, varying degrees of mental retardation, motor problems, heart defects, and facial abnormalities (Figure 5.7). Even in milder cases, those who were exposed to prenatal alcohol show impairments in learning, memory, language, and attention (Kodituwakku, 2007).

The mechanism of fetal alcohol syndrome relates partly to apoptosis: Remember that to prevent apoptosis, a neuron must receive neurotrophins from the incoming axons as well as from its own axon's target cell. Alcohol suppresses the release of glutamate, the brain's main excitatory transmitter, and enhances activity of GABA, the main inhibitory transmitter. Consequently, many neurons receive less excitation and neurotrophins than normal, and they undergo apoptosis (Ikonomidou et al., 2000). Alcohol also impairs brain development by altering the migration pattern of small neurons (Cuzon, Yeh, Yanagawa, Obata, & Yeh, 2008).

Prenatal exposure to other substances can be dangerous, too. On average, children of mothers who use cocaine or smoke cigarettes during pregnancy have an increased risk of attention-deficit disorder and other behavioral deficits (B. L. Thompson, Levitt, & Stanwood, 2009). Children whose mother used antidepressant drugs during pregnancy have increased risk of heart problems (Thompson et al., 2009). Because these are correlational studies, we cannot be sure of cause and effect. Mothers who smoke or use cocaine tend to be of lower socioeconomic status, less educated, and so forth, so the effect of smoking is probably smaller than the results suggest (Thapar et al., 2003).

Finally, the immature brain is highly responsive to influences from the mother. If a mother rat is exposed to stressful experiences, she becomes more fearful, she spends less than the

AP Images

FIGURE 5.7 Child with fetal alcohol syndrome
Note the facial pattern. Many children exposed to smaller amounts of alcohol before birth have behavioral deficits without facial signs.

usual amount of time licking and grooming her offspring, and her offspring become permanently more fearful in a variety of situations (Cameron et al., 2005). Analogously, the children of impoverished and abused women have, on average, increased problems in both their academic and social lives. The mechanisms in humans are not exactly the same as those in rats, but the overall principles are similar: Stress to the mother changes her behavior in ways that change her offspring's behavior.

> **Stop & Check**

10. Anesthetic drugs increase inhibition of neurons, blocking most action potentials. Why would we predict that exposure to anesthetics might be dangerous to the brain of a fetus?

ANSWER

10. Prolonged exposure to anesthetics might produce effects similar to fetal alcohol syndrome. Fetal alcohol syndrome occurs because alcohol increases inhibition and therefore increases apoptosis of developing neurons.

Differentiation of the Cortex

Neurons in different brain areas differ in shape and chemistry. When and how does a neuron "decide" which kind of neuron it is going to be? It is not a sudden decision. Immature neurons experimentally transplanted from one part of the developing cortex to another develop the properties characteristic of their new location (S. K. McConnell, 1992). However, neurons transplanted at a slightly later stage develop some new properties while retaining some old ones (Cohen-Tannoudji, Babinet, & Wassef, 1994). It is like the speech of immigrant children: Those who enter a country when very young master the correct pronunciation, whereas older children retain an accent.

In one fascinating experiment, researchers explored what would happen to the immature auditory portions of the brain if they received input from the eyes instead of the ears. Ferrets—mammals in the weasel family—are born so immature that their optic nerves (from the eyes) have not yet reached the thalamus. On one side of the brain, researchers damaged the superior colliculus and the occipital cortex, the two main targets for the optic nerves. On that side, they also damaged the auditory input. Therefore, the optic nerve could not attach to its usual target, and the auditory area of the thalamus lacked its usual input. As a result, the optic nerve attached to what is usually the auditory area of the thalamus. What would you guess happened? Did the visual input cause auditory sensations, or did the auditory areas of the brain turn into visual areas?

The result, surprising to many, was this: What would have been auditory thalamus and cortex reorganized, developing some (but not all) of the characteristic appearance of visual areas (Sharma, Angelucci, & Sur, 2000). But how do we know whether the animals treated that activity as vision? Remember that the researchers performed these procedures on one side of the brain. They left the other side intact. The researchers presented stimuli to the normal side of the brain and trained the ferrets to turn one direction when they heard something and the other direction when they saw a light, as shown in Figure 5.8. After the ferrets learned this task well, the researchers presented a light that the rewired side could see. The result: The ferrets turned the way they had been taught to turn when they saw something. In short, the rewired temporal cortex, receiving input from the optic nerve, produced visual responses (von Melchner, Pallas, & Sur, 2000).

> **Stop & Check**

11. In the ferret study, how did the experimenters determine that visual input to the auditory portions of the brain actually produced a visual sensation?

ANSWER 11. They trained the ferrets to respond to stimuli on the normal side, turning one direction in response to sounds and the other direction to lights. Then they presented light to the rewired side and saw that the ferret again turned in the direction it had associated with lights.

Fine-Tuning by Experience

The blueprints for a house determine its overall plan, but because architects can't anticipate every detail, construction workers often have to improvise. The same is true for your nervous system. Because of the unpredictability of life, our brains have evolved the ability to remodel themselves (within limits) in response to our experience (Shatz, 1992).

Experience and Dendritic Branching

Decades ago, researchers doubted that adult neurons substantially changed their shape. We now know that axons and den-

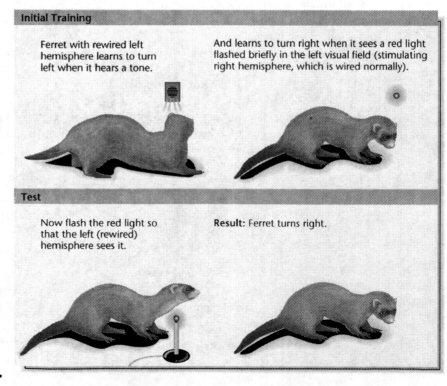

Initial Training

Ferret with rewired left hemisphere learns to turn left when it hears a tone.

And learns to turn right when it sees a red light flashed briefly in the left visual field (stimulating right hemisphere, which is wired normally).

Test

Now flash the red light so that the left (rewired) hemisphere sees it.

Result: Ferret turns right.

FIGURE 5.8 A ferret with rewired temporal cortex

First, the normal (right) hemisphere is trained to respond to a red light by turning to the right. Then, the rewired (left) hemisphere is tested with a red light. The fact that the ferret turns to the right indicates that it regards the stimulus as light, not sound. (© Cengage Learning 2013)

drites continue to modify their structure throughout life. Dale Purves and R. D. Hadley (1985) developed a method of injecting a dye that enabled them to examine the structure of a living neuron at different times, days to weeks apart. They found that some dendritic branches extended between one viewing and another, whereas others retracted or disappeared (Figure 5.9). About 6% of dendritic spines appear or disappear within a month (Xu, Pan, Yang, & Gan, 2007). The gain or loss of spines means a turnover of synapses, which relates to learning (Yang, Pan, & Gan, 2009).

Experiences guide the neuronal changes. Let's start with a simple example. Decades ago, it was typical for a laboratory rat to live alone in a small gray cage. Imagine by contrast a group of rats in a larger cage with a few objects to explore. Researchers called this an enriched environment, but it was enriched only in contrast to the deprived experience of a typical rat cage. A rat in the more stimulating environment developed a thicker cortex, more dendritic branching, and improved learning (Greenough, 1975; Rosenzweig & Bennett, 1996). An enriched environment enhances sprouting of axons and dendrites in many other species also (Coss, Brandon, & Globus, 1980) (Figure 5.10). As a result of this research, most rats today are kept in a more enriched environment than was typical in the past.

We might suppose that the neuronal changes in an enriched environment depend on new and interesting experiences, and many of them do. For example, after practice of particular skills, the connections relevant to those skills proliferate, while other connections retract. Nevertheless, much of the enhancement produced by the enriched environment is due to physical activity. Using a running wheel enhances growth of axons and dendrites, even for rats in isolation (Pietropaolo, Feldon, Alleva, Cirulli, & Yee, 2006; Rhodes et al., 2003; van Praag, Kempermann, & Gage, 1999). Activity also improves learning and memory (Van der Borght, Havekes, Bos, Eggen, & Van der Zee, 2007).

Can we extend these results to humans? Could we, for example, improve people's intelligence by giving them a more enriched environment? It's not that easy. Educators have long operated on the assumption that training children to do something difficult will enhance their intellect in general. Long ago, British schools taught children Greek and Latin. Today it might be Shakespeare's plays or advanced math, but in any case, the idea is to teach one thing and hope students get smarter in other ways, too. The psychological term is "far transfer." (*Near transfer* is training on one task and finding improvement on a very similar task.) In general, far transfer is weak and hard to demonstrate. Most attempted interventions to improve people's memory and reasoning produce only small benefits (Hertzog, Kramer, Wilson, & Lindenberger, 2009). Many companies offer computer programs designed to "train your brain." How well do they work? In one careful evaluation, researchers studied more than 11,000 people who did the computer-guided exercises several times a week for 6 weeks. At the end of that time, participants had improved substantially on the tasks the computer trained them to do, but they showed no sign of improvement on other cognitive tasks (Owen et al., 2010). That is, they showed no far transfer. This is not to say that *no* training method has benefits. For example, certain complex video games improve people's attention patterns (Boot, Kramer, Simons, Fabiani, & Gratton, 2008; Hertzog et al., 2009). But your brain isn't like a muscle, where you could exercise it to be bigger and stronger.

Similarly, many people advise old people to do crossword puzzles or Sudoku puzzles to "exercise their brains." Many correlational studies show that people who engage in such activities remain mentally alert longer than others do, but we cannot conclude cause and effect. Perhaps working puzzles helps keep the brain active, but the other interpretation is that people who already have active brains are more likely than average to work puzzles. Experimental studies suggest that practicing crossword puzzles doesn't help people remember where they left their keys, what time they were planning to meet someone for lunch, or anything else other than crossword puzzles (Salthouse, 2006).

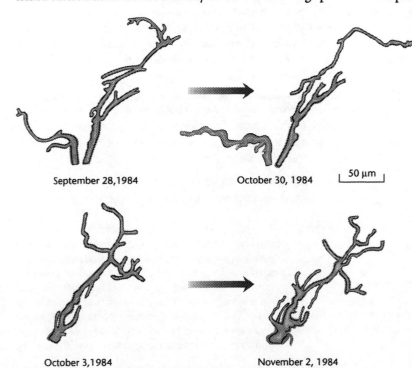

September 28, 1984   October 30, 1984 | 50 μm |

October 3, 1984   November 2, 1984

FIGURE 5.9 Changes in dendritic trees of two neurons
During a month, some branches elongated and others retracted. The shape of the neuron is in flux even during adulthood. (*Source: Reprinted from "Changes in Dendritic Branching of Adult Mammalian Neurons Revealed by Repeated Imaging in Situ," by D. Purves and R. D. Hadley, Nature, 315, p. 404–406. Copyright © 1985 Macmillan Magazines, Ltd. Reprinted by permission of D. Purves and Macmillan Magazines, Ltd.*)

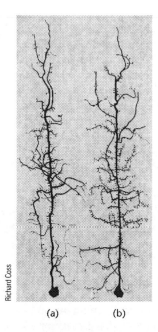

Richard Coss

(a)   (b)

FIGURE 5.10 Effect of a stimulating environment
(a) A jewel fish reared in isolation develops neurons with fewer branches. (b) A fish reared with others has more neuronal branches.

One of the best-documented ways to maintain intellectual vigor in old age is the same thing that works so well for laboratory animals—physical activity. Experimental studies, in which older people were randomly assigned to daily aerobic exercise or sedentary activities, confirm that the physical activity enhances both cognitive processes and brain anatomy (Rosano et al., 2010; P. J. Smith et al., 2010).

 **Stop & Check**

12. An enriched environment promotes growth of axons and dendrites. What is known to be one important reason for this effect?

ANSWER

12. Animals in an enriched environment are more active, and their exercise enhances growth of axons and dendrites.

Effects of Special Experiences

Attempts to enhance overall brain development produce at best modest effects. However, prolonged experience of a particular type profoundly enhances the brain's ability to perform the same function again.

Brain Adaptations in People Blind Since Infancy

What happens to the brain if one sensory system is impaired? Recall the experiment on ferrets, in which axons of the visual system, unable to contact their normal targets, attached instead to the brain areas usually devoted to hearing and managed to convert them into more or less satisfactory visual areas (p. 132). Might anything similar happen in the brains of people born deaf or blind?

People often say that blind people become better than usual at touch and hearing, or that deaf people develop a finer sense of touch and vision. Those statements are true in a way, but we need to be more specific. Being blind does not change the touch receptors in the fingers or the receptors in the ears. However, it increases attention to touch and sound, and the brain adapts to that attention.

In several studies, investigators asked sighted people and people blind since infancy to feel Braille letters or other objects and say whether two items were the same or different. On average, blind people performed more accurately than sighted people, as you would guess. More surprisingly, PET and fMRI scans indicated substantial activity in the occipital cortex of blind people while they performed these tasks (Burton et al., 2002; Sadato et al., 1996, 1998). Evidently, touch information activated this cortical area, which is ordinarily devoted to vision alone. In people blind since birth or early childhood, auditory stimuli also produce increased responses in what are usually visual areas of the cortex (Gougoux et al., 2009; Wan, Wood, Reutens, & Wilson, 2010).

To double-check this conclusion, researchers asked blind and sighted people to perform the same kind of task during temporary inactivation of the occipital cortex. As discussed in Chapter 4, intense magnetic stimulation on the scalp temporarily inactivates neurons beneath the magnet. Applying this procedure to the occipital cortex of people who are blind interferes with their ability to identify Braille symbols, whereas it does not impair touch perception in sighted people. In short, blind people, unlike sighted people, use the occipital cortex to help identify what they feel (L. G. Cohen et al., 1997).

Similar changes can occur even in adulthood, to a limited extent. Researchers blindfolded healthy sighted adults for five days while they learned Braille. By the end of that time, the participants' occipital cortex became responsive to touch stimuli. Furthermore, magnetic stimulation over the occipital scalp interfered with their Braille performance, indicating that the occipital cortex was indeed contributing to touch perception (Merabet et al., 2008). Evidently what happens in long-term blindness is simply an extreme case of what is potentially present in everyone.

 **Stop & Check**

13. Name two kinds of evidence indicating that touch information from the fingers activates the occipital cortex of people blind since birth.

14. Under what circumstance would the occipital cortex of a sighted adult become responsive to touch?

ANSWERS

13. First, brain scans indicate increased activity in the occipital cortex while blind people perform tasks such as feeling two objects and saying whether they are the same or different. Second, temporary inactivation of the occipital cortex blocks blind people's ability to perform that task, without affecting the ability of sighted people. **14.** A sighted person who practices tactile discrimination for a few days, such as learning Braille while blindfolded, begins to use the occipital cortex for touch.

Learning to Read

If you learn to read, and then spend a few hours every day reading, does your brain change? Ordinarily, this hypothesis is difficult to test, because children learn to read while their brains are changing in many ways already. Also, in most countries, nearly all children are learning to read. Experimenters took advantage of an unusual opportunity: In Colombia, many children became guerrilla fighters instead of going to school, but many of them returned to society as adults. Of those, some were taught to read and others were not. Researchers found several differences between the brains of those who learned to read in adulthood and those who did not. Those who learned had more gray matter (presumably expanded neuron cell bodies and dendrites) in five gyri of the cerebral cortex, and greater thickness in part of the corpus callosum (Carreiras et al., 2009).

Music Training

People who develop expertise in any area spend enormous amounts of time practicing, and it seems reasonable to look for corresponding changes in their brains. Of the various kinds of expertise, which would you want to examine? Researchers' favorite choice has been musicians, for two reasons. First, we have a good idea of where in the brain to look for changes—the brain areas responsible for hearing and finger control. Second, serious musicians are numerous and easy to find. Almost any big city has an orchestra, and so do most universities. Most orchestra members have been practicing for hours every day for years.

One study used magnetoencephalography (MEG, described in Chapter 4) to record responses of the auditory cortex to pure tones. The responses in professional musicians were about twice as strong as those in nonmusicians. An examination of their brains, using MRI, found that one area of the temporal cortex in the right hemisphere was about 30% larger in professional musicians (Schneider et al., 2002). Other studies found enhanced responses of subcortical brain structures

to musical sounds and speech sounds, compared to nonmusicians (Herdener et al., 2010; Lee, Skoe, Kraus, & Ashley, 2009; Musacchia, Sams, Skoe, & Kraus, 2007). These brain changes help musicians attend to key sounds in tonal languages. For example, in Chinese, *nián* (with a rising tone) means year, and *niàn* (with a falling tone) means study. Musicians learn to recognize these differences faster than other people do (Wong, Skoe, Russo, Dees, & Kraus, 2007).

According to a study using MRI, gray matter of several brain areas was thicker in professional musicians than in amateurs and thicker in amateurs than in nonmusicians, as shown in Figure 5.11 (Gaser & Schlaug, 2003). The most strongly affected areas related to hand control and vision (which is important for reading music). A related study on stringed instrument players found that a larger than normal section of the postcentral gyrus in the right hemisphere was devoted to representing the fingers of the left hand, which they use to control the strings (Elbert, Pantev, Wienbruch, Rockstroh, & Taub, 1995). The area devoted to the left fingers was largest in those who began their music practice early and therefore also continued for more years.

These results suggest that practicing a skill reorganizes the brain to maximize performance of that skill. However, an alternative hypothesis is that brain characteristics that people were born with attract them to one occupation or another. Phoneticians—people who specialize in analyzing details of speech, including regional accents—are more likely than other people to have certain features of the auditory cortex that are known to form before birth (Golestani, Price, & Scott, 2011). Might it also be the case that inborn brain features attract certain people to music? One way to address that question is with a longitudinal study. Researchers examined 15 6-year-olds who were beginning piano lessons and 16 other children not taking music lessons. At the start of training, neither brain scans nor cognitive tests showed any significant difference between the two groups. After 15 months, the trained group performed better

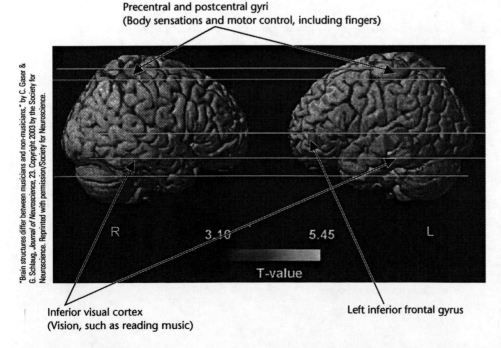

Precentral and postcentral gyri
(Body sensations and motor control, including fingers)

R   3.10   5.45   L

T-value

Inferior visual cortex
(Vision, such as reading music)

Left inferior frontal gyrus

FIGURE 5.11 Brain correlates of music practice
Areas marked in red showed thicker gray matter among professional keyboard players than in amateurs and thicker among amateurs than in nonmusicians. Areas marked in yellow showed even stronger differences in that same direction.

on measures of rhythm and melody discrimination, and they showed enlargements of brain areas responsible for hearing and hand movements, similar to those seen in adult musicians (Hyde et al., 2009a, 2009b). These results imply that the brain differences are the result of musical training, not the cause.

Another issue is whether music training produces bigger effects if it begins early in life, while the brain is more easily modified. Several studies have found major differences between young adults who started music training in childhood and those who began as teenagers. However, those studies do not separate the effects of age at starting from those of total years of practice. A later study compared people who started music training before age 7 with people who started later but

continued for just as many years. The result was that those who started younger showed an advantage on several tasks (Watanabe, Savion-Lemieux, & Penhune, 2007).

➡️ **Stop & Check**

15. Which brain area shows expanded representation of the left hand in people who began practicing stringed instruments in childhood and continued for many years?

ANSWER

15. Postcentral gyrus (somatosensory cortex) of the right hemisphere

When Brain Reorganization Goes Too Far

If playing music—or practicing anything else—expands a relevant brain area, the change is good, right? Usually it is, but not always. As mentioned, when people play piano or string instruments many hours a day for years, the representation of the hand increases in the somatosensory cortex. Imagine the normal representation of the fingers in the cortex:

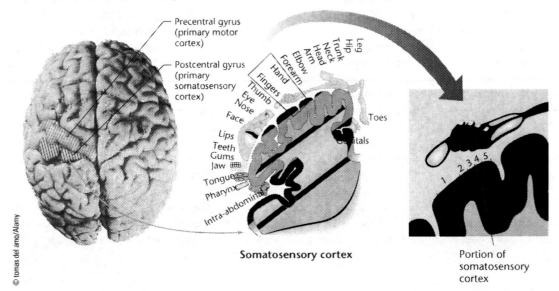

With extensive musical practice, the expanding representations of the fingers might spread out like this:

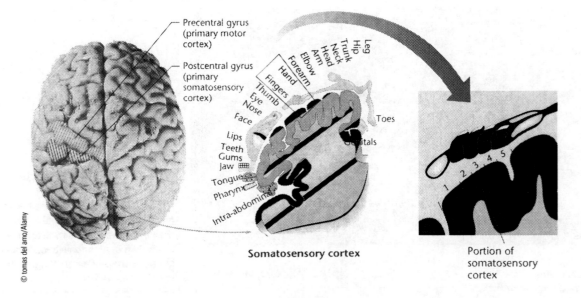

Or the representations of all fingers could grow from side to side without spreading out so that representation of each finger overlaps that of its neighbor:

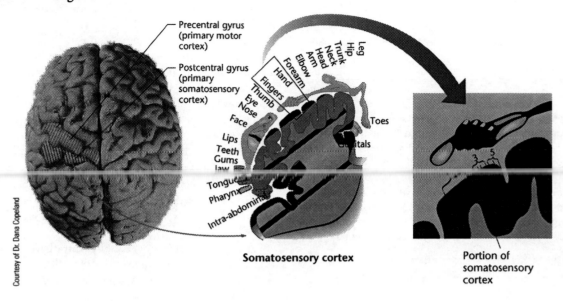

Somatosensory cortex

Portion of somatosensory cortex

In some cases, the latter process does occur, such that stimulation on one finger excites mostly the same cortical areas as another finger (Byl, McKenzie, & Nagarajan, 2000; Elbert et al., 1998; Lenz & Byl, 1999; Sanger, Pascual-Leone, Tarsy, & Schlaug, 2001; Sanger, Tarsy, & Pascual-Leone, 2001). If you can't clearly feel the difference between one finger and another, it is difficult to move them independently. Furthermore, the motor cortex changes also. Representation of the middle fingers expands, overlapping and displacing representation of the index finger and little finger. As a result, the person has trouble controlling the index finger and little finger. One or more fingers may go into constant contraction (Beck et al., 2008; Burman, Lie-Nemeth, Brandfonbrener, Parisi, & Meyer, 2009). This condition, known as "musician's cramp" or more formally as **focal hand dystonia**, is often a career ender for a musician. Some people who spend all day writing develop the same problem, in which case it is known as "writer's cramp."

Previously, physicians assumed that musician's cramp or writer's cramp was in the hands themselves, in which case the treatment would be hand surgery or injection of some drug into the hand. Now that we have identified brain reorganization as the problem, the approach is to find an appropriate type of retraining. Here is one promising possibility: Researchers gave periodic bursts of vibration stimuli to various hand muscles, in random sequence, instructing people with musician's cramp to attend carefully to the stimuli and any changes in their vibration frequency. A mere 15-minute treatment produced improvement in finger sensations and use, which lasted up to 24 hours (Rosenkranz, Butler, Williamson, & Rothwell, 2009). Further development of this technique or something similar may help people with this disorder.

Someone with musician's cramp or writer's cramp has difficulty moving one finger independently of others. One or more fingers may twitch or go into a constant contraction.

Stop & Check

16. What change in the brain is responsible for musician's cramp?

17. What procedure is most promising for treating musician's cramp?

ANSWERS

(upside-down text:)

16. Extensive practice of violin, piano, or other instruments causes expanded representation of the fingers in the somatosensory cortex, as well as displacement of representation of one or more fingers in the motor cortex. If the sensory representation of two fingers overlaps too much, the person cannot feel them separately or move them separately. **17.** The most promising treatment so far is training the person to attend to specific sensations in the hand. The training is intended to reorganize the brain representation.

Brain Development and Behavioral Development

Behavior changes as people grow older. How much of that change has to do with the brain? Let's consider adolescence and old age.

Adolescence

Adolescents are widely regarded as impulsive and prone to seek immediate pleasure. Neither of those characteristics is unique to adolescents, as children are even more impulsive and eager for immediate pleasure. Still, on average, adolescents differ in these regards from adults. Impulsiveness is a problem if it leads to risky driving, drinking, sex, spending sprees, and so forth.

Impulsiveness means a difficulty inhibiting an impulse. Here is a simple way to measure it: Hold your hands to the left and right of someone's head. Instruct the person that when you wiggle a finger, he or she should look at the *other* hand. Before age 5 to 7 years, most children find it almost impossible to look away from the wiggling finger. They are "impulsive" in that they do not inhibit their strong tendency to look at a moving object. Similarly, if a face suddenly appears on one side of a screen, people find it difficult to look in the opposite direction (Morand, Grosbras, Caldara, & Harvey, 2010). Looking away from a powerful attention-getter is called the **antisaccade task**. A saccade is a voluntary eye movement, and an antisaccade is a voluntary eye movement away from the normal direction.

TRY IT YOURSELF

Ability to perform this task improves sharply between ages 7 to 11, and then gradually improves during the teenage years, depending on areas of the prefrontal cortex that mature slowly (Michel & Anderson, 2009; Munoz & Everling, 2004).

As you might guess, children with attention-deficit hyperactivity disorder (ADHD), who tend to be impulsive in other ways, also have difficulty with the antisaccade task (Loe, Feldman, Yasui, & Luna, 2009).

In addition to being more impulsive than adults, adolescents (and children) tend to "discount the future," preferring a smaller pleasure now over a larger one later. Which would you prefer, $100 now or $125 a year from now? What about $100 now vs. $150 a year from now? $175? How much bigger would the payoff have to be next year to make you willing to wait? Adolescents are more likely to choose an immediate reward than are older adults, in a variety of situations (Steinberg et al., 2009). However, to be fair, the situation is not the same for people of different ages. Most adolescents have little cash on hand and need the money right now. Most older adults are more financially secure and can afford to wait for a higher reward.

Adolescents are not equally impulsive in all situations. In an argument before the U.S. Supreme Court, the American Psychological Association (APA) took the position that adolescents are mature enough to make their own decisions about a possible abortion. Later, the APA took the position that an adolescent who commits murder is too immature to be held to the same legal standard as an adult. Was the APA flip-flopping about adolescent maturity, based on the political decisions they favored? Could be, but the argument is more defensible than it might sound at first. According to the research, most adolescents make reasonable, mature decisions when they have time to consider their options carefully. However, they are impulsive when making quick decisions, especially in the face of peer pressure (Luna, Padmanabhan, & O'Hearn, 2010; Reyna & Farley, 2006).

Many studies have found that adolescent brains show stronger responses than older adults when anticipating rewards, and weaker responses in the areas of the prefrontal cortex responsible for inhibiting behaviors (Geier, Terwilliger, Teslovich, Velanova, & Luna, 2010; Luna, et al., 2010). But should we conclude that adolescents are impulsive *because* their prefrontal cortex is less active? Maybe, but not necessarily. Consider this analogy: Imagine a college professor who has spent the afternoon sitting at his desk writing this chapter. If you monitored his leg muscles you would find that they had a low activity level all afternoon. Would you conclude that he sat working on writing this chapter *because* his leg muscles were inactive? I assume you would not. If those leg muscles were *incapable* of moving, they would help explain why someone spent an afternoon at a computer. But when someone simply fails to use healthy leg muscles, monitoring their activity explains nothing. Similarly, if we found that certain parts of the adolescent prefrontal cortex are *incapable* of strong activity, we may have an explanation for impulsive behavior. But most research simply reports that adolescents' prefrontal cortex *is* relatively inactive in certain situations, and that result is not sufficient to explain the behavior.

Stop & Check

18. Under what circumstances are adolescents most likely to make an impulsive decision?

19. When people claim that adolescents make risky decisions because of a lack of inhibition, which brain area do they point to as being responsible for inhibition?

ANSWERS

18. Adolescents are most likely to make an impulsive decision when they have to decide quickly in the presence of peer pressure. 19. The prefrontal cortex

Old Age

Many studies confirm that, on average, people's memory and reasoning fade beyond age 60, if not sooner. In old age, neurons alter their synapses more slowly (Gan, Kwon, Feng, Sanes, & Lichtman, 2003; Grutzendler, Kasthuri, & Gan, 2002). The thickness of the temporal cortex shrinks by about half a percent per year, on average (Fjell et al., 2009). The volume of the hippocampus also gradually declines, and certain aspects of memory decline in proportion to the loss of hippocampus (Erickson et al., 2010). The frontal cortex begins thinning at age 30 (Brans et al., 2010)!

Nevertheless, most chief executives of major corporations, world political leaders, college presidents, and so forth are over 60 years old. Is this a problem? Should we fire them and replace them with 25-year-olds?

Much of the research underestimates older people, for several reasons. First, people vary. Some people deteriorate markedly, but others show little sign of loss in either behavior or brain anatomy well into old age. If we take an average, it appears that everyone is decaying a little each year, but averages can be misleading. Second, as people grow older, they may be slower in many intellectual activities, but they have a greater base of knowledge and experience. On certain kinds of questions, older people do significantly better than younger people (Queen & Hess, 2010). Third, many older people find ways to compensate for any losses. In one study, a certain memory task activated the right prefrontal cortex in young adults and in older adults who did poorly on the task. For older people who did well, the task activated the prefrontal cortex of *both* hemispheres (Cabeza, Anderson, Locantore, & McIntosh, 2002). That is, high-performing older adults activate more brain areas to make up for less efficient activity.

Stop & Check

20. What is one way in which older adults compensate for less efficient brain functioning?

ANSWER

20. Many of them compensate by activating additional brain areas.

MODULE 5.1 ■ IN CLOSING

Brain Development

Considering the number of ways in which abnormal genes and chemicals can disrupt brain development, let alone the possible varieties of abnormal experience, it is a wonder that any of us develop normally. Evidently, the system has enough margin for error that we can function even if all of our connections are not quite perfect. Development can go wrong in many ways, but somehow, the system usually manages to work.

SUMMARY

1. In vertebrate embryos, the central nervous system begins as a tube surrounding a fluid-filled cavity. Developing neurons proliferate, migrate, differentiate, myelinate, and generate synapses. Neuron proliferation varies among species mainly by the number of cell divisions. Migration depends on a large number of chemicals that guide immature neurons to their destinations. **124**

2. Even in adults, new neurons can form in the olfactory system, the hippocampus, and the song-producing brain areas of some bird species. Although controversy persists, new neurons apparently also form in the adult primate cerebral cortex following damage to the nervous system. How long such neurons survive is not known. **125**

3. Growing axons find their way close to the right locations by following chemicals. Then they array themselves over a target area by following chemical gradients. **126**

4. After axons reach their targets based on chemical gradients, the postsynaptic cell adjusts the connections

based on experience, accepting certain combinations of axons and rejecting others. This kind of competition among axons continues throughout life.   **129**

5. Initially, the nervous system develops far more neurons than will actually survive. Some axons make synaptic contacts with cells that release to them nerve growth factor or other neurotrophins. The neurons that receive neurotrophins survive, and the others die in a process called apoptosis.   **129**

6. The developing brain is vulnerable to chemical insult. Many chemicals that produce only mild, temporary problems for adults can permanently impair early brain development.   **131**

7. At an early stage of development, the cortex is sufficiently plastic that visual input can cause what would have been the auditory cortex to develop different properties and now respond visually.   **132**

8. Enriched experience leads to greater branching of axons and dendrites, partly because animals in enriched environments are more active than those in deprived environments. However, this enrichment effect has been demonstrated in comparison to a standard laboratory environment that is extremely deprived.   **132**

9. Specialized experiences can alter brain development, especially early in life. For example, in people who are born blind, representation of touch and hearing expands in areas usually reserved for vision.   **134**

10. Extensive practice of a skill expands the brain's representation of sensory and motor information relevant to that skill. For example, the representation of fingers expands in people who regularly practice musical instruments.   **135**

11. Although expanded representation in the brain is ordinarily a good thing, it can be harmful if carried too far. Some musicians and others who use their hands many hours each day develop brain changes that interfere with their ability to feel or use one finger independently of the others.   **136**

12. Compared to adults, adolescents tend to be impulsive and centered more on present pleasures than future prospects. Research demonstrates increased response of their brain to anticipated pleasures, and decreased activity in the prefrontal cortex, responsible for inhibiting behavior tendencies. However, it is not clear that these brain phenomena explain the behaviors.   **138**

13. On average, people in old age show declining memory and reasoning, and shrinkage of certain brain areas. However, these averages do not apply to all individuals or all situations. Many older people compensate for inefficiency of certain brain functions by recruiting activity in additional brain areas.   **139**

KEY TERMS

Terms are defined in the module on the page number indicated. They're also presented in alphabetical order with definitions in the book's Subject Index/Glossary, which begins on page 561. Interactive flashcards and crossword puzzles are among the online resources available to help you learn these terms and the concepts they represent.

antisaccade task   **138**
apoptosis   **130**
differentiates   **125**
fetal alcohol syndrome   **131**

focal hand dystonia   **137**
migrate   **125**
myelination   **125**
nerve growth factor (NGF)   **130**
neural Darwinism   **129**

neurotrophin   **130**
proliferation   **124**
stem cells   **125**
synaptogenesis   **125**

THOUGHT QUESTION

Biologists can develop antibodies against nerve growth factor (i.e., molecules that inactivate nerve growth factor). What would happen if someone injected such antibodies into a developing nervous system?

Plasticity After Brain Damage

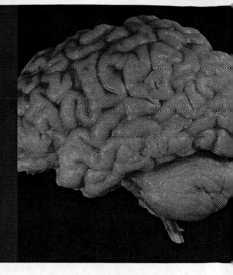

An American soldier who suffered a wound to the left hemisphere of his brain during the Korean War was at first unable to speak at all. Three months later, he could speak in short fragments. When he was asked to read the letterhead, "New York University College of Medicine," he replied, "Doctors—little doctors." Eight years later, when someone asked him again to read the letterhead, he replied, "Is there a catch? It says, 'New York University College of Medicine'" (Eidelberg & Stein, 1974).

Almost all survivors of brain damage show behavioral recovery to some degree. Some of the mechanisms rely on the growth of new branches of axons and dendrites, similar to the mechanisms of brain development discussed in the first module. Understanding the process leads to better therapies for people with brain damage and contributes to our understanding of brain functioning.

Brain Damage and Short-Term Recovery

The possible causes of brain damage include tumors, infections, exposure to radiation or toxic substances, and degenerative conditions such as Parkinson's disease and Alzheimer's disease. In young people, the most common cause is **closed head injury**, a sharp blow to the head resulting from an accident or assault that does not puncture the brain. The effects of closed head injury depend on severity and frequency. Many, probably most, children and young adults sustain at least a mild blow to the head from falling off a bicycle or similar accident, from which they recover within a few days. Repeated head injuries, common in certain sports, are more worrisome (Shaughnessy, 2009). After a severe head injury, recovery is slow and often incomplete (Forsyth, Salorio, & Christensen, 2010).

One cause of damage after closed head injury is the rotational forces that drive brain tissue against the inside of the skull. Another cause is blood clots that interrupt blood flow to the brain (Kirkpatrick, Smielewski, Czosnyka, Menon, & Pickard, 1995).

APPLICATIONS AND EXTENSIONS

How Woodpeckers Avoid Concussions

Speaking of blows to the head, have you ever wondered how woodpeckers manage to avoid giving themselves concussions? If you repeatedly banged your head into a tree at 6 or 7 meters per second (about 15 miles per hour), you would quickly harm yourself.

Using slow-motion photography, researchers found that woodpeckers usually start with a couple of quick preliminary taps against the wood, much like a carpenter lining up a nail with a hammer. Then the birds make a hard strike in a straight line, keeping a rigid neck. They almost completely avoid rotational forces and whiplash (May, Fuster, Haber, & Hirschman, 1979).

The researchers suggested that football helmets, race car helmets, and so forth would give more protection if they extended down to the shoulders to prevent rotation and whiplash. They also suggest that if you see a crash about to happen, you should tuck your chin to your chest and tighten your neck muscles.

Reducing the Harm from a Stroke

A common cause of brain damage, especially in older people, is temporary interruption of normal blood flow to a brain area during a **stroke**, also known as a **cerebrovascular accident**. The more common type of stroke is **ischemia** (iss-KEE-me-uh), the result of a blood clot or other obstruction in an artery. The less common type is **hemorrhage** (HEM-oh-rage), the result of a ruptured artery. Effects of strokes vary from barely noticeable to immediately fatal. Figure 5.12 shows the brains of three people: one who died immediately after a stroke, one who survived long after a stroke, and a bullet wound victim. For a good collection of information about stroke, visit the website of the National Stroke Association at http://www.stroke.org/.

In ischemia, the neurons deprived of blood lose much of their oxygen and glucose supplies. In hemorrhage, they are

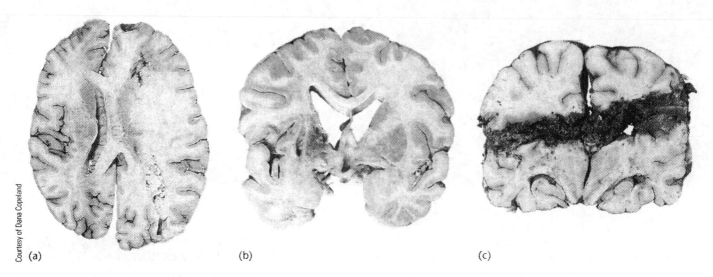

Courtesy of Dana Copeland

(a)   (b)   (c)

FIGURE 5.12 Three damaged human brains
(a) Brain of a person who died immediately after a stroke. Note the swelling on the right side. (b) Brain of someone who survived for a long time after a stroke. Note the cavities on the left side, where many cells were lost. (c) Brain of a person who suffered a gunshot wound and died immediately.

flooded with blood and excess oxygen, calcium, and other chemicals. Both ischemia and hemorrhage lead to many of the same problems, including **edema** (the accumulation of fluid), which increases pressure on the brain and the probability of additional strokes (Unterberg, Stover, Kress, & Kiening, 2004). Both ischemia and hemorrhage also impair the sodium–potassium pump, leading to an accumulation of sodium inside neurons. The combination of edema and excess sodium provokes excess release of the transmitter glutamate (Rossi, Oshima, & Attwell, 2000), which overstimulates neurons: Sodium and other ions enter the neurons faster than the sodium–potassium pump can remove them. The excess positive ions block metabolism in the mitochondria and kill the neurons (Stout, Raphael, Kanterewicz, Klann, & Reynolds, 1998). As neurons die, microglia cells proliferate, removing the products of dead neurons and supplying neurotrophins that promote survival of the remaining neurons (Lalancette- Hébert, Gowing, Simard, Weng, & Kriz, 2007).

Immediate Treatments

As recently as the 1980s, hospitals had little to offer to a stroke patient. Today, prospects are good for ischemia if physicians act quickly. A drug called **tissue plasminogen activator (tPA)** breaks up blood clots (Barinaga, 1996). To get significant benefit, a patient should receive tPA within 3 hours after a stroke, although slight benefits are possible during the next several hours. Emergency wards have improved their response times, but the limiting factor is that most stroke victims don't get to the hospital quickly enough (Evenson, Foraker, Morris, & Rosamond, 2009).

It is difficult to determine whether someone has had an ischemic or hemorrhagic stroke. Given that tPA is useful for

ischemia but could only make matters worse in a hemorrhage, what is a physician to do? An MRI scan distinguishes between the two kinds of stroke, but MRIs take time, and time is limited. The usual decision is to give the tPA. Hemorrhage is less common and usually fatal anyway, so the risk of making a hemorrhage worse is small compared to the hope of alleviating ischemia.

What other treatments might be effective shortly after a stroke? Given that strokes kill neurons by overstimulation, one approach has been to decrease stimulation by blocking glutamate synapses, blocking calcium entry, or other means. Many such techniques have shown benefits in laboratory animals (e.g., Sun et al., 2009), but so far none has produced much benefit in humans. It is fair to object that they haven't been given a fair try. Nearly all of the clinical studies have used small doses (to avoid side effects such as hallucinations), and nearly all have given the treatments 12 or more hours after a stroke, despite evidence from laboratory animals that the treatments are effective only within the first 3 to 6 hours (Ginsberg, 2008).

The most effective known method of preventing brain damage after strokes in laboratory animals is to cool the brain. Cooling slows a variety of harmful processes. People can be cooled safely to about 34–35° C (93–95° F). What matters is temperature at the core of the body, so it is possible to keep the skin warm enough to prevent shivering, while cooling the interior of the body. This procedure has shown much promise, and additional research is under way (Ginsberg, 2008; Steiner, Ringleb, & Hacke, 2001).

Another procedure might surprise you: Exposure to cannabinoids (the chemicals found in marijuana) minimizes the damage caused by strokes in laboratory animals. You might wonder how anyone thought of trying such a thing. Research-

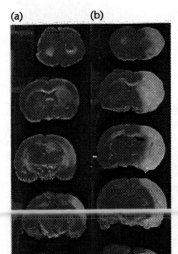

(a)   (b)

FIGURE 5.13 Effects of a cannabinoid on stroke damage
Row (a) shows slices through the brains of 5 rats treated with a high dose of a cannabinoid shortly after a stroke. Row (b) shows slices for rats not treated with cannabinoids. The white areas on the right of each brain show the extent of the damage. *(From Schomacher, M., Müller, H. D., Sommer, C., Schwab, S., & Schäbitz, W.-R. (2008). Endocannabinoids mediate neuroprotection after transient focal cerebral ischemia. Brain Research, 1240, 213–220.)*

ers had a theoretical rationale: As mentioned in Chapter 3, cannabinoids decrease the release of glutamate. If excessive glutamate is one of the reasons for cell loss, then cannabinoids might be helpful. They do, in fact, minimize the damage after a stroke, as shown in Figure 5.13, although the explanation is not yet clear (Schomacher, Müller, Sommer, Schwab, & Schäbitz, 2008). In addition to putting the brakes on glutamate, cannabinoids exert anti-inflammatory effects and alter brain chemistry in other ways that might protect against damage. So far, physicians have made only limited attempts to apply cannabinoids to human stroke patients, and again the limiting factor is that the chemicals are effective only within the first few hours after a stroke. In fact, the research on laboratory animals indicates that cannabinoids are most effective if taken shortly *before* the stroke. It would be difficult to apply that advice in humans!

> **Stop & Check**

21. What are the two kinds of stroke, and what causes each kind?

22. Why is tPA not helpful in cases of hemorrhage?

23. If one of your relatives has a stroke and a well-meaning person offers a blanket, what should you do?

ANSWERS

21. The more common form, ischemia, is the result of an occlusion of an artery. The other form, hemorrhage, breaks up blood clots, and hemorrhage results from is the result of a ruptured artery. **22.** The drug tPA a ruptured blood vessel, not a blood clot. **23.** Refuse the blanket. Recovery will be best if the stroke victim remains cold.

Later Mechanisms of Recovery

After the first days following brain damage, many of the surviving brain areas increase or reorganize their activity (Nishimura et al., 2007). In some cases, one area more or less takes over the function of another, damaged area. For example, after damage to the connections from one brain hemisphere to the leg on the opposite side of the body, the hemisphere on the same side increases its connections to that leg (Ghosh et al., 2009). In other cases, surviving brain areas do not take over the functions of the damaged area, but they compensate in various ways.

Increased Brain Stimulation

A behavioral deficit after brain damage reflects more than just the cells that died. After damage to any brain area, other areas that have lost part of their normal input become less active. For example, shortly after damage in one brain hemisphere, its input to the other hemisphere declines, and therefore the other hemisphere shows deficits also (van Meer et al., 2010). Recovery from a stroke depends largely on increasing activity for the opposite side of the brain (Takatsuru et al., 2009).

Diaschisis (di-AS-ki-sis, from a Greek term meaning "to shock throughout") refers to the decreased activity of surviving neurons after damage to other neurons. If diaschisis contributes to behavioral deficits following brain damage, then increased stimulation should help. Researchers studied one man who had been in a "minimally conscious state" for 6 years, showing almost no activity or response to stimulation. Electrical stimulation of his central thalamus led to substantial improvements, including self-feeding and some intelligible speech (Schiff et al., 2007).

Stimulant drugs also promote recovery. In a series of experiments, D. M. Feeney and colleagues measured the behavioral effects of cortical damage in rats and cats. Depending on the location of the damage, the animals showed impairments in movement or depth perception. Injecting amphetamine significantly enhanced both behaviors, and animals that practiced the behaviors under the influence of amphetamine showed long-lasting benefits. Injecting a different drug to block dopamine synapses impaired behavioral recovery (Feeney & Sutton, 1988; Feeney, Sutton, Boyeson, Hovda, & Dail, 1985; Hovda & Feeney, 1989; Sutton, Hovda, & Feeney, 1989). Stimulant drugs may be helpful after other kinds of brain damage, too, and not just strokes (Huey, Garcia, Wassermann, Tierney, & Grafman, 2008).

Although amphetamine is too risky for use with human patients, other stimulant drugs are more promising (Whyte et al., 2005). A related idea is to use drugs that block the release of GABA, the brain's main inhibitory neurotransmitter. As with amphetamine, GABA blockers are effective in promoting recovery after stroke in laboratory animals (Clarkson, Huang, MacIsaac, Mody, & Carmichael, 2010).

![Stop & Check arrow]

24. After someone has had a stroke, would it be best (if possible) to direct stimulant drugs to the cells that were damaged or somewhere else?

ANSWER 24. It is best to direct the amphetamine to the cells that had been receiving input from the damaged cells. Presumably, the loss of input has produced diaschisis.

Regrowth of Axons

Although a destroyed cell body cannot be replaced, damaged axons do grow back under certain circumstances. A neuron of the peripheral nervous system has its cell body in the spinal cord (for motor neurons) or in a ganglion near the spinal cord (for sensory neurons). In either case, the axon extends into one of the limbs. A crushed axon grows back toward the periphery at a rate of about 1 mm per day, following its myelin sheath to the original target. If the axon is cut instead of crushed, the myelin on the two sides of the cut may not line up correctly, and the regenerating axon may not have a sure path to follow. In that case, a motor nerve may attach to the wrong muscle, as Figure 5.14 illustrates.

Within a mature mammalian brain or spinal cord, damaged axons do not regenerate, or do so only slightly (Schwab, 1998). However, in many kinds of fish, axons do regenerate across a cut in the spinal cord and restore nearly normal functioning (Bernstein & Gelderd, 1970; Rovainen, 1976; Scherer, 1986; Selzer, 1978). Why do damaged CNS axons regenerate so much better in fish than in mammals? Can we find ways to improve axon regeneration in mammals?

Several problems limit axon regeneration in mammals. First, a cut in the nervous system causes a scar to form (thicker in mammals than in fish), creating a mechanical barrier. That scar tissue is beneficial immediately after the damage, but it blocks regrowth of axons later (Rolls, Shechter, & Schwartz, 2009). Second, neurons on the two sides of the cut pull apart. Third, the glia cells that react to CNS damage release chemicals that inhibit axon growth (Yiu & He, 2006).

These problems are formidable, but hope remains. Researchers developed a way to build a protein bridge, providing a path for axons to regenerate across a scar-filled gap. When they applied this technique to hamsters with a cut in the optic nerve, many axons from the eye grew back and established synapses, enabling most hamsters to regain partial vision (Ellis-Behnke et al., 2006). Also, injecting neurotrophins at appropriate locations helps axons grow and establish normal synapses (Alto et al., 2009). A third possibility: Infant axons grow under the influence of a protein called mTOR (which stands for mammalian Target Of Rapamycin). As the individual matures, mTOR levels decrease and axons in the spinal cord lose their capacity for regrowth. Deleting a gene responsible for inhibiting mTOR enables regrowth of axons in the adult spinal cord (Liu et al., 2010). So far, these methods have been tried only in laboratory animals, and we don't know about their feasibility with humans.

Axon Sprouting

Ordinarily, the surface of dendrites and cell bodies is covered with synapses, and a vacant spot doesn't stay vacant for long. After a cell loses input from an axon it secretes neurotrophins that induce other axons to form new branches, or **collateral sprouts**, that take over the vacant synapses (Ramirez, 2001) (Figure 5.15). In the area near the damage, new synapses form at a high rate, especially for the first 2 weeks (C. E. Brown, Li, Boyd, Delaney, & Murphy, 2007).

Is collateral sprouting helpful or harmful? It depends on whether the sprouting axons convey information similar to those that they replace. For example, the hippocampus receives much input from an area called the entorhinal cortex. If the entorhinal cortex is damaged in one hemisphere, then axons from the entorhinal cortex of the other hemisphere sprout, take over the vacant synapses, and largely restore behavior (Ramirez, Bulsara, Moore, Ruch, & Abrams, 1999; Ramirez, McQuilkin, Carrigan, MacDonald, & Kelley, 1996). However, if the entorhinal cortex is damaged in both hemispheres, then axons from other locations sprout into the vacant synapses, conveying different information. Under those conditions, the sprouting interferes with behavior and prevents recovery (Ramirez, 2001; Ramirez et al., 2007).

Here is another example where sprouting is either useless or harmful: Imagine a stroke that damages the axons bringing information from the upper-left visual field—that is, everything that appears to the viewer as being in the upper left. Suppose this stroke does not damage the visual cortex. Now the area of visual cortex that used to receive input from the upper left has lost its input, and axons represent-

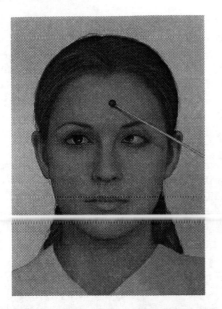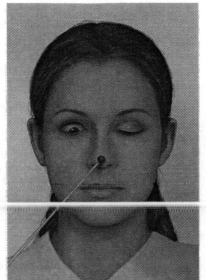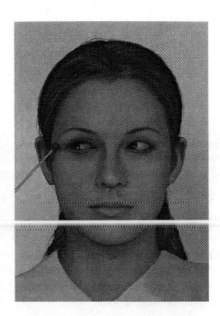

FIGURE 5.14 What can happen if damaged axons regenerate to incorrect muscles
Damaged axons to the muscles of the patient's right eye regenerated but attached incorrectly. When she looks down, her right eyelid opens wide instead of closing like the other eyelid. Her eye movements are frequently misaimed, and she has trouble moving her right eye upward or to the left. (© Cengage Learning 2013)

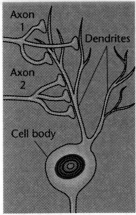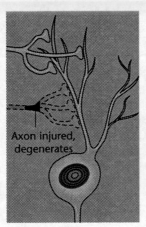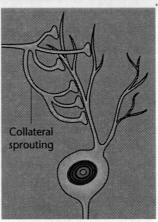

Axon 1 — Dendrites — Axon 2 — Cell body

Axon injured, degenerates

Collateral sprouting

At first   Loss of an axon   Sprouting to fill vacant synapses

FIGURE 5.15 Collateral sprouting
A surviving axon grows a new branch to replace the synapses left vacant by a damaged axon. (© Cengage Learning 2013)

ing another part of the visual field—the lower left—sprout into the vacant synapses. As that happens, a stimulus that should look as shown here on the left begins to look like the stimulus on the right (Dilks, Serences, Rosenau, Yantis, & McCloskey, 2007):

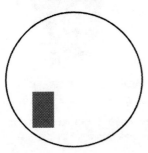

Denervation Supersensitivity

Neurons make adjustments to maintain a nearly constant level of arousal. After learning strengthens one set of synapses, other synapses weaken. (If this didn't happen, every time you learned something your brain would get more and more aroused.) Something similar happens after certain kinds of brain damage: If most of the axons that transmit dopamine to some brain area die or become inactive, the remaining dopamine synapses become more responsive, more easily stimulated. This process of enhanced response is known as **denervation supersensitivity** or *receptor supersensitivity* (Kostrzewa, Kostrzewa, Brown, Nowak, & Brus, 2008).

Denervation supersensitivity helps compensate for decreased input. In some cases, it enables people to maintain nearly normal behavior even after losing most of the axons in some pathway (Sabel, 1997). However, it can also have unpleasant consequences, such as chronic pain. Because spinal injury damages many axons, postsynaptic neurons develop increased sensitivity to the remaining ones. Therefore, even mild input produces enhanced responses (Hains, Everhart, Fullwood, & Hulsebosch, 2002).

> **Stop & Check**

25. Is collateral sprouting a change in axons or dendritic receptors?

26. Is denervation supersensitivity a change in axons or dendritic receptors?

27. Many people with schizophrenia take drugs that block dopamine synapses. After prolonged use, the side effects include frequent involuntary movements. What is one possible explanation?

ANSWERS

25. Axons **26.** Dendritic receptors **27.** Denervation supersensitivity. The decreased input may have led to hyperresponsive receptors.

Reorganized Sensory Representations and the Phantom Limb

If a brain area loses a set of incoming axons, we can expect some combination of increased response (denervation supersensitivity) by the remaining axons and collateral sprouting by other axons that ordinarily attach to some other target. Let's imagine how these processes might apply in the case of an amputation.

Reexamine Figure 4.24: Each section along the somatosensory cortex receives input from a different part of the body. Within the area marked "fingers" in that figure, a closer examination reveals that each subarea responds more to one finger than to another. Figure 5.16 shows the arrangement for a monkey brain. In one study, experimenters amputated finger 3 of an owl monkey. The cortical cells that previously responded to information from finger 3 lost their input. Soon various cells became more responsive to finger 2, finger 4, or part of the palm, until the cortex developed the pattern of responsiveness shown in Figure 5.16b (Kaas, Merzenich, & Killackey, 1983; Merzenich et al., 1984).

What happens if an entire arm is amputated? For many years, neuroscientists assumed that the cortical area corresponding to that arm would remain permanently silent, because axons from other cortical areas could not sprout far enough to reach the area representing the arm. Then came a surprise. Investigators recorded from the cerebral cortices of monkeys whose sensory nerves from one forelimb had been cut 12 years previously. They found that the stretch of cortex previously responsive to the limb was now responsive to the face (Pons et al., 1991). After loss of sensory input from the forelimb, the axons representing the forelimb degenerated, leaving vacant synaptic sites at several levels of the CNS. Evidently, axons representing the face sprouted into those sites in the spinal cord, brainstem, and thalamus (Florence & Kaas, 1995; E. G. Jones & Pons, 1998). Or perhaps axons from the face were already present but became stronger through denervation supersensitivity. Brain scan studies confirm that the same processes occur with humans. Reorganization also occurs in other brain areas that respond to skin sensations (Tandon, Kambi, Lazar, Mohammed, & Jain, 2009).

Now consider what happens when something activates the neurons in a reorganized cortex. Previously, those cells responded to arm stimulation, but now they receive information from the face. Does it feel like stimulation on the face or on the arm?

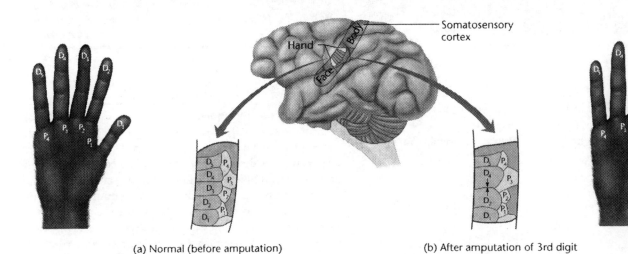

(a) Normal (before amputation)   (b) After amputation of 3rd digit

FIGURE 5.16 Somatosensory cortex of a monkey after a finger amputation
Note that the cortical area previously responsive to the third finger (D_3) becomes responsive to the second and fourth fingers (D_2 and D_4) and part of the palm (P_3). (Redrawn from the Annual Review of Neuroscience, Vol. 6, © 1983, by Annual Reviews, Inc. Reprinted by permission of Annual Reviews, Inc. and Jon H. Kaas.)

The answer: It feels like the arm (K. D. Davis et al., 1998). Physicians have long noted that many people with amputations experience a **phantom limb**, a continuing sensation of an amputated body part. That experience can range from occasional tingling to intense pain. It is possible to have a phantom hand, foot, or anything else that has been amputated. The phantom sensation might last days, weeks, or a lifetime (Ramachandran & Hirstein, 1998).

Until the 1990s, no one knew what caused phantom pains, and most believed that the sensations came from the stump of the amputated limb. Some physicians performed additional amputations, removing more of the limb in a futile attempt to eliminate the phantom sensations. Modern methods have demonstrated that phantom limbs develop only if the relevant portion of the somatosensory cortex reorganizes and becomes responsive to alternative inputs (Flor et al., 1995). For example, suppose axons representing the face come to activate the cortical area previously devoted to an amputated hand. A touch on the face now produces a facial sensation but it also produces a sensation in the phantom hand. Figure 5.17 shows a map of which face area stimulates sensation in which part of the phantom hand, for one person (Aglioti, Smania, Atzei, & Berlucchi, 1997).

Note in Figure 4.24 that the part of the cortex responsive to the feet is adjacent to the part responsive to the genitals. Two patients with foot amputations felt a phantom foot during sexual arousal! One reported feeling orgasm in the phantom foot as well as the genitals—and enjoyed it intensely (Ramachandran & Blakeslee, 1998). Evidently, the representation of the genitals had spread into the cortical area responsible for foot sensation.

Is there any way to relieve a painful phantom sensation? In some cases, yes. Amputees who learn to use an artificial arm report that their phantom sensations gradually disappear (Lotze et al., 1999). They start attributing sensations to the artificial arm, and in doing so, they displace abnormal connections from the face. Similarly, a study of one man found that after his hands were amputated, the area of his cortex that usually responds to the hands partly shifted to face sensitivity, but after he received hand transplants, his cortex gradually shifted back to hand sensitivity (Giraux, Sirigu, Schneider, & Dubernard, 2001). Another patient had a hand amputated at age 19; 35 years later, a new hand was grafted in its place. Within months, he was starting to feel normal sensations in that hand (Frey, Bogdanov, Smith, Watrous, & Breidenbach, 2008). Evidently the brain areas that start off as hand areas, face areas, or whatever retain those properties even after decades without normal input.

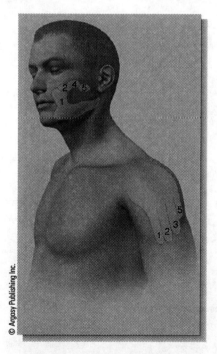

FIGURE 5.17 Sources of phantom sensation for one person
Stimulation in the areas marked on the cheek produced phantom sensations of digits 1 (thumb), 2, 4, and 5. Stimulation on the shoulder also evoked phantom sensations of digits 1, 2, 3, and 5. *(Based on Figure 5.29 from* Phantoms in the Brain *by V. S. Ramachandran, M.D., PhD, and Sandra Blakeslee. Copyright © 1998 by V. S. Ramachandran and Sandra Blakeslee. Reprinted by permission of HarperCollins Publishers and authors.)*

Amputees who feel a phantom limb are likely to lose those phantom sensations if they learn to use an artificial arm or leg.

> **Stop & Check**

28. What is responsible for the phantom limb experience?

ANSWER 28. Synapses that used to receive input from the now-amputated part become vacant. Axons representing another part of the body take over those synapses. Now stimulation of this other part activates the synapses associated with the amputated area, but that stimulation feels like the amputated area.

Learned Adjustments in Behavior

So far, the discussion has focused on anatomical changes. In fact, much recovery from brain damage is based on learning.

If you can't find your keys, perhaps you accidentally dropped them into the trash (so they are gone forever), or perhaps you absentmindedly put them in an unusual place (where you will find them if you keep looking). Similarly, someone with brain damage may have lost some ability totally or may be able to find it with enough effort. Much recovery from brain damage depends on learning to make better use of the abilities that were spared. For example, if you lose your peripheral vision, you learn to move your head from side to side to compensate (Marshall, 1985).

Sometimes, a person or animal with brain damage appears unable to do something but is in fact not trying. Consider an animal that incurred damage to the sensory nerves linking a forelimb to the spinal cord, as in Figure 5.18. The animal no longer feels the limb, although the motor nerves still connect to the muscles. We say the limb is **deafferented** because it has lost its afferent (sensory) input. A monkey with a deafferented limb does not spontaneously use it for walking, picking up objects, or any other voluntary behaviors (Taub & Berman, 1968). At first investigators assumed that a monkey *can't* use a deafferented limb. In a later experiment, however, they cut the afferent nerves of both forelimbs. Despite this more extensive damage, the monkey used both deafferented

limbs to walk, climb, and pick up food. Apparently, a monkey fails to use a deafferented forelimb only because walking on three limbs is easier than using an impaired limb. When it has no choice but to use its deafferented limbs, it does.

Now consider a rat with damage to its visual cortex. Before the damage, it learned to approach a white card instead of a black card for food, but after the damage, it approaches one card or the other randomly. Has it completely forgotten the discrimination? Evidently not, because it can more easily relearn to approach the white card than learn to approach the black card (T. E. LeVere & Morlock, 1973) (Figure 5.19). Thomas LeVere (1975) proposed that a lesion to the visual

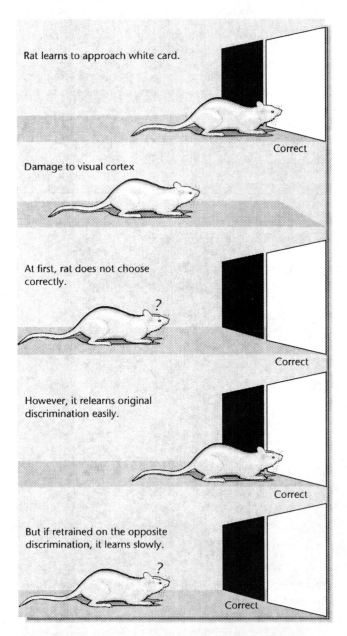

FIGURE 5.19 Memory impairment after cortical damage
Brain damage impairs retrieval but does not destroy the memory. *(Source: Based on T. E. LeVere & Morlock, 1973)*

Rat learns to approach white card. / Correct

Damage to visual cortex

At first, rat does not choose correctly. / Correct

However, it relearns original discrimination easily. / Correct

But if retrained on the opposite discrimination, it learns slowly. / Correct

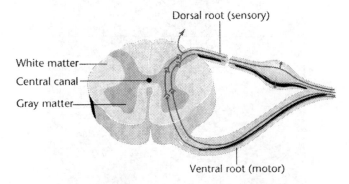

FIGURE 5.18 Cross-section through the spinal cord
A cut through the dorsal root (as shown) deprives the animal of touch sensations from part of the body but leaves the motor nerves intact. *(© Cengage Learning 2013)*

Dorsal root (sensory)

White matter

Central canal

Gray matter

Ventral root (motor)

cortex does not destroy the memory trace but merely impairs the rat's ability to find it. As the animal recovers, it regains access to misplaced memories.

Similarly, therapy for people with brain damage focuses on encouraging them to practice skills that are impaired but not lost. Treatment begins with careful evaluation of a patient's abilities and disabilities. Such evaluations are the specialty of neuropsychologists, who develop tests to try to pinpoint the problems. For example, someone who has trouble carrying out spoken instructions might be impaired in hearing, memory, language, muscle control, or alertness. After identifying the problem, a neuropsychologist might refer a patient to a physical therapist or occupational therapist, who helps the patient practice the impaired skills. Therapists get their best results if they start soon after a patient's stroke, and animal researchers find the same pattern. In one study, rats with damage to the parietal cortex of one hemisphere showed poor coordination of the contralateral forepaw. Some of the rats received experiences designed to encourage them to use the impaired limb. Those who began practice 5 days after the damage recovered better than those who started after 14 days, who in turn recovered better than those who started after 30 days (Biernaskie, Chernenko, & Corbett, 2004). As other kinds of evidence have confirmed, the brain has increased plasticity during the first days after damage.

One important note is that behavior recovered after brain damage is effortful, and its recovery is precarious. A person with brain damage who appears to be functioning normally is working harder than usual. The recovered behavior deteriorates markedly after drinking alcohol, physical exhaustion, or other kinds of stress that would minimally affect most other people (Fleet & Heilman, 1986). It also deteriorates in old age (Corkin, Rosen, Sullivan, & Clegg, 1989).

> **Stop & Check**

29. Suppose someone has suffered a spinal cord injury that interrupts all sensation from the left arm. Now he or she uses only the right arm. Of the following, which is the most promising therapy: electrically stimulate the skin of the left arm, tie the right arm behind the person's back, or blindfold the person?

ANSWER

29. Tie the right arm behind the back to force the person to use the impaired arm instead of only the normal arm. Stimulating the skin of the left arm would accomplish nothing, as the sensory receptors have no input to the CNS. Blindfolding would be either irrelevant or harmful (by decreasing the visual feedback from left-hand movements).

MODULE 5.2 ■ IN CLOSING

MODULE 5.2 ■ IN CLOSING

Brain Damage and Recovery

The mammalian body is well equipped to replace lost blood cells or skin cells but poorly prepared to deal with lost brain cells. Even the responses that do occur after brain damage, such as collateral sprouting of axons or reorganization of sensory representations, are not always helpful. It is tempting to speculate that we failed to evolve mechanisms to recover from brain damage because, through most of our evolutionary history, an individual with brain damage was not likely to survive long enough to recover. Today, many people with brain and spinal cord damage survive for years, and we need continuing research on how to improve their lives.

SUMMARY

1. Brain damage has many causes, including blows to the head, obstruction of blood flow to the brain, or a ruptured blood vessel in the brain. Strokes kill neurons largely by overexcitation. **141**

2. During the first 3 hours after an ischemic stroke, tissue plasminogen activator (tPA) can reduce cell loss by breaking up the blood clot. Theoretically, it should also be possible to minimize cell loss by preventing overexcitation of neurons, but so far, procedures based on this idea have been ineffective. Cooling the brain or providing cannabinoids can reduce cell loss. **142**

3. When one brain area is damaged, other areas become less active than usual because of their loss of input. Stimulant drugs can help restore normal function of these undamaged areas. **143**

4. After an area of the CNS loses its usual input, other axons begin to excite it as a result of either sprouting or denervation supersensitivity. In some cases, this abnormal input produces odd sensations such as the phantom limb. **144**

5. Many individuals with brain damage are capable of more than they show because they avoid using skills that have become impaired or difficult. **148**

KEY TERMS

Terms are defined in the module on the page number indicated. They're also presented in alphabetical order with definitions in the book's Subject Index/Glossary, which begins on page 561. Interactive flashcards and crossword puzzles are among the online resources available to help you learn these terms and the concepts they represent.

cerebrovascular accident   **141**

closed head injury   **141**

collateral sprouts   **144**

deafferented   **148**

denervation supersensitivity   **145**

diaschisis   **143**

edema   **142**

hemorrhage   **141**

ischemia   **141**

phantom limb   **147**

stroke   **141**

tissue plasminogen activator (tPA)   **142**

THOUGHT QUESTIONS

1. Ordinarily, patients with advanced Parkinson's disease (who have damage to dopamine-releasing axons) move very slowly if at all. However, during an emergency (e.g., a fire in the building), they may move rapidly and vigorously. Suggest a possible explanation.

2. Drugs that block dopamine synapses tend to impair or slow limb movements. However, after people have taken such drugs for a long time, some experience involuntary twitches or tremors in their muscles. Based on material in this chapter, propose a possible explanation.

CHAPTER 5 Interactive Exploration and Study

The **Psychology CourseMate** for this text brings chapter topics to life with interactive learning, study, and exam preparation tools, including quizzes and flashcards for the Key Concepts that appear throughout each module, as well as an interactive media-rich eBook version of the text that is fully searchable and includes highlighting and note taking capabilities and interactive versions of the book's **Stop & Check** quizzes and **Try It Yourself Online** activities. The site also features **Virtual Biological Psychology Labs, videos,** and **animations** to help you better understand concepts—logon and learn more at **www.cengagebrain.com**, which is your gateway to all of this text's complimentary and premium resources, including the following:

Virtual Biological Psychology Labs

© 2013 Cengage Learning

Explore the experiments that led to modern-day understanding of biopsychology with the Virtual Biological Psychology Labs, featuring a realistic lab environment that allows you to conduct experiments and evaluate data to better understand how scientists came to the conclusions presented in your text. The labs cover a range of topics, including perception, motivation, cognition, and more. You may purchase access at **www.cengagebrain.com**, or login at **login.cengagebrain.com** if an access card was included with your text.

Videos

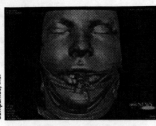

Traumatic Brain Damage

Also available—

- Brain Development in Childhood and Adolescence
- Waking from a Coma
- Brain Regrowth
- Stroke Robots

Animations

Phantom Limb

Also available—

- Sperry Experiment

Suggestions for Further Exploration

Books

Levi-Montalcini, R. (1988). *In praise of imperfection.* New York: Basic Books. Autobiography by the discoverer of nerve growth factor.

Ramachandran, V. S., & Blakeslee, S. (1998). *Phantoms in the brain.* New York: Morrow. One of the most thought-provoking books ever written about human brain damage, including the phantom limb phenomenon.

Websites

The Psychology CourseMate for this text provides regularly updated links to relevant online resources for this chapter, such as the **National Stroke Association** and instructions on how to experience an illusion similar to the phantom limb.

Emotional Behaviors

12

MAIN IDEAS

1. Emotions include cognitions, actions, and feelings. Several kinds of evidence support the theory that emotional feelings result from actions of the muscles or organs.

2. Many brain areas contribute to emotions. It is not clear that different emotions are localized differently in the brain.

3. Aggressive and fearful behaviors represent the combined outcome of many biological and environmental influences.

4. The amygdala responds quickly to emotional stimuli. Damage to the amygdala interferes with attention to information that is relevant to emotions.

OPPOSITE: People express emotions by facial expressions, gestures, and postures.

5. Stressful events arouse the sympathetic nervous system and later the adrenal cortex. Prolonged or severe stress produces many of the same bodily responses that illness does.

We know the meaning [of consciousness] so long as no one asks us to define it.

William James (1892/1961, p. 19)

Unfortunately, one of the most significant things ever said about emotion may be that everyone knows what it is until they are asked to define it.

Joseph LeDoux (1996, p. 23)

Suppose researchers have discovered a new species—let's call it species X—and psychologists begin testing its abilities. They place food behind a green card and nothing behind a red card and find that after a few trials, X always goes to the green card. So we conclude that X shows learning, memory, and hunger. Then researchers offer X a green card and a variety of gray cards; X still goes to the green, so it must have color vision and not just brightness discrimination. Next they let X touch a blue triangle that is extremely hot. X makes a loud sound and backs away. Someone picks up the blue triangle (with padded gloves) and starts moving with it rapidly toward X. As soon as X sees this happening, it makes the same sound, turns, and starts moving rapidly away. Shall we conclude that it feels fear?

If you said yes, now let me add: I said this was a new species, and so it is, but it's a new species of robot, not animal. Do you still think X feels fear? Most people are willing to talk about artificial learning, memory, intelligence, and motivation, but not emotion.

If such behavior isn't adequate evidence for emotion in a robot, is it adequate evidence for an animal? Emotion is a difficult topic because it implies conscious feelings that we cannot observe. Biological researchers therefore concentrate mostly on emotional *behaviors*, which are observable, even if the emotional feelings are not. Still, most of us eventually hope to learn something about the emotional experiences themselves.

What Is Emotion?

By one definition, emotion includes "cognitive evaluations, subjective changes, autonomic and neural arousal, and impulses to action" (Plutchik, 1982, p. 551). That sounds okay, but by that definition, don't hunger and thirst count as emotions? One definition of motivation is "an internal process that modifies the way an organism responds to a certain class of external stimuli" (Numan & Woodside, 2010). By that definition, don't happiness, sadness, fear, and anger count as motivations? Distinguishing between motivation and emotion is difficult, and possibly not worth the effort. Still, the term *emotion* provides a convenient category to discuss some important, interesting topics.

Regardless of how we word the definition, or whether we define it at all, psychologists generally agree that emotion has three components—cognitions ("This is a dangerous situation"), feelings ("I feel frightened"), and actions ("Run for the nearest exit"). Of these, feelings are the most central to our concept of emotion. If someone reports feeling frightened, we attribute emotion to that person at once. However, if someone coolly calculates, "This is a dangerous situation," but feels no tenseness or arousal, we would be less inclined to attribute emotion. What are emotional feelings, what causes them, and what function do they serve?

Emotions, Autonomic Arousal, and the James-Lange Theory

Emotional situations arouse the autonomic nervous system, which has two branches—the sympathetic and the parasympathetic (Figure 12.1). Walter Cannon was the first to understand that the sympathetic nervous system prepares the body for brief, vigorous "fight-or-flight" responses. The parasympathetic nervous system increases digestion and other processes that save energy and prepare for later events. However, each situation evokes its own special mixture of sympathetic and parasympathetic arousal (Wolf, 1995). For example, nausea is associated with sympathetic stimulation of the stomach (decreasing its contractions and secretions) and parasympathetic stimulation of the intestines and salivary glands.

How does the autonomic nervous system relate to emotions? Common sense holds that first you feel an emotion,

National Library of Medicine

Walter B. Cannon
(1871–1945)

As a matter of routine I have long trusted unconscious processes to serve me…. [One] example I may cite was the interpretation of the significance of bodily changes which occur in great emotional excitement, such as fear and rage. These changes—the more rapid pulse, the deeper breathing, the increase of sugar in the blood, the secretion from the adrenal glands—were very diverse and seemed unrelated. Then, one wakeful night, after a considerable collection of these changes had been disclosed, the idea flashed through my mind that they could be nicely integrated if conceived as bodily preparations for supreme effort in flight or in fighting.

which then changes your heart rate and prompts other responses. In contrast, according to the **James-Lange theory** (James, 1884), the autonomic arousal and skeletal actions come first. What you experience as an emotion is the label you give to your responses: You feel afraid *because* you run away; you feel angry *because* you attack.

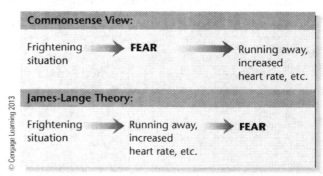

You might object, "How would I know to run away before I was scared?" In a later paper, William James (1894) clarified his position. An emotion has three components: cognitions, actions, and feelings. The cognitive aspect comes first. You quickly appraise something as good, bad, frightening, or whatever. Your appraisal of the situation leads to an appropriate

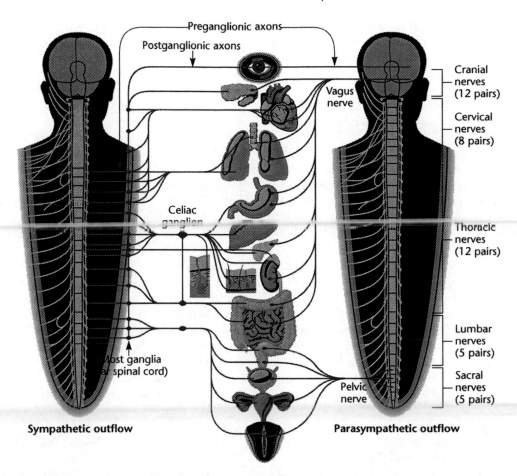

FIGURE 12.1 The sympathetic and parasympathetic nervous systems
Review Chapter 4 for more information. (© *Cengage Learning 2013*)

action, such as running away, attacking, or sitting motionless with your heart racing. When William James said that arousal and actions led to emotions, he meant the *feeling* aspect of an emotion. That is,

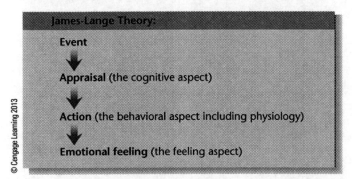

If a feeling is a kind of sensation, it is hard to know where the sensation would come from if not from some change in the body. Nevertheless, we want to test the idea. The James-Lange theory leads to two predictions: People with weak autonomic or skeletal responses should feel less emotion, and causing or increasing someone's responses should enhance an emotion. Let's consider the evidence.

Is Physiological Arousal *Necessary* for Emotions?

People with damage to the spinal cord are paralyzed from the level of the damage downward. People who cannot move their arms and legs certainly cannot attack or run away. Most of them report that they feel emotions about the same as before their injury (Cobos, Sánchez, Pérez, & Vila, 2004). This finding indicates that emotions do not require feedback from muscle movements. However, paralysis does not affect the autonomic nervous system, so it remains possible that emotional feelings depend on feedback from autonomic responses.

In people with an uncommon condition called **pure autonomic failure**, output from the autonomic nervous system to the body fails, either completely or almost completely. Heartbeat and other organ activities continue, but the nervous system no longer regulates them. Someone with this condition does not react to stressful experiences with changes in heart rate, blood pressure, or sweating. According to the James-Lange theory, we would expect such people to report no emotions. In fact, they report "having" the same emotions as anyone else. They have little difficulty identifying what emotion a character in a story would probably experience (Heims,

Critchley, Dolan, Mathias, & Cipolotti, 2004). However, they say they *feel* their emotions much less intensely than before (Critchley, Mathias, & Dolan, 2001). Presumably, when they report emotions, they refer to the cognitive aspect: "Yes, I'm angry, because this is a situation that calls for anger." But they do not *feel* the anger, or if they do, they feel it weakly. Their decreased emotional feeling is consistent with predictions from the James-Lange theory.

Here is another example: Botulinum toxin ("BOTOX") blocks transmission at synapses and nerve-muscle junctions. Physicians sometimes use it to paralyze the muscles for frowning and thereby remove frown lines on people's faces. One result is that people become slightly slower at reading unhappy sentences. Ordinarily, when people read something unpleasant, they frown just a bit. Evidently an inability to frown interferes with processing unpleasant information (Havas, Glenberg, Gutowski, Lucarelli, & Davidson, 2010). A related study examined people with BOTOX injections that temporarily paralyzed all the facial muscles. These people reported weaker than usual emotional responses when they watched short videos (Davis, Senghas, Brandt, & Ochsner, 2010). Another study found that people with brain damage that prevents voluntary facial movements have trouble recognizing other people's emotional expressions, especially expressions of fear (Pistoia et al., 2010). The implication of all these studies is that feeling a body change is important for feeling an emotion.

Evidence pointing away from this conclusion comes from a study of people with two kinds of brain damage. People with damage to the right somatosensory cortex had normal autonomic responses to emotional music but reported little subjective experience. People with damage to part of the prefrontal cortex had weak autonomic responses but normal subjective responses (Johnson, Tranel, Lutgendorf, & Adolphs, 2009). However, it was not clear whether people's reports of their "emotional experience" accurately recorded the feeling aspect of emotion, as opposed to the cognitive aspect.

Is Physiological Arousal *Sufficient* for Emotions?

According to the James-Lange theory, emotional feelings result from the body's actions. If your heart started racing and you started sweating and breathing rapidly, would you feel an emotion? Well, it depends. If you had those responses because you ran a mile, you would attribute your feelings to the exercise, not emotion. However, if they occurred spontaneously, you might indeed interpret your increased sympathetic nervous system arousal as fear. Rapid breathing in particular makes people worry that they are suffocating, and they experience a **panic attack**, marked by extreme sympathetic nervous system arousal (Klein, 1993).

What about other emotions? For example, if you find yourself smiling, do you become happier? To test this hypothesis, how could we get people to smile? Yes, of course, we could tell them to smile. However, if we tell people to smile and then

ask whether they are happy, people guess what the experiment is about and say what they think we want to hear. Clever researchers found a way to get people to smile while concealing the purpose of the study. It is a method you could easily try yourself: Hold a pen in your mouth, either with your teeth or with your lips, as shown in Figure 12.2. Now examine a page of newspaper comic strips. Mark each one + for very funny, ✓ for somewhat funny, or − for not funny. Most people rate cartoons funnier when holding a pen with their teeth—which forces a smile—than when holding it with their lips—which prevents a smile (Strack, Martin, & Stepper, 1988). That is, the sensation of smiling increases happiness, although only slightly. (Telling a depressed person to cheer up and smile does not help.)

Researchers also found a clever way to ask people to frown without saying so. They said they wanted to test people's ability to do a cognitive task and a motor task at the same time. The cognitive task was to examine photographs and rate their pleasantness or unpleasantness. For the motor task, researchers attached golf tees to each of the person's eyebrows and said to try to keep the tips of the golf tees touching each other. The only way to do that was to frown. People given this instruction rated the photographs as more unpleasant than the average for people who were not induced to frown (Larsen, Kasimatis, & Frey, 1992).

However, although smiles and frowns slightly alter happiness, smiles are not *necessary* for happiness. People with a rare condition called *Möbius syndrome* cannot move their facial muscles to make a smile, as shown in Figure 12.3. They nevertheless experience happiness and amusement, although they have trouble making friends because other people react to the lack of smiling. The girl shown in the figure underwent surgery to give her an artificial smile (G. Miller, 2007b).

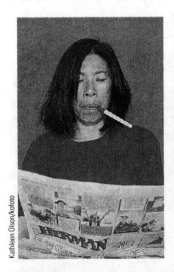

FIGURE 12.2 Effect of facial expression on emotion
People who hold a pen in their teeth, and who are therefore forced to smile, are more likely to report amusement than are people with a pen in their lips, who therefore cannot smile.

Courtesy of Lori Thomas

FIGURE 12.3 Möbius syndrome
People with this condition cannot move their facial muscles to smile. This girl went through surgery to give her an artificial smile, as shown. The lack of a smile before surgery did not rob her of happiness or a sense of humor, although it interfered with her ability to make friends.

Overall, the results suggest that our perceptions of the body's actions contribute to our emotional feelings, as the James-Lange theory proposed. Many psychologists therefore refer to emotions as "embodied"—that is, they depend on responses of the body. The theory does not insist that we can tell one emotion apart from another by our physiological responses.

> **STOP & CHECK**

1. According to the James-Lange theory, what kind of person should feel no emotions?

2. How did researchers get people to smile or frown without using those words?

ANSWERS 1. Someone who had no muscle movements and no perceivable changes in any organ should feel no emotions. However, such a person might still recognize the cognitive aspects of emotion. ("This is a sad situation.") 2. They got people to smile by telling them to hold a pen between their teeth. They got people to frown by attaching golf tees to their eyebrows and then telling them to keep the two tees touching each other.

Brain Areas Associated with Emotion

Do different emotions activate different brain areas? Moreover, which brain areas react most strongly to emotions?

Attempts to Localize Specific Emotions

Traditionally, the **limbic system**—the forebrain areas surrounding the thalamus—has been regarded as critical for emotion (Figure 12.4). We consider one part of it, the amygdala, in more detail later in this chapter. Much of the cerebral cortex also reacts to emotional situations.

Whereas many brain areas respond to emotion in one way or another, it is theoretically important to know whether different brain areas respond to different emotions. For example, does one brain area respond during happiness and another during sadness? Many researchers have used PET or fMRI techniques to identify the cortical areas that respond while people look at emotional pictures or listen to emotional stories. In Figure 12.5, each dot represents one research study that found significant activation of a particular cortical area associated with happiness, sadness, disgust, fear, or anger (Phan,

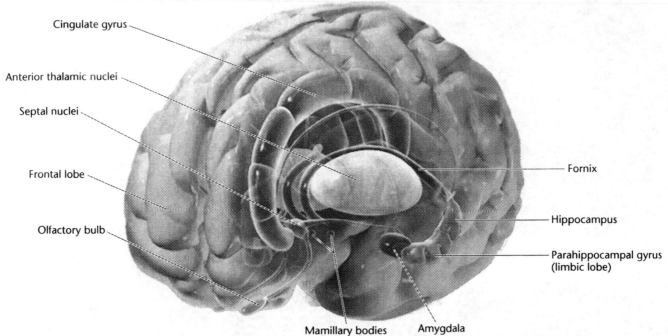

FIGURE 12.4 The limbic system
The limbic system is a group of stuctures in the interior of the brain. Here you see them as if the exterior of the brain were transparent. (© Argosy Publishing Inc.)

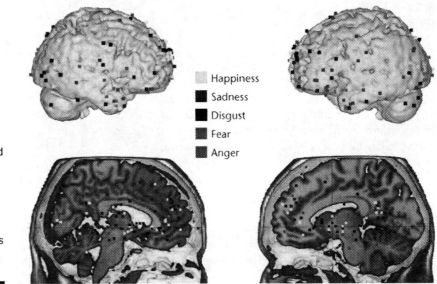

FIGURE 12.5 Brain areas associated with particular emotions
Each dot represents a study that found increased activity in a given brain area associated with the emotion designated by the color of the dot. (Reprinted from NeuroImage, 16, Phan, K. L., Wagner, T., Taylor, S. F., & Liberzon, I., "Functional neuroanatomy of emotion: A meta-analysis of emotion activation studies in PET and fMRI," pages 331–348, Copyright 2002, with permission from Elsevier.)

Wager, Taylor, & Liberzon, 2002). The frontal and temporal cortices show many dots, and other kinds of research also point to these areas as important for emotions (Kringelbach, 2005). However, the most salient point of this figure is the variability of location for each emotion. The results apparently depend more on the details of procedure than on which emotion was targeted.

Sometimes, physicians insert electrodes directly into the brains of patients with epilepsy to monitor their responses over time. In one study, researchers used these implanted electrodes to record responses to emotional pictures. They did find partic-

ular cells that responded mainly to pleasant pictures and others that responded mainly to unpleasant pictures (Kawasaki et al., 2005). However, no one has demonstrated cells that respond only to a particular unpleasant emotion, such as sadness or fear.

Of all emotions, only disgust seems to be associated with the response of a particular brain area. The *insular cortex*, or *insula*, is strongly activated if you see a disgusting picture (F. C. Murphy, Nimmo-Smith, & Lawrence, 2003; M. L. Phillips et al., 1997) or the facial expression of someone who is feeling disgusted (Wicker et al., 2003). That is, if you see someone who looks disgusted, you feel disgusted, too. In fact, different parts of the insula respond to different types of disgusting scenes, such as a video of a surgical operation and a video of someone vomiting (Harrison, Gray, Gianaros, & Critchley, 2010).

Locating disgust in the insula is interesting because that is the primary taste cortex (Figure 7.21). *Disgust* is literally *disgust*, or bad taste. To react with disgust is to react as if something tasted bad; we want to spit it out. One man with damage to his insular cortex not only failed to experience disgust in daily life but also had trouble recognizing other people's disgust expressions. When he heard a retching sound, he did not recognize that it meant nausea or vomiting. How disgusted would you be if you found a cockroach in your soup? What if you saw someone whose intestines were spilling out through a hole in the abdomen? What if you saw people with feces on their hands and faces? To questions like these, this patient gave much lower ratings than other people do (Calder, Keane, Manes, Antoun, & Young, 2000).

However, the insula also responds to frightening pictures (Schienle et al., 2002) and pictures of angry faces (Fusar-Poli et al., 2009), not just to items suggesting disgust. Therefore, we should not too closely equate the insula with disgust.

▶ STOP & CHECK

3. The insula is important for which kind of emotion, and which kind of sensation?

ANSWER 3. The insula is important for disgust and taste.

Contributions of the Left and Right Hemispheres

Another hypothesis relates the two hemispheres of the brain to different categories of emotion. Activity of the left hemisphere, especially its frontal and temporal lobes, relates to what Jeffrey Gray (1970) called the **Behavioral Activation System (BAS)**, marked by low to moderate autonomic arousal and a tendency to approach, which could characterize either happiness or anger. Increased activity of the frontal and temporal lobes of the right hemisphere is associated with the **Behavioral Inhibition System (BIS)**, which increases attention and arousal, inhibits action, and stimulates emotions such as fear and disgust (Davidson & Fox, 1982; Davidson & Henriques, 2000; F. C. Murphy et al., 2003; Reuter-Lorenz & Davidson, 1981).

The difference between the hemispheres relates to personality: On average, people with greater activity in the frontal cortex of the left hemisphere tend to be happier, more outgoing, and more fun-loving. People with greater right-hemisphere activity tend to be socially withdrawn, less satisfied with life, and prone to unpleasant emotions (Knyazev, Slobodskaya, & Wilson, 2002; Schmidt, 1999; Shackman, McMenamin, Maxwell, Greischar, & Davidson, 2009; Urry et al., 2004).

The right hemisphere appears to be more responsive to emotional stimuli than the left. For example, listening to either laughter or crying activates the right amygdala more than the left (Sander & Scheich, 2001). When people look at faces, drawing their attention to the emotional expression increases the activity in the right temporal cortex (Narumoto, Okada, Sadato, Fukui, & Yonekura, 2001). People with damage to the right temporal cortex have trouble identifying other people's emotional expressions or even saying whether two people are expressing the same emotion or different ones (H. J. Rosen et al., 2002).

In one fascinating study, people watched videotapes of 10 people. All 10 described themselves honestly during one speech and completely dishonestly during another. The task of the observers was to guess which of the two interviews was the honest one. The task is more difficult than it might sound, and most people are no more correct than chance (about 5 of 10). The only group tested that performed better than chance was a group of people with left-hemisphere brain damage (Etcoff, Ekman, Magee, & Frank, 2000). They got only 60% correct—not great, but at least better than chance. Evidently, the right hemisphere is better not only at expressing emotions but also at detecting other people's emotions. With the left hemisphere out of the way, the right hemisphere was free to do what it does best.

In another study, 11 patients went through a procedure in which one hemisphere at a time was anesthetized by drug injection into one of the carotid arteries, which provide blood to the head. (This procedure, called the Wada procedure, is sometimes used before certain kinds of brain surgery.) All 11 patients had left-hemisphere language, so they could not be interviewed with the left hemisphere inactivated. When they were tested with the right hemisphere inactivated, something fascinating happened: They could still describe any of the sad, frightening, or irritating events they had experienced in life, but they remembered only the facts, not the emotion. For example, one patient remembered a car wreck, another remembered visiting his mother while she was dying, and another remembered a time his wife threatened to kill him. But they denied they had felt any significant fear, sadness, or anger. When they described the same events with both hemispheres active, they remembered strong emotions. So evidently, when the right hemisphere is inactive, people do not experience strong emotions and do not even remember feeling them (Ross, Homan, & Buck, 1994).

▶ STOP & CHECK

4. What are the contributions of the right hemisphere to emotional behaviors and interpreting other people's emotions?

ANSWER 4. Activation of the right hemisphere is associated with withdrawal from events and social contact. The right hemisphere is also more specialized than the left for interpreting other people's expressions of emotions.

▌The Functions of Emotions

If we evolved the capacity to experience and express emotions, emotions must have been adaptive for our ancestors, and probably for us as well. What good do emotions do?

For certain emotions, the answer is clear. Fear alerts us to escape from danger. Anger directs us to attack an intruder. Disgust tells us to avoid something that might cause illness. The adaptive value of happiness, sadness, embarrassment, and other emotions is less obvious, although researchers have suggested some plausible possibilities.

Also, emotions provide a useful guide when we need to make a quick decision. Sometimes, your "gut feeling" is useful. In one study, college students viewed a series of slides of snakes and spiders, each presented for just 10 ms, followed by a masking stimulus—a random array of unrecognizable patterns. Under these conditions, people cannot identify whether they saw a snake or a spider. For each participant, one kind of stimulus—either the snakes or the spiders—was always followed by a mild shock 5.6 seconds later. Most of those shocked after spider pictures developed a bigger heart rate increase after

spider pictures, and people shocked after snake pictures learned an increased heart rate after snake pictures, even though neither group could consciously identify the pictures. On certain trials, participants were asked to report any perceived changes in their heart rate, which were compared to measurements of their actual heart rate. On other trials, after the stimulus, they guessed whether a shock was forthcoming. In general, those who were most accurate at reporting their heart rate increases were the most accurate at predicting whether they were about to get a shock (Katkin, Wiens, & Öhman, 2001). The interpretation is that people who are good at detecting their autonomic responses may have valid gut feelings about dangers that they cannot identify consciously.

Emotions and Moral Decisions

We base many important decisions partly on emotional considerations—how we think one outcome or another will make us feel. Consider the following moral dilemmas, of which Figure 12.6 illustrates three.

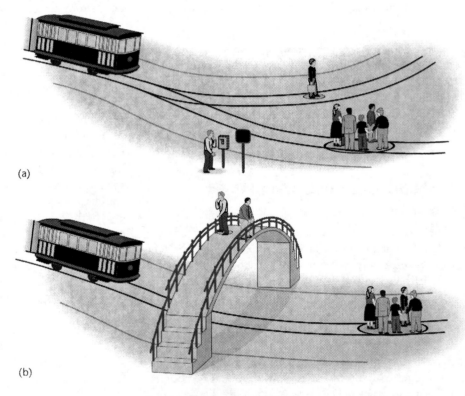

(a)

(b)

FIGURE 12.6 Three moral dilemmas
(a) Would you divert a runaway train so it kills one person instead of five? (b) Would you push someone off a footbridge so a runaway train kills him instead of five others? (c) Would you push someone off a sinking lifeboat to save yourself and four others?
(© Cengage Learning 2013)

(c)

The Trolley Dilemma. A runaway trolley is headed toward five people on a track. The only way you can prevent their death is to switch the trolley onto another track, where it will kill one person. Would it be right to pull the switch?

The Footbridge Dilemma. You are standing on a footbridge overlooking a trolley track. A runaway trolley is headed toward five people on a track. The only way you can prevent their death is to push a heavy-set stranger off the footbridge and onto the track so that he will block the trolley. Would it be right to push him?

The Lifeboat Dilemma. You and six other people are on a lifeboat in icy waters, but it is overcrowded and starting to sink. If you push one of the people off the boat, the boat will stop sinking and the rest of you will survive. Would it be right to push someone off?

The Hospital Dilemma. You are a surgeon, and five of your patients will die soon unless they get organ transplants. Each needs the transplant of a different organ. You haven't been able to find organ donors for any of them. Then a nurse bursts into your office: "Good news! A visitor to the hospital has just arrived, who has exactly the same tissue type as all five of your patients! We can kill this visitor and use the organs to save the five others!" Would it be right to do so?

In each of these dilemmas, you can save five people (including yourself in the lifeboat case) by killing one person. However, although that may be true logically, the decisions do not feel the same. Most people (though not all) say it is right to pull the switch in the trolley dilemma. Fewer say yes in the footbridge and lifeboat dilemmas. Almost no one endorses killing one person to save five others in the hospital dilemma. Brain scans show that contemplating the footbridge or lifeboat dilemma activates brain areas known to respond to emotions, including parts of the prefrontal cortex and cingulate gyrus (Greene, Sommerville, Nystrom, Darley, & Cohen, 2001). Responses in the amygdala are also important. We don't want to act to harm someone, because we identify with that other person and begin to feel the pain that our actions might cause that other person (Pfaff, 2007). In short, when we are making a decision about right and wrong, we seldom work it out rationally. One decision or the other immediately "feels" right. After we have already decided, we try to think of a logical justification (Haidt, 2001).

Decision Making After Brain Damage that Impairs Emotions

Damage to parts of the prefrontal cortex blunts people's emotions in most regards, except for an occasional outburst of anger. It also impairs decision making. People with such damage often make impulsive decisions without pausing to consider the consequences, including how they will feel after a possible mistake. When given a choice, they frequently make a quick decision and then immediately sigh or wince, knowing that

they have made the wrong choice (Berlin, Rolls, & Kischka, 2004). You might think of impulsive decisions as emotional, but these people's decisions often seem unemotional. For example, if confronted with the trolley car dilemma or the other dilemmas we just discussed, people with prefrontal damage are more likely than average to choose the utilitarian option of killing one to save five, even in situations where most people find the choice emotionally unacceptable (Koenigs et al., 2007). And they make that utilitarian decision quickly and calmly.

The most famous case of a person with prefrontal damage is that of Phineas Gage. In 1848, an explosion sent an iron rod through Gage's prefrontal cortex. Amazingly, he survived. During the next few months, his behavior was impulsive and he made poor decisions. These are common symptoms of prefrontal damage. However, the reports about his behavior provide little detail. Over the years, with multiple retellings, people elaborated and exaggerated the meager facts available (Kotowicz, 2007).

We know more about a modern case. Antonio Damasio (1994) examined a man with prefrontal cortex damage who expressed almost no emotions. Nothing angered him. He was never very sad, even about his own brain damage. Nothing gave him much pleasure, not even music. Far from being brilliantly rational, he frequently made bad decisions that cost him his job, his marriage, and his savings. When tested in the laboratory, he successfully predicted the probable outcomes of various decisions. For example, when asked what would happen if he cashed a check and the bank teller handed him too much money, he knew the probable consequences of returning it or walking away with it. But he admitted, "I still wouldn't know what to do" (A. R. Damasio, 1994, p. 49). He knew that one action would win him approval and another would get him in trouble, but he apparently did not anticipate that approval would feel good and trouble would feel bad. In a sense, any choice requires consideration of values and emotions—how we think one outcome or another will make us feel. In Damasio's words, "Inevitably, emotions are inseparable from the idea of good and evil" (A. Damasio, 1999, p. 55).

After damage to a particular part of the prefrontal cortex—the ventromedial prefrontal cortex—people seem deficient in their sense of guilt, both in everyday life and in laboratory situations. Consider two economic games: In the one-shot Dictator game, you are the Dictator, and you are given some money to divide between yourself and another person, whatever way you choose. Most people split it evenly or almost evenly, keeping a little more than half for themselves. People with ventromedial prefrontal damage keep about 90%, on average. In the Trust game (also mentioned in Chapter 11), one person gets some money and has the option of giving some of it to a Trustee. If so, the amount given triples in value, and the Trustee can return any amount of it, such as half, to the first person. People with ventromedial prefrontal damage give less, showing decreased trust. If they are in the position of Trustee, they keep all or nearly all of the money instead of returning it (Krajbich, Adolphs, Tranel, Denburg, &

Camerer, 2009). In short, they show less than normal concern for others. If most people didn't show a reasonable amount of concern for others, civilization would fall apart.

Here is an experiment to explore further the role of emotions in decisions. In the Iowa Gambling Task, people can draw one card at a time from four piles. They always win $100 in play money from decks A and B, or $50 from C and D. However, some of the cards also have penalties:

| Gain $100; one-half of all cards also have penalties averaging $250 | Gain $100; one-tenth of all cards also have penalties of $1250 | Gain $50; one-half of all cards also have penalties averaging $50 | Gain $50, one-tenth of all cards also have penalties of $250 |

© Cengage Learning 2013

When you see all the payoffs laid out, you can easily determine that the best strategy is to pick cards from decks C and D. In the experiment, however, people have to discover the payoffs by trial and error. Ordinarily, as people sample from all four decks, they gradually start showing signs of nervous tension whenever they draw a card from A or B, and they start shifting their preference toward C and D. People with damage to either the prefrontal cortex or the amygdala (part of the temporal lobe) are slow in processing emotional information. In this experiment, they show no nervous tension when drawing from decks A and B, and they continue choosing those decks (Bechara, Damasio, Damasio, & Lee, 1999). In short, failure to anticipate the unpleasantness of likely outcomes leads to bad decisions.

Of course, it is also true that emotions sometimes interfere with good decisions. If you were driving and suddenly started skidding on a patch of ice, what would you do? A patient with damage to his prefrontal cortex who happened to face this situation calmly followed the advice he had always heard: Take your foot off the accelerator and steer in the direction of the skid (Shiv, Loewenstein, Bechara, Damasio, & Damasio, 2005). Most people in this situation panic, hit the brakes, and steer away from the skid, making a bad situation worse.

> **STOP & CHECK**

5. If brain damage impairs someone's emotions, what happens to the person's decision making?

ANSWER

5. After brain damage that impairs emotion, people make impulsive decisions, evidently because they do not quickly imagine how bad a poor decision might make them feel.

MODULE 12.1 ■ IN CLOSING

Emotions and the Nervous System

Although we regard emotions as nebulous internal states, they are fundamentally biological. As William James observed in the early days of psychology, emotions are "embodied"—an emotional feeling requires some action and a perception of that action.

Biological research sheds light on many of the central questions about the psychology of emotions. For example, one issue is whether people have a few "basic" emotions or continuous dimensions along which emotions vary. If researchers found that different emotions depended on different brain areas or different neurotransmitters, that evidence would strongly support the idea of basic emotions. However, so far, researchers have found no evidence that each emotion has a specific physiology, with the possible exception of disgust.

Studies of people with brain damage also shed light on the functions of emotion, particularly with relation to moral behavior and decision making. Far from being an impediment to intelligent behavior, emotional reactions are often a useful quick guide to appropriate actions. In short, understanding emotions and understanding their biology go hand in hand.

SUMMARY

1. According to the James-Lange theory, the feeling aspect of an emotion results from feedback from actions of the muscles and organs. **356**

2. Consistent with the James-Lange theory, people who have impaired autonomic responses have weaker emotional feelings, although they continue to identify the cognitive aspects of emotion. **357**

3. Feedback from facial movements or other actions can strengthen an emotional feeling, but they are not necessary for such feelings. **358**

4. Emotional experiences arouse many brain areas, as measured by fMRI scans or EEG recordings. So far, the research does not convincingly assign different emotions to different brain areas, with the possible exception of disgust. **359**

5. Activation of the frontal and temporal areas of the left hemisphere is associated with approach and the Behavioral Activation System. The corresponding areas of the right hemisphere are associated with withdrawal, decreased activity, and the Behavioral Inhibition System. The right hemisphere is more effective than the left for recognizing emotional expressions.   361

6. Brain damage that impairs emotional feelings and responses also impairs decision making. One interpreta-tion is that people decide badly because they do not quickly imagine their emotional reactions to possible consequences.   362

7. People with damage to the ventromedial prefrontal cortex show little concern for other people. They appar-ently lack a normal sense of guilt.   363

KEY TERMS

Terms are defined in the module on the page number indicated. They're also presented in alphabetical order, with definitions, in the book's Subject Index/Glossary, which begins on page 561. Interactive flashcards and crossword puzzles are among the online re-sources available to help you learn these terms and the concepts they represent.

Behavioral Activation System (BAS)   361

Behavioral Inhibition System (BIS)   361

James-Lange theory   356

limbic system   359

panic attack   358

pure autonomic failure   357

THOUGHT QUESTION

According to the James-Lange theory, we should expect peo-ple with pure autonomic failure to experience weaker than average emotions. What kind of people might experience stronger than average emotions?

Attack and Escape Behaviors

Have you ever watched a cat play with a rat or mouse before killing it? It might kick, bat, toss, pick up, shake, and carry the rodent. Is the cat sadistically tormenting its prey? No. Most of what we call its "play" behaviors are a compromise between attack and escape: When the rodent is facing away, the cat approaches; if the rodent turns around and bares its teeth to the cat, the cat bats it or kicks it defensively (Pellis et al., 1988). A cat usually goes for a quick kill if the rodent is small and inactive or if the cat has been given drugs that lower its anxiety. The same cat withdraws altogether if confronted with a large, menacing rodent. "Play" occurs in intermediate situations (Adamec, Stark-Adamec, & Livingston, 1980; Biben, 1979; Pellis et al., 1988).

Most of the vigorous emotional behaviors we observe in animals fall into the categories of attack and escape, and it is no coincidence that we describe the sympathetic nervous system as the fight-or-flight system. These behaviors and their corresponding emotions—anger and fear—are closely related both behaviorally and physiologically.

▌Attack Behaviors

Attack behavior depends on the individual as well as the situation. If a hamster intrudes into another hamster's territory, the home hamster sniffs the intruder and eventually attacks, but usually not at once. Suppose the intruder leaves, and a little later, another hamster intrudes. The home hamster attacks faster and more vigorously than before. The first attack increases the probability of a second attack against any intruder for the next 30 minutes or more (Potegal, 1994). It is as if the first attack gets the hamster in the mood to attack again. During that period, activity builds up in the corticomedial area of the amygdala (Figure 12.7), and as it does so, it increases the hamster's probability of attacking (Potegal, Ferris, Hebert, Meyerhoff, & Skaredoff, 1996; Potegal, Hebert, DeCoster, & Meyerhoff, 1996). Something similar happens in people, although we can only speculate about whether the brain mechanism is the same: If you hold a toddler's arm to prevent him or her from playing with a toy, the result is sometimes screaming and other signs of anger. If you pause 30 seconds and then do

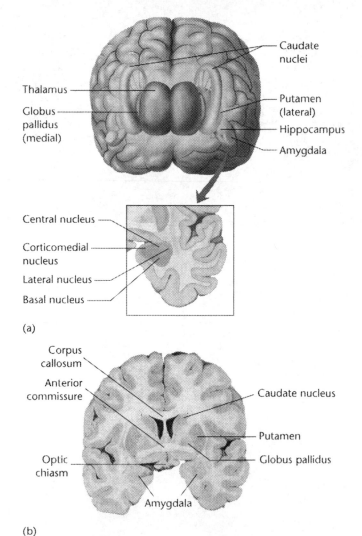

(a)

(b)

FIGURE 12.7 Location of amygdala in the human brain
The amygdala, located in the interior of the temporal lobe, receives input from many cortical and subcortical areas. Part (a) shows several nuclei of the amygdala. *([a] After Hanaway, Woolsey, Gado, & Roberts, 1998; Nieuwenhuys, Voogd, & vanHuijzen, 1988; [b] Photo courtesy of Dr. Dana Copeland)*

it again, the anger is more rapid and more intense (Potegal, Robison, Anderson, Jordan, & Shapiro, 2007).

The same is true for adults. You may have noticed times when one person annoys you and a few minutes later you get angry with someone else. You have probably been told, "If you become angry, count to 10 before you act." Counting to a few thousand would work better, but the idea is correct. Lying on your back is another way to decrease anger. Research has shown that it is easier to feel angry while standing (and therefore in a position to attack) than while lying in a more helpless position (Harmon-Jones & Peterson, 2009). As in several cases in the first module, this finding supports the idea that emotion is embodied: What you are doing or about to do affects how you feel.

Heredity and Environment in Violence

Why do some people turn to violence more readily than others do? Some environmental factors are easy to identify. Certainly people who were abused in childhood, people who witnessed violent abuse between their parents, and people who live in a violent neighborhood are at greater risk of violence themselves. Another environmental factor is exposure to lead, which is harmful to developing brains. Since the banning of lead-based paints and the rise of unleaded gasoline, the prevalence of violent crime has declined, possibly as a result of the decreased lead in the environment (Nevin, 2007).

What about heredity? Monozygotic twins resemble each other more closely than dizygotic twins do with regard to violent and criminal behaviors, and adopted children resemble their biological parents more closely than their adoptive parents (Rhee & Waldman, 2002). However, various kinds of aggressive behavior occur under different circumstances, and we cannot expect to find a single gene or set of genes that will account for all the variations (Yeh, Coccaro, & Jacobson, 2010). For example, researchers found one gene linked to aggressive behavior that is common only among people of Finnish ancestry (Bevilacqua et al., 2010).

After researchers repeatedly failed to find a strong link between any single gene and aggressive behavior, they explored the possibility of interactions between heredity and environment. Several studies have found that violence is particularly enhanced in people with both a genetic predisposition *and* a troubled early environment (Cadoret, Yates, Troughton, Woodworth, & Stewart, 1995; Caspi et al., 2002; Enoch, Steer, Newman, Gibson, & Goldman, 2010; Widom & Brzustowicz, 2006). Figure 12.8 illustrates the effects of genetic differences in production of the enzyme *monoamine oxidase A* (*MAO$_A$*). This enzyme breaks down the neurotransmitters dopamine, norepinephrine, and serotonin, thus lowering the available amounts. Researchers find little difference in aggressive or other antisocial behavior, on average, between people with high or low amounts of MAO$_A$. However, the effects of this gene apparently interact with childhood experience. As the figure shows, the rate of antisocial behavior was low among people who were treated well in childhood, regardless

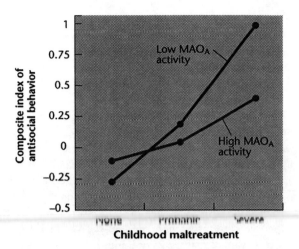

FIGURE 12.8 Genes, environment, and antisocial behavior in men
The y axis represents a complex score combining several types of measurement. Higher scores indicate more aggressive behaviors. *(From "Role of genotype in the cycle of violence in maltreated children," from Caspi, A., et al., Science, 297, 851–854. © 2002 AAAS.)*

of their MAO$_A$ levels. In those who endured a small amount of mistreatment in childhood, the rate of antisocial behavior increased, but their MAO$_A$ levels did not make much difference. However, among those who were seriously maltreated in childhood, the rate of antisocial behavior was significantly higher for those with low MAO$_A$ activity (Caspi et al., 2002). This result is fascinating because of its apparent demonstration of an interaction between genetics and environment. However, from a theoretical standpoint, it is not clear why decreased MAO$_A$ should be linked to increased aggression, or why the effect of this gene should depend on the environment. We can look forward to more detailed investigations of this relationship.

STOP & CHECK

6. What relationship did Caspi et al. (2002) report between the enzyme MAO$_A$ and antisocial behavior?

ANSWER

6. Overall, people with genes for high or low production of MAO$_A$ do not differ significantly in their probability of antisocial behavior. However, among those who suffered serious maltreatment during childhood, people with lower levels of the enzyme showed higher rates of antisocial behavior.

Hormones

Most fighting in the animal kingdom is by males competing for mates or females defending their young. Male aggressive behavior depends heavily on testosterone, which is highest for adult males in the reproductive season. Even in species that do not have a particular season for breeding, testosterone increases are linked with increased striving for social dominance (Beehner et al., 2009).

Similarly, throughout the world, men fight more often than women, commit more violent crimes, shout more insults at one another, and so forth. Moreover, young adult men, who have the highest testosterone levels, have the highest rate of aggressive behaviors and violent crimes. Women's violent acts are in most cases less severe (Archer, 2000).

If we compare men of the same age, do men with higher testosterone levels also commit more violent behavior? Yes, on average, although the effects are often smaller than most people expect (Archer, Birring, & Wu, 1998; Archer, Graham-Kevan, & Davies, 2005). Figure 12.9 shows one set of results. Note that high testosterone levels were more common among men convicted of violent crimes than for those convicted of less violent crimes, but also note that the differences are small. According to the "triple imbalance hypothesis," the reason testosterone's effects are unimpressive is that violence depends on other chemicals as well, especially cortisol and serotonin (van Honk, Harmon-Jones, Morgan, & Schutter, 2010). Cortisol, which increases under stressful conditions, increases fear, and a decrease in cortisol is associated with loss of inhibitions. Therefore, aggression tends to be highest when testosterone levels are high and cortisol levels low. Men with high levels of both testosterone and cortisol are likely to inhibit their violent impulses. Serotonin also tends to inhibit violent impulses.

To test the effects of testosterone, correlational studies are not ideal, because men with high testosterone levels may be unusual in other regards besides testosterone. Several studies used the idea of temporarily increasing testosterone levels in women. Because most women start with low testosterone levels, researchers can readily measure the effects of an increase. In one study, women received either testosterone or placebo and then played the Ultimatum game. In this game, the first person is given $10 and then must propose how to split it with a second person—$5 each, or $7 for me and $3 for you, or whatever. The second person can then accept the offer, or veto it, in which case neither person receives anything. We might expect that giving testosterone to the first person would lead to a greedy offer, but in fact the women receiving testosterone offered their partner a bit *more* money, on average, than did those receiving a placebo (Eisenegger, Naef, Snozzi, Heinrichs, & Fehr, 2010). That reaction doesn't make sense in terms of aggression, although it might make sense in terms of enhancing one's status. That is, someone who offers the other person a good share of the money is saying, "I'm so successful that I can afford to be generous with you."

In another study, the women's task was to examine photos of faces and try to identify the expressed emotions among six choices: anger, disgust, fear, happiness, sadness, and surprise. The photos were morphed from 0% (neutral expression) to 100% expression of an emotion. Figure 12.10 shows the example for anger.

The result was that after women received testosterone, most became less accurate at recognizing facial expressions of anger (van Honk & Schutter, 2007). Meanwhile, other research shows that testosterone *increases* responses of the amygdala to photos showing angry expressions (Hermans, Ramsey, & van Honk, 2008). Evidently, testosterone affects certain brain areas differently, increasing the responses of emotion-related areas, while decreasing the ability of the cerebral cortex to identify the emotion consciously. We can speculate that the result might be increased emotional arousal and decreased ability to regulate that emotion deliberately.

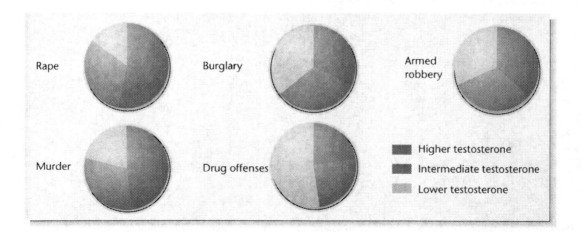

FIGURE 12.9 Testosterone levels for male prisoners
Testosterone levels are higher, on average, for men convicted of murder or rape than for those convicted of burglary or drug offenses.
(Based on Dabbs, Carr, Frady, & Riad, 1995)

FIGURE 12.10 Stimuli to measure people's ability to identify emotion
For each of six emotions, researchers prepared views ranging from 0% to 100% expression of the emotion. In this case, the emotion is anger. Women identified the expression more quickly, on average, after a placebo injection than after a testosterone injection. *(From van Honk, J., & Schutter, D. J. L. G. "Testosterone reduces conscious detection of signals serving social correction," Psychological Science, 18, 663–667. Used by permission of Blackwell Publishing.)*

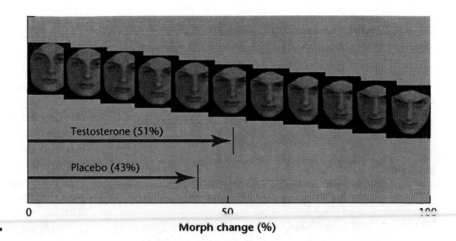

Morph change (%)

> STOP & CHECK

7. How does testosterone influence emotional and cognitive responses to a facial expression of anger?

ANSWER

7. It decreases the ability to recognize the expression consciously but increases the responses in emotion-related areas of the brain.

Serotonin Synapses and Aggressive Behavior

Several lines of evidence link aggressive behavior to low serotonin release. Let's examine some of this evidence.

Nonhuman Animals

Much of the earliest evidence came from studies on mice. Luigi Valzelli (1973) found that isolating male mice for 4 weeks increased their aggressive behavior and decreased their serotonin *turnover*. When neurons release serotonin, they reabsorb most of it and synthesize enough to replace the amount that washed away. Thus, the amount present in neurons remains fairly constant, and if we examine that amount, we have little idea how much the neurons have been releasing. However, if we measure the serotonin metabolites in body fluids, we gauge the **turnover**, which is the amount that neurons released and replaced. Researchers estimate serotonin turnover from the concentration of **5-hydroxyindoleacetic acid (5-HIAA)**, serotonin's main metabolite, in the cerebrospinal fluid (CSF). Measuring the amount in the blood or urine is a simpler but less accurate alternative.

Comparing different genetic strains of mice, Valzelli and his colleagues found that social isolation lowered serotonin turnover by the greatest amount in the genetic strains that reacted with the greatest amount of fighting after social isolation (Valzelli & Bernasconi, 1979). Social isolation does not decrease serotonin turnover in female mice in any genetic strain, and it does not make the females aggressive.

That is, serotonin's effects combine with those of testosterone, as in the triple imbalance hypothesis mentioned previously. Serotonin activity is lower in juvenile rodents than in adults, and aggressive behavior is higher in the juveniles (Taravosh-Lahn, Bastida, & Delville, 2006). Serotonin release is also below average in highly aggressive hamsters (Cervantes & Delville, 2009).

In a fascinating study, investigators measured 5-HIAA levels in 2-year-old male monkeys living in a natural environment and then observed their behavior closely. The monkeys in the lowest quartile for 5-HIAA, and therefore the lowest serotonin turnover, were the most aggressive, had the greatest probability of attacking larger monkeys, and incurred the most injuries. Most of them died by age 6. In contrast, monkeys with high serotonin turnover survived (Higley et al., 1996). Female monkeys with low 5-HIAA levels are also likely to get injured and die young (Westergaard, Cleveland, Trenkle, Lussier, & Higley, 2003).

If most monkeys with low turnover die young, why hasn't natural selection eliminated the genes for low serotonin turnover? One possibility is that evolution selects for an intermediate amount of aggression and anxiety (Trefilov, Berard, Krawczak, & Schmidtke, 2000). The most fearless animals get into fights and die young, but those with too much fear have other problems. We could say the same about humans: People with too little fear take excessive risks—wrestling alligators, bungee jumping with a frayed cord, things like that. Those with too much fear are withdrawn and unlikely to succeed (Nettle, 2006).

We can also see aggressiveness as a high-risk, high-payoff strategy: A monkey with low 5-HIAA starts many fights and probably dies young. However, a monkey who wins enough of those fights survives and achieves a dominant status within the group (Howell et al., 2007). In female monkeys, too, those with low 5-HIAA levels tend to achieve higher status in the troop (Riddick et al., 2009). Under some circumstances, taking aggressive risks to achieve a dominant status might be a reasonable gamble.

> **STOP & CHECK**

8. If we want to know how much serotonin the brain has been releasing, what should we measure?

9. Given that monkeys with low serotonin turnover pick many fights and in most cases die young, what keeps natural selection from eliminating the genes for low serotonin turnover?

ANSWERS

8. We can measure the concentration of 5-HIAA, a serotonin metabolite, in the cerebrospinal fluid or other body fluids. The more 5-HIAA, the more serotonin has been released and presumably resynthesized. 9. Although most monkeys with low serotonin turnover die young, many of the survivors achieve a dominant status that enables them to get more of the food and to reproduce more frequently. Monkeys with high serotonin turnover survive, but at the cost of accepting a low status.

Humans

Many studies have found low serotonin turnover in people with a history of violent behavior, including people convicted of arson and other violent crimes (Virkkunen, Nuutila, Goodwin, & Linnoila, 1987) and people who attempt suicide by violent means, as illustrated in Figure 12.11 (G. L. Brown et al., 1982; Edman, Åsberg, Levander, & Schalling, 1986; Mann, Arango, & Underwood, 1990; Pandey et al., 1995; Roy, DeJong, & Linnoila, 1989; Sher et al., 2006; Spreux-Varoquaux et al., 2001). Follow-up studies on people released from prison have found that those with lower serotonin turnover had a greater probability of further convictions for violent crimes (Virkkunen, DeJong, Bartko, Goodwin, &

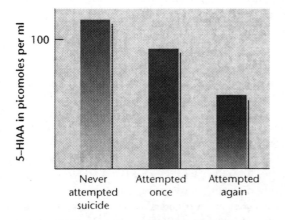

FIGURE 12.11 Levels of 5-HIAA in the CSF of depressed people
Measurements for the suicide-attempting groups were taken after the first attempt. Low levels of 5-HIAA indicate low serotonin turnover. (Based on results of Roy, DeJong, & Linnoila, 1989)

Linnoila, 1989; Virkkunen, Eggert, Rawlings, & Linnoila, 1996). However, although each of these relationships is statistically reliable, the effects are not sufficiently powerful that we could use blood tests to make important decisions about individuals, such as which prisoners should be eligible for parole. Furthermore, although the research points to a relationship between low serotonin turnover and highly violent criminal or suicidal acts, the results are less clear for aggressive behavior in the normal population (where extreme violence is uncommon). In the normal population, studies often find a weak relationship, and sometimes a relationship in the opposite direction—that is, somewhat *less* aggression by people with low 5-HIAA (Coccaro & Lee, 2010).

It is possible to alter serotonin synthesis by changes in diet. Neurons synthesize serotonin from tryptophan, an amino acid found in small amounts in proteins. Tryptophan crosses the blood–brain barrier by an active transport channel that it shares with phenylalanine and other large amino acids. Thus, a diet high in other amino acids impairs the brain's ability to synthesize serotonin. One study found that many young men on such a diet showed an increase in aggressive behavior a few hours after eating (Moeller et al., 1996). Considering these results, it would seem prudent for anyone with aggressive or suicidal tendencies to reduce consumption of aspartame (NutraSweet, which is 50% phenylalanine) and maize (American corn), which is high in phenylalanine and low in tryptophan (Lytle, Messing, Fisher, & Phebus, 1975).

Much of the variation in serotonin activity, and therefore violence, relates to genetics. People vary in the gene that controls *tryptophan hydroxylase*, the enzyme that converts tryptophan into serotonin. People with less active forms of this enzyme are more likely than average to report frequent anger and aggression (Hennig, Reuter, Netter, Burk, & Landt, 2005; Rujescu et al., 2002) and more likely to make violent suicide attempts (Abbar et al., 2001).

How Do We Explain Serotonin Effects?

If some treatment suddenly lowered your serotonin level, would you at once become violent? When researchers have used drugs or diet to suppress serotonin levels, some people felt depressed, others became more aggressive or impulsive, and those with previous drug problems reported a craving for drugs (Kaplan, Muldoon, Manuck, & Mann, 1997; Van der Does, 2001; S. N. Young & Leyton, 2002). In short, serotonin's role is not specific to aggression. A better hypothesis is that high levels of serotonin inhibit a variety of impulses, and low levels remove inhibitions. Then the resulting behavior depends on what had been inhibited, which varies from one person to another. In an interesting study that illustrated inhibition, people ate a diet rich in other amino acids but lacking tryptophan. That diet temporarily reduced their serotonin levels. Then they had to learn a response to avoid a loud buzzing noise and a loss of money. People low in serotonin learned the response, but they differed from the placebo group in this regard: Ordinarily, when people receive punishments, such as a loss of money, they become inhibited. They become inactive or slow to respond in a variety of situations. The people low in serotonin failed to show that kind of generalized inhibition (Crockett, Clark, & Robbins, 2009).

The serotonin-aggression relationship is complex in another way also: Although most studies imply that serotonin inhibits aggressive behavior, the brain releases serotonin during aggressive behavior (van der Vegt et al., 2003). Apparently, a low level of serotonin activity prior to aggravation magnifies the response when serotonin is suddenly released at the start of an aggressive encounter (Nelson & Trainor, 2007).

10. What change in diet can alter the production of serotonin?

Fear and Anxiety

What is the "right" amount of anxiety? It depends. If you are sitting with family or friends at a restaurant, a low level of anxiety is appropriate. If you are walking alone at night and you hear footsteps approaching you, it is time to turn up your anxiety level.

Nevertheless, even among people in the same situation, some show much more anxiety than others do, partly for genetic reasons (Aleman, Swart, & van Rijn, 2008; Chen et al., 2006; Lonsdorf et al., 2009, 2010; Wray et al., 2009). Both experiences and genetics modify activity in the amygdala, one of the main areas for regulating anxiety.

Fear, Anxiety, and the Amygdala

Do we have any built-in, unlearned fears? Yes, at least one: Even newborns are frightened by loud noises. The response to an unexpected loud noise, known as the **startle reflex**, is extremely fast: Auditory information goes first to the cochlear nucleus in the medulla and from there directly to an area in the pons that commands tensing the muscles, especially the neck muscles. Tensing the neck muscles is important because the neck is so vulnerable to injury. (Chapter 5 discussed how woodpeckers protect their necks while pecking a tree.) Information reaches the pons within 3 to 8 ms after a loud noise, and the full startle reflex occurs in less than two tenths of a second (Yeomans & Frankland, 1996).

Although you don't have to learn to fear loud noises, your current mood or situation modifies your reaction. Your startle reflex is more vigorous if you are already tense. People with

Joe McBride/Getty Images

People's choices of activities depend in part on how easily they develop anxiety.

post-traumatic stress disorder, who are certainly known for their intense anxiety, show a much enhanced startle reflex (Grillon, Morgan, Davis, & Southwick, 1998).

Studies of Rodents

Psychologists measure variations in the startle reflex as a gauge of fear or anxiety. In research with nonhumans, psychologists first measure the normal response to a loud noise. Then they repeatedly pair a stimulus, such as a light, with shock. Finally, they present the light just before the loud noise and determine how much the light increases the startle response. A control group is tested with a stimulus that has not been paired with shock. Results of such studies consistently show that after animals have learned to associate a stimulus with shock, that stimulus becomes a fear signal, and presenting the fear signal just before a sudden loud noise enhances the startle response. Conversely, a stimulus previously associated with pleasant stimuli or the absence of danger becomes a safety signal that decreases the startle reflex (Schmid, Koch, & Schnitzler, 1995).

Investigators have determined that the amygdala (Figures 12.7 and 12.12) is important for enhancing the startle reflex. Many cells in the amygdala, especially in the basolateral and central nuclei, get input from pain fibers as well as vision or hearing, so the circuitry is well suited to establishing conditioned fears (Uwano, Nishijo, Ono, & Tamura, 1995). Some cells in the amygdala respond strongly to rewards, others to punishments, and still others to surprises in either direction (Belova, Paton, Morrison, & Salzman, 2007).

Output from the amygdala to the hypothalamus controls autonomic fear responses, such as increased blood pressure. The amygdala also has axons to areas of the prefrontal cortex that control approach and avoidance responses (Garcia, Vouimba, Baudry, & Thompson, 1999; Lacroix, Spinelli, Heidbreder, & Feldon, 2000). Additional axons extend to midbrain areas that relay information to the pons to control the startle reflex (LeDoux, Iwata, Cicchetti, & Reis, 1988; Zhao & Davis, 2004). Figure 12.12 shows the connections.

If a rat has damage to the amygdala, it still shows a normal startle reflex, but signals before the noise do not modify the reflex. In one study, rats were repeatedly exposed to a light followed by shock and then tested for their responses to a loud noise. Intact rats showed a moderate startle reflex to the loud noise and an enhanced response if the light preceded the noise. In contrast, rats with damage in the path from the amygdala to the hindbrain showed the same startle reflex with or without the light (Hitchcock & Davis, 1991).

Do these results indicate that amygdala damage destroys fear? Not necessarily. An alternative explanation is that the rats have trouble interpreting or understanding stimuli with emotional consequences. The same issue arises with humans, as we shall see.

An odd parasite has evolved a way to exploit the consequences of amygdala damage (Berdoy, Webster, & Macdonald, 2000). *Toxoplasma gondii* is a protozoan that infects many mammals but reproduces only in cats. Cats excrete the parasite's eggs in their feces, thereby releasing them into the ground. Rats that burrow in the ground can become infected with the parasite. When the parasite enters a rat, it migrates to the brain where it apparently damages the amygdala. The rat then fearlessly approaches a cat, guaranteeing that the cat will eat the rat and that the parasite will find its way back into a cat!

The amygdala is important for learning what to fear (Antoniadis, Winslow, Davis, & Amaral, 2007; Kwon & Choi, 2009; Wilensky, Schafe, Kristensen, & LeDoux, 2006). That is not the only type of fear conditioning. If a rat has received shocks after a particular stimulus in a particular cage, it learns to fear the stimulus (by changes in the amygdala) but it also learns to fear the cage... and new cages... and new situations. The same

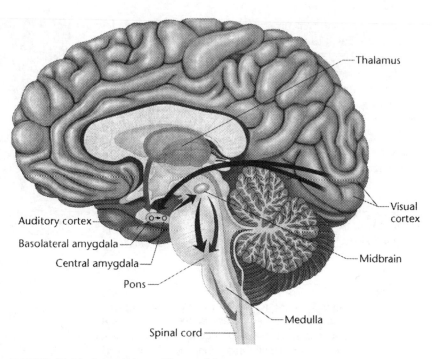

FIGURE 12.12 Amygdala and learned fears
The central amygdala receives sensory input from the lateral and basolateral amygdala. It sends output to the central gray area of the midbrain, which relays information to a nucleus in the pons responsible for the startle reflex. Damage anywhere along the route from amygdala to pons interferes with learned fears that modify the startle reflex. (© Cengage Learning 2013)

is true for humans. If you are attacked or if you have other traumatic experiences, you become more fearful in a wide variety of situations. It is as if your brain has decided, "This is a dangerous world. I need to be alert for new threats." This long-term, generalized emotional arousal depends on a brain area called the **bed nucleus of the stria terminalis** (Duvarci, Bauer, & Paré, 2009; Toufexis, 2007). The stria terminalis is a set of axons that connect this nucleus to the amygdala, as shown in Figure 12.13.

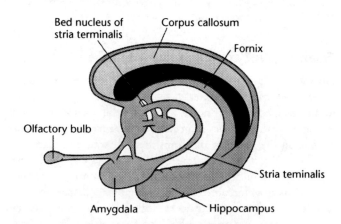

FIGURE 12.13 The bed nucleus of the stria terminalis
The bed nucleus is critical for long-term adjustments of anxiety, whereas the amygdala is responsible for fear of individual items. The stria terminalis is a set of axons connecting its bed nucleus to the amygdala. (© Cengage Learning 2013)

11. What brain mechanism enables the startle reflex to be so fast?

12. How could a researcher use the startle reflex to determine whether some stimulus causes fear?

ANSWERS 11. Loud noises activate a path from the cochlea to cells in the pons that trigger a tensing of neck muscles. 12. Present the stimulus before giving a loud noise. If the stimulus increases the startle reflex beyond its usual level, then the stimulus produced fear.

Studies of Monkeys

The effect of amygdala damage in monkeys was described in classic studies early in the 1900s and is known as the *Klüver-Bucy syndrome*, from the names of the primary investigators. Monkeys showing this syndrome are tame and placid. They attempt to pick up lighted matches and other objects that they ordinarily avoid. They display less than the normal fear of snakes or of larger, more dominant monkeys (Kalin, Shelton, Davidson, & Kelley, 2001).

However, not all monkeys with amygdala damage react with the full Klüver-Bucy syndrome. The most prominent effect is an alteration of monkeys' social behaviors, although the exact results vary depending on the age of the monkeys, the social situation, and the exact location of the damage. Some monkeys with damage to the amygdala are withdrawn and fearful, but others are friendly and fearless (Bauman, Toscano, Mason, Lavenex, & Amaral, 2006; Emery et al., 2001; Kalin, Shelton, & Davidson, 2004; Machado et al., 2008; Rosvold, Mirsky, & Pribram, 1954). Among intact monkeys, those with a more vigorously reactive amygdala tend to show the greatest fear in response to a noise or an intruder (Oler et al., 2010).

Response of the Human Amygdala to Visual Stimuli

Studies using fMRI show that the human amygdala responds strongly when people look at photos that arouse fear or photos of faces showing fear. To a lesser extent it also responds to faces showing happiness or sadness (Fusar-Poli et al., 2009). Instructing people to pay attention to pleasant stimuli increases the amygdala's responses to them (Cunningham, Van Bavel & Johnsen, 2008).

Contrary to what we might guess, the amygdala responds most strongly when a facial expression is a bit ambiguous or difficult to interpret. Consider angry and frightened faces. As a rule, it is easy to interpret an angry face looking straight at you, but a fearful face looking straight at you is more puzzling. Frightened people almost always stare at whatever is frightening them, and so you will almost never see someone stare at you with a fearful expres-

sion unless the person is afraid of *you*! Consequently, you recognize an angry expression faster if it is directed toward you and a fearful expression faster if it is directed to the side (Adams & Kleck, 2005). The amygdala, however, responds more strongly to a fearful face directed toward you (Adams et al., 2003) (Figure 12.14). That is, the amygdala responds more strongly to the expression that is harder to interpret. Presumably the arousal indicates that it is working harder to make sense of the stimulus.

Individual Differences in Amygdala Response and Anxiety

Most people's tendency toward anxiety generally remains fairly consistent over time. Most infants with an "inhibited" temperament develop into shy, fearful children and then into shy adults who show an enhanced amygdala response to the sight of any unfamiliar face (Beaton et al., 2008; Schwartz, Wright, Shin, Kagan, & Rauch, 2003). One study found a strong relationship between amygdala activation and fearfulness. College students carried a beeper for 28 days. It beeped at unpredictable times each day, calling for the student to record his or her emotional state at the moment. A year later the students came into a laboratory for the second part of the study, in which an fMRI recorded their amygdala response to very brief presentations of frightening pictures. The amygdala responses correlated highly with the number of unpleasant emotions they had recorded the previous year (Barrett, Bliss-Moreau, Duncan, Rauch, & Wright, 2007). Presumably they recorded so many unpleasant emotions because they were biologically predisposed to react strongly.

In a study of Israeli soldiers, researchers first measured their amygdala responses to briefly flashed unpleasant photos, at the

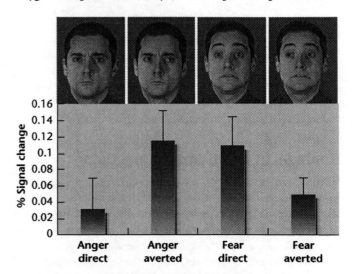

FIGURE 12.14 Amygdala response and direction of gaze
The amygdala responds more strongly to an angry face directed away from the viewer and to a frightened face directed toward the viewer. *(From Adams, R. B. et al. "Effects of gaze on amygdala sensitivity to anger and fear faces," Science, 2003, 300:1536. Reprinted with permission from AAAS/Science Magazine.)*

time of the soldiers' induction into the army. Later they measured the soldiers' responses to combat stress. Those with the greatest amygdala response at the start reported the greatest amount of combat stress (Admon et al., 2009). Again, it appears that amygdala response is closely related to fear reactivity.

Fear reactivity, in turn, affects much of life—even, according to one study, political attitudes. People were asked a series of questions about their support for use of military force, police powers, the death penalty, gun ownership, and so forth. Researchers also measured each person's responses to sudden loud noises, repeated numerous times. As shown in Figure 12.15, those showing high support for military and police action showed a greater startle response to the loud noises, which we know indicates amygdala activity (Oxley et al., 2008). The interpretation is that people with a highly reactive amygdala are likely to perceive dangers, and therefore to support strong protection against those dangers. (This relationship, of course, says nothing about whether the high support or low support group is *correct*. It just indicates that when we are arguing about policy, our brain physiology influences our decision, just as facts and logic do.)

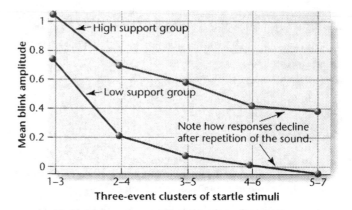

FIGURE 12.15 Fear responses and political attitudes
On average, people who show a stronger startle response to loud noises tend to favor greater reliance on military and police powers. *(From Oxley, D. R., Smith, K. B., Alford, J. R., Hibbing, M. V., Miller, J. L., Scalora, M., et al. (2008). Political attitudes vary with physiological traits. Science, 321, 1667–1670. Reprinted by permission from the American Association for the Advancement of Science.)*

> **STOP & CHECK**
>
> **13.** What evidence indicates that amygdala activity corresponds to the effort needed for interpreting emotional information?
>
> **14.** What can we predict about someone if we know the strength of that person's amygdala responses to upsetting pictures or loud noises?

ANSWERS

13. The amygdala responds more strongly to a fearful face directed at the viewer, rather than a similar face looking to the side. People usually find it easier to understand a fearful face looking to the side. **14.** People with a highly reactive amygdala are likely to report many negative emotional experiences during a day, to show strong responses to stressful experiences, and to favor strong reliance on military and police power.

Damage to the Human Amygdala

With laboratory animals, researchers can intentionally damage the amygdala to see the effects. With humans, they have to rely on damage that occurs spontaneously. For example, some people suffer a stroke that damages the amygdala and surrounding areas, at least in one hemisphere. They are impaired in some ways and not others. When they examine emotional pictures, they can classify them as pleasant vs. unpleasant about as well as anyone else. However, they experience little arousal from viewing unpleasant pictures (Berntson, Bechara, Damasio, Tranel, & Cacioppo, 2007). That is, they continue to experience the cognitive aspect of unpleasant emotions, but not the feeling aspect.

It is possible to study damage limited to the amygdala only in people with the rare genetic disorder *Urbach-Wiethe disease*. They suffer skin lesions, and many also accumulate calcium in the amygdala until it wastes away. Much of the research on this condition deals with a woman known by her initials, SM. SM describes herself as fearless, and she certainly acts that way. When she viewed 10 clips from the scariest movies the researchers could find, she reported feeling only excitement, no fear. Researchers took her to an exotic pet store. In spite of insisting that she hates snakes and spiders, she was happy to hold a snake (Figure 12.16), and the staff repeatedly had to restrain her from touching or poking the tarantulas and venomous snakes they had. When the researchers took her to a "haunted house," she led the way without hesitation, venturing down dark hallways. When people dressed as monsters jumped out, other people in the group screamed, but SM laughed, started poking one of the monsters out of curiosity, and scared the monster! Her fearlessness is dangerous to her. She has been held up at gun point and knife point and has been physically assaulted repeatedly. Evidently she plunges into dangerous situations without the caution other people would show. When she describes these events, she remembers feeling angry, but not afraid (Feinstein, Adolphs, Damasio, & Tranel, 2011).

Here is another example of her fearlessness: Suppose you are standing, and a person you don't know approaches you, face to face. How close could that person come before you began to feel uncomfortable? Most people stand about 0.7 m (2 feet) away from another person, but SM's preferred distance is about half that. When a man unknown to her, instructed by the experimenters, approached her so close that their noses touched, with eye-to-eye contact, she showed and reported no discomfort (Kennedy, Gläscher, Tyszka, & Adolphs, 2009).

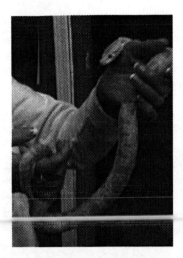

FIGURE 12.16 SM, a woman with amygdala damage, holds a snake at an exotic pet store
Although she said she hates snakes, she was curious to hold this one and wanted to touch the others, including venomous ones. *(From Feinstein, J. S., Adolphs, R., Damasio, A., & Tranel, D. (2011). The human amygdala and the induction and experience of fear. Current Biology, 21, 34–38 with permission from Elsevier)*

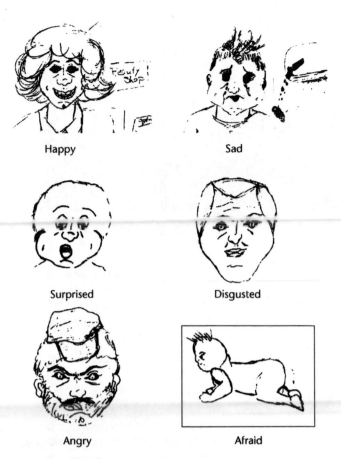

FIGURE 12.17 Drawings by SM, who has a damaged amygdala
She at first declined to draw a fearful expression because, she said, she could not imagine it. When urged to try, she remembered that frightened people are often depicted with their hair on end, at least in cartoons. *(From "Fear and the human amygdala," by R. Adolphs, D. Tranel, H. Damasio, and A. Damasio, Journal of Neuroscience, 15, pp. 5879–5891. Copyright © 1995 by Oxford University Press. Reprinted by permission.)*

SM and other people with Urbach-Wiethe disease often fail to recognize the emotional expressions in faces, especially expressions of fear or disgust (Boucsein, Weniger, Mursch, Steinhoff, & Irle, 2001). Even when they recognize an expression as fear or disgust, they rate it as less intense than other people do, and they are less likely than average to remember a photo of an emotional expression if they see the same photo an hour later (Siebert, Markowitsch, & Bartel, 2003).

When SM was asked to draw faces showing certain emotions (Figure 12.17), she made good drawings of most expressions but had trouble drawing a fearful expression, saying that she did not know what such a face would look like. When the researcher urged her to try, she drew someone crawling away with hair on end, as cartoonists often indicate fear (Adolphs, Tranel, Damasio, & Damasio, 1995).

Why do SM and others with amygdala damage have trouble identifying facial expressions of fear? At first, the assumption was that someone with amygdala damage doesn't feel fear and therefore can't understand it in others. But then Ralph Adolphs and his colleagues observed that SM focuses almost entirely on the nose and mouth of each photograph. Also, in everyday life, she seldom makes eye contact, looking at the mouth instead (Spezio, Huang, Castelli, & Adolphs, 2007). Suppose you are looking at a computer screen, and a face is flashed briefly on the screen, located such that your eyes are fixated on the mouth. Almost instantaneously, you would move your gaze to focus on the eyes, and you would be especially impelled to do so if you saw at first glance that the face was showing fear (Gamer & Büchel, 2009). She has no reluctance to make eye contact, but someone's eyes simply don't at-

tract her attention the way they do for other people (Kennedy & Adolphs, 2010). When researchers asked her to look at the eyes, she quickly recognized fearful expressions (Adolphs et al., 2005). Seeing the eyes is particularly important for recognizing fear. People express happiness with the mouth, but fear mainly with the eyes (Morris, deBonis, & Dolan, 2002; Vuilleumier, 2005). Figure 12.18 shows only the whites of the eyes of people expressing fear (left) and happiness (right). Most people recognize the fear expression from the eyes alone, but not the happy expression (Whalen et al., 2004).

These observations suggest an alternative interpretation of the function of the amygdala. Instead of being responsible for *feeling* fear or other emotions, perhaps it is responsible for detecting emotional information and directing other brain areas to pay attention to it in the proper way. The distinction between these interpretations is difficult to test. As is often the case, good research points the way for further research.

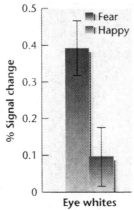

Fear   Happy   Eye whites

FIGURE 12.18 Eye expressions for fear and happiness
The eye whites alone enable most people to guess that the person on the left was feeling afraid. *(From "Human amygdala responsivity to masked fearful eye whites," by P. J. Whalen et al. (2004). Science, 306, 2061. Reprinted by permission from AAAS/Science magazine.)*

Ralph Adolphs

Will a better understanding of the social brain lead to a better understanding of social behavior? And can such knowledge ultimately be used to help our species negotiate and survive in the vastly complex social world it has helped create? To approach such questions, social neuroscientists will need to establish dialogues with other disciplines in the social and behavioral sciences, and to be highly sensitive to the public consequences of the data they generate. (Adolphs, personal communication)

STOP & CHECK

15. Why do people with amygdala damage have trouble recognizing expressions of fear?

ANSWER 15. They focus their vision on the nose and mouth. Expressions of fear depend almost entirely on the eyes.

▌Anxiety Disorders

Most psychological disorders include increased anxiety as one of the symptoms. In generalized anxiety disorder, phobia, and panic disorder, the only major symptom is increased anxiety. **Panic disorder** is characterized by frequent periods of anxiety and occasional attacks of rapid breathing, increased heart rate, sweating, and trembling—that is, extreme arousal of the sympathetic nervous system. It is more common in women than in men and far more common in adolescents and young adults than in older adults (Shen et al., 2007; Swoboda, Amering,

Windhaber, & Katschnig, 2003). Twin studies suggest a genetic predisposition, although no single gene has been identified (Hettema, Neale, & Kendler, 2001; Kim, Lee, Yang, Hwang, & Yoon, 2009). Curiously, panic disorder occurs in about 15% of people with *joint laxity*, commonly known as being "double-jointed" (able to bend the fingers backward farther than usual). Even when people with joint laxity do not have panic disorder, they tend to have stronger fears than most other people do (Bulbena et al., 2004; Bulbena, Gago, Sperry, & Bergé, 2006).

The research so far links panic disorder to some abnormalities in the hypothalamus and not necessarily the amygdala. Panic disorder is associated with decreased activity of the neurotransmitter GABA and increased levels of orexin. Orexin, as discussed in Chapters 9 and 10, is associated with maintaining wakefulness and activity. We might not have guessed that it would also be associated with anxiety, but apparently it is, and drugs that block orexin receptors block panic responses (Johnson et al., 2010).

Pharmacological Relief from Anxiety

People with excessive anxiety sometimes seek relief through medications. A variety of studies indicate that anxiety is increased by the transmitters orexin and CCK (cholecystokinin) in the amygdala or hippocampus (C. Becker et al., 2001; Frankland, Josselyn, Bradwejn, Vaccarino, & Yeomans, 1997). So far, no drugs based on orexin or CCK have been approved. However, many drugs are available to increase activity of the transmitter GABA, which inhibits anxiety.

The most common anti-anxiety drugs ("anxiolytic drugs") are the **benzodiazepines** (BEN-zo-die-AZ-uh-peens), such as diazepam (trade name Valium), chlordiazepoxide (Librium), and alprazolam (Xanax). Benzodiazepines bind to the **GABA$_A$ receptor**, which includes a site that binds GABA as well as sites that modify the sensitivity of the GABA site (Figure 12.19). (The brain also has other kinds of GABA receptors, such as GABA$_B$, with different behavioral effects.)

At the center of the GABA$_A$ receptor is a chloride channel. When open, it permits chloride ions (Cl$^-$) to cross the membrane into the neuron, hyperpolarizing the cell. (That is, the synapse is inhibitory.) Surrounding the chloride channel are four units, each containing one or more sites sensitive to GABA. Benzodiazepines bind to additional sites on three of those four units (labeled α in Figure 12.19). When a benzodiazepine molecule attaches, it neither opens nor closes the chloride channel but twists the receptor so that the GABA binds more easily (Macdonald, Weddle, & Gross, 1986). Benzodiazepines thus facilitate the effects of GABA.

Benzodiazepines exert their anti-anxiety effects in the amygdala, hypothalamus, midbrain, and several other areas. A minute amount of benzodiazepines injected directly into a rat's amygdala decreases learned shock-avoidance behaviors (Pesold & Treit, 1995), relaxes the muscles, and increases social approaches to other rats (S. K. Sanders & Shekhar, 1995). Benzodiazepines also decrease the responses in a rat's brain to the smell of a cat. Ordinarily, that smell triggers an apparently built-in fear (McGregor, Hargreaves, Apfelbach, & Hunt, 2004).

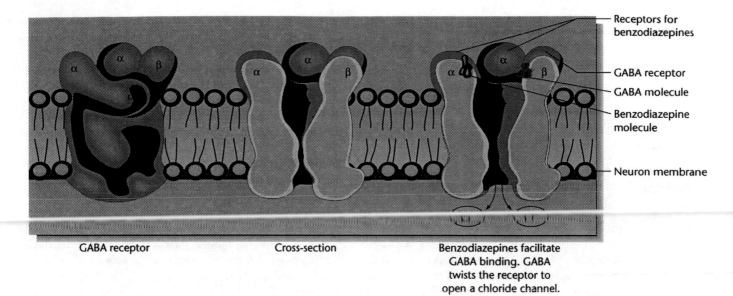

GABA receptor   Cross-section   Benzodiazepines facilitate GABA binding. GABA twists the receptor to open a chloride channel.

FIGURE 12.19 The GABA_A receptor complex
Of its four receptor sites sensitive to GABA, the three α sites are also sensitive to benzodiazepines. *(Based on Guidotti, Ferrero, Fujimoto, Santi, & Costa, 1986)*

Benzodiazepines produce a variety of additional effects, including the possibility of addiction (Tan et al., 2010). When they reach the thalamus and cerebral cortex, they induce sleepiness, block epileptic convulsions, and impair memory (Rudolph et al., 1999). The mixture of effects is a problem. For example, you might want to reduce your anxiety without becoming sleepy, and presumably, you don't want to impair your memory. Researchers hope to develop drugs with more specific and limited effects (Korpi & Sinkkonen, 2006).

FIGURE 12.20 Two rats that were given the same amount of alcohol
The rat on the right was later given the experimental drug Ro15-4513. Within 2 minutes, its performance and coordination improved significantly.

APPLICATIONS AND EXTENSIONS

Alcohol as an Anxiety Reducer

Alcohol promotes the flow of chloride ions through the GABA_A receptor complex by binding strongly at a special site found on only certain kinds of GABA_A receptors (Glykys et al., 2007). Alcohol influences the brain in other ways as well, but the effects on GABA are responsible for alcohol's anti-anxiety and intoxicating effects. Drugs that block the effects of alcohol on the GABA_A receptor complex also block most of alcohol's behavioral effects. One experimental drug, known as Ro15-4513, is particularly effective in this regard (Suzdak et al., 1986). Besides affecting the GABA_A receptor complex, Ro15-4513 blocks the effects of alcohol on motor coordination, its depressant action on the brain, and its ability to reduce anxiety (H. C. Becker, 1988; Hoffman, Tabakoff, Szabó, Suzdak, & Paul, 1987; Ticku & Kulkarni, 1988) (Figure 12.20).

Could Ro15-4513 be useful as a "sobering-up" pill or as a treatment to help people who want to stop drinking alcohol? Hoffman-LaRoche, the company that discovered it, concluded that the drug would be too risky. People who relied on the pill might think they were sober and try to drive home when they were still impaired. Furthermore, giving such a pill to alcoholics would probably backfire. Because alcoholics drink to get drunk, a pill that decreased their feeling of intoxication would probably increase their drinking. Ro15-4513 reduces but does not eliminate alcohol's effects, especially with large amounts of alcohol (Poling, Schlinger, & Blakely, 1988). ∎

National Institute of Mental Health

STOP & CHECK

16. What would be the effect of benzodiazepines on someone who had no GABA?

ANSWER

16. Benzodiazepines facilitate the effects of GABA, so a person without GABA would have no response to benzodiazepines.

Relearning as Relief from Anxiety

To the extent that anti-anxiety drugs provide relief, the relief is temporary. If you have a long-term problem of excessive anxiety, you probably shouldn't try to solve it with daily benzodiazepines. If your fear is based on a particular traumatic experience, an alternative is to try to extinguish the learned fear. Suppose, for sake of illustration, that you once almost drowned in the ocean, and now you are terribly afraid to go near it. A reasonable approach is to expose you to your feared object, perhaps a little at a time, in hopes of extinction (in the classical-conditioning sense). First you wade through a puddle, then set foot into a pond, then a bigger pond, and you work up through lakes until you are ready to face the ocean. Clinical psychologists generally use that approach to relieve phobias, with good success. The problem is, extinction training suppresses original learning or overhangs it with new learning, but does not eliminate it. Young children sometimes fully extinguish a learned reaction, but adults seldom do, and the original fear might return, especially after a time of stress (Gogolla, Caroni, Lüthi, & Herry, 2009).

How could we extinguish a learned fear more fully? In general, it is easier to extinguish a learned response immediately after original learning than it is later. After time has passed, the learning becomes stronger. Psychologists say it has *consolidated*. Ordinarily, if you have a traumatic experience, no one is there to extinguish the learning in the next few minutes. However, if an event strongly revives the original experience, that connection again becomes temporarily labile (unconsolidated) and available for either reconsolidation or highly effective extinction.

This process has been demonstrated for both rats (Monfils, Cowansage, Klann, & LeDoux, 2009) and humans. Here is the human study (Schiller et al., 2010): Imagine you watch as a series of red squares and blue squares appear. When you see a red square, nothing happens, but when you see a blue square, 38% of the time you receive a mildly painful shock. Before long, you show distinct signs of anxiety at the sight of that blue square. A day later, you return to the laboratory and you see a blue square, just once, with no shock, just enough to give you a strong reminder of the experience. Later you undergo extinction training, with many presentations of both the red and blue squares, without shock. If you get this extinction training about 10 minutes after the reminder, it is highly effective, and your learned fear virtually disappears, long term. If you receive the extinction training 6 hours after the reminder, or after no reminder, the extinction suppresses the fear temporarily, but it may return later.

A related approach uses *propanolol*, a drug that interferes with protein synthesis at certain synapses in the amygdala. Suppose you learn a fear of some stimulus. Later you are exposed to that stimulus under the influence of propanolol. Exposure awakens the memory and makes the memory trace labile, but propanolol evidently blocks the reconsolidation. The result is a much weaker emotional response, although you can still describe the experience in words (Kindt, Soeter, & Vervliet, 2009). Psychiatrists have successfully applied this method to post-traumatic stress disorder by asking people to describe their traumatic experience under the influence of propanolol. The result was a persisting decrease in fear intensity (Brunet et al., 2008).

STOP & CHECK

17. Why is extinction more effective a few minutes after a brief reminder of the original learning?

ANSWER

17. The reminder brings the representation of the learning into a labile state from which it can be reconsolidated or extinguished.

MODULE 12.2 ■ IN CLOSING

Doing Something About Emotions

It is hard to foresee future developments, but suppose researchers make sudden advances in linking emotional behaviors to physiological measurements. Imagine if we could take a blood sample—measuring 5-HIAA or whatever—plus an fMRI scan and a few other measurements and then predict which people will commit violent crime. What would we want to do with that information, if anything?

And what about anxiety? Suppose research enables us to modulate people's anxiety precisely without undesirable side effects. Would it be a good idea to use these methods to assure that everyone had the "right" anxiety level—not too much, not too little? Future research will give us new options and opportunities. Deciding what to do with them is another matter.

SUMMARY

1. An experience that gradually provokes an attack leaves the individual more ready than usual to attack again. 366

2. Aggressive behavior relates to both genetic and environmental influences. Some studies indicate that one gene increases aggressive behavior mainly among people who had abusive experiences in childhood. 367

3. Differences in testosterone levels correlate weakly with variations in aggressive behavior. Aggressive behavior depends on a combination of chemicals, with testosterone increasing the probability and both cortisol and serotonin decreasing it. 367

4. Low serotonin turnover is associated with an increased likelihood of impulsive behavior, sometimes including violence. Monkeys with low serotonin turnover get into many fights and in most cases die young. However, those that survive have a high probability of achieving a dominant status. 369

5. Researchers measure enhancement of the startle reflex as an indication of anxiety or learned fears. 371

6. The amygdala is critical for increasing or decreasing the startle reflex on the basis of learned information. 372

7. According to studies using fMRI, the human amygdala responds strongly to fear stimuli and any other stimuli that evoke strong emotional processing. It responds most strongly when the processing is effortful. 373

8. People with damage to the amygdala fail to focus their attention on stimuli with important emotional content. One woman with damage limited to the amygdala seems almost entirely fearless. 374

9. Damage to the amygdala impairs recognition of fear expressions largely because of lack of attention to the eyes. 375

10. Panic disorder is associated with increased orexin release and decreased GABA release in the hippocampus. 376

11. Anti-anxiety drugs decrease fear by facilitating the binding of the neurotransmitter GABA to the GABA$_A$ receptors, especially in the amygdala. 376

12. A behavioral approach to reducing anxiety is to reawaken a learned fear and then apply extinction procedures while the memory is in a labile state. 378

KEY TERMS

Terms are defined in the module on the page number indicated. They're also presented in alphabetical order with definitions in the book's Subject Index/Glossary, which begins on page 561. Interactive flashcards and crossword puzzles are among the online resources available to help you learn these terms and the concepts they represent.

THOUGHT QUESTIONS

1. Much of the play behavior of a cat can be analyzed into attack and escape components. Is the same true for children's play?

2. People with amygdala damage approach other people indiscriminately instead of trying to choose people who look friendly and trustworthy. What might be a possible explanation?

Stress and Health

In the early days of scientific medicine, physicians made little allowance for the relation of personality or emotions to health and disease. If someone became ill, the cause had to be structural, like a virus or bacterium. Today, **behavioral medicine** emphasizes the effects on health of diet, smoking, exercise, stressful experiences, and other behaviors. We accept the idea that emotions and other experiences influence people's illnesses and patterns of recovery. This view does not imply mind-body dualism. Stress and emotions are brain activities, after all.

▌Concepts of Stress

The term *stress*, like the term *emotion*, is hard to define or quantify. Hans Selye (1979) defined **stress** as the nonspecific response of the body to any demand made upon it. When Selye was in medical school, he noticed that patients with a wide variety of illnesses have much in common: They develop a fever, they lose their appetite, they become inactive, they are sleepy most of the day, and their immune systems become more active. Later, when doing laboratory research, he found that rats exposed to heat, cold, pain, confinement, or the sight of a cat responded to these dissimilar stimuli in similar ways, including increased heart rate, breathing rate, and adrenal secretions. Selye inferred that any threat to the body, in addition to its specific effects, activated a generalized response to stress, which he called the **general adaptation syndrome**. The initial stage, which he called *alarm*, is characterized by increased activity of the sympathetic nervous system, readying the body for brief emergency activity. During the second stage, *resistance*, the sympathetic response declines, but the adrenal cortex secretes **cortisol** and other hormones that enable the body to maintain prolonged alertness, fight infections, and heal wounds. After intense, prolonged stress, the body enters the third stage, *exhaustion*. During this stage, the individual is tired, inactive, and vulnerable because the nervous system and immune systems no longer have the energy to sustain their heightened responses (Sapolsky, 1998).

Stress-related illnesses and psychiatric problems are widespread in industrial societies, possibly because of changes in the type of stresses that we face. As Robert Sapolsky (1998) has argued, many of our crises are prolonged, such as advancing in a career, paying a mortgage, or caring for a relative with a chronic health problem. If a long-term, almost inescapable issue activates the general adaptation syndrome, the result can be exhaustion.

Selye's concept of stress included any *change* in one's life, such as either getting fired from your job or getting promoted. Bruce McEwen (2000, p. 173) proposed an alternative definition that is better for most purposes: "events that are interpreted as threatening to an individual and which elicit physiological and behavioral responses." Although this definition differs from Selye's, the idea remains that many kinds of events can be stressful, and the body reacts to all kinds of stress in similar ways.

▌Stress and the Hypothalamus-Pituitary-Adrenal Cortex Axis

Stress activates two body systems. One is the sympathetic nervous system, which prepares the body for brief emergency responses—"fight or flight." The other is the **HPA axis**—the hypothalamus, pituitary gland, and adrenal cortex. Activation of the hypothalamus induces the anterior pituitary gland to secrete **adrenocorticotropic hormone (ACTH)**, which in turn stimulates the human adrenal cortex to secrete cortisol, which enhances metabolic activity and elevates blood levels of sugar and other nutrients (Figure 12.21). Many researchers refer to cortisol as a "stress hormone" and use measurements of cortisol level as an indication of someone's recent stress level. Compared to the autonomic nervous system, the HPA axis reacts more slowly, but it becomes the dominant response to prolonged stressors, such as living with an abusive parent or spouse.

Stress that releases cortisol helps the body mobilize its energies to fight a difficult situation, but the effects depend on amount and duration. Brief or moderate stress improves attention and memory formation (Krugers, Hoogenraad, & Groc, 2010). It improves performance on relatively simple tasks, although it impairs performance that requires complex, flexible thinking (Arnsten, 2009). Stress also enhances activity of the immune system, helping it fight illnesses (Benschop

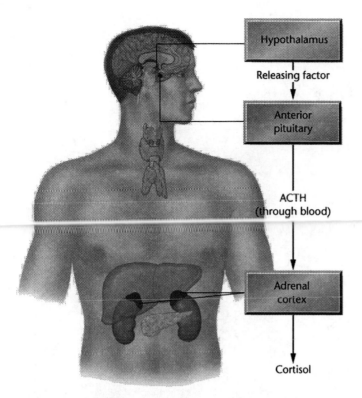

FIGURE 12.21 The hypothalamus-pituitary-adrenal cortex axis
Prolonged stress increases secretion of the adrenal hormone corti-sol, which elevates blood sugar and increases metabolism. These changes help the body sustain prolonged activity but at the expense of decreased immune system activity. *(© Cengage Learning 2013)*

et al., 1995). However, prolonged stress impairs memory and immune activity. To see why, we start with an overview of the immune system.

The Immune System

The **immune system** consists of cells that protect the body against viruses, bacteria, and other intruders. The immune system is like a police force: If it is too weak, the "criminals" (viruses and bacteria) run wild and create damage. If it becomes too strong and unselective, it starts attacking "law-abiding citizens" (the body's own cells). When the immune system attacks normal cells, we call the result an *autoimmune disease*. Myasthenia gravis and rheumatoid arthritis are examples of autoimmune diseases.

Leukocytes

The most important elements of the immune system are the **leukocytes**, commonly known as white blood cells (Kiecolt-Glaser & Glaser, 1993; O'Leary, 1990).

We distinguish several types of leukocytes, including B cells, T cells, and natural killer cells (Figure 12.22):

- *B cells*, which mature mostly in the bone marrow, secrete **antibodies**, which are Y-shaped proteins that attach to particular kinds of antigens, just as a key fits a lock. Every cell has surface proteins called **antigens** (antibody-generator molecules), and your body's antigens are as unique as your fingerprints. The B cells recognize the "self" antigens, but when they find an unfamiliar antigen, they attack the cell. This kind of attack defends the body against viruses and bacteria. It also causes rejection of organ transplants, unless physicians take special steps to minimize the attack. After the body has made antibodies against a particular intruder, it "remembers" the intruder and quickly builds more of the same kind of antibody if it encounters that intruder again.

- *T cells* mature in the thymus gland. Several kinds of T cells attack intruders directly (without secreting antibodies), and some help other T cells or B cells to multiply.

- *Natural killer cells*, another kind of leukocytes, attack tumor cells and cells that are infected with viruses. Whereas each B or T cell attacks a particular kind of foreign antigen, natural killer cells attack all intruders.

In response to an infection, leukocytes and other cells produce small proteins called **cytokines** (e.g., interleukin-1, or IL-1) that combat infections and also communicate with the brain to elicit appropriate behaviors (Maier & Watkins, 1998). Cytokines are the immune system's way of telling the brain that the body is ill. They trigger the hypothalamus to produce fever, sleepiness, lack of energy, lack of appetite, and loss of sex drive. The immune system also reacts to infection by increased production of *prostaglandins*, additional chemicals that promote sleepiness. In other words, cytokines and prostaglandins are responsible for what Selye called the general adaptation syndrome.

Note also that what we usually consider symptoms are actually part of the body's way of fighting the illness. Most people think of fever and sleepiness as something the illness did to them, but in fact, fever and sleepiness are strategies that evolved for fighting the illness. As discussed in Chapter 10, a moderate fever helps fight many infections. Sleep and inactivity are ways of conserving energy so that the body can devote more energy to its immune attack against the intruders.

STOP & CHECK

18. What kind of cell releases cytokines?

19. What behavioral changes do cytokines stimulate?

ANSWERS
18. Leukocytes, which are part of the immune system, release cytokines. **19.** Cytokines stimulate neurons to produce fever, decreased hunger, decreased sex drive, and increased sleepiness.

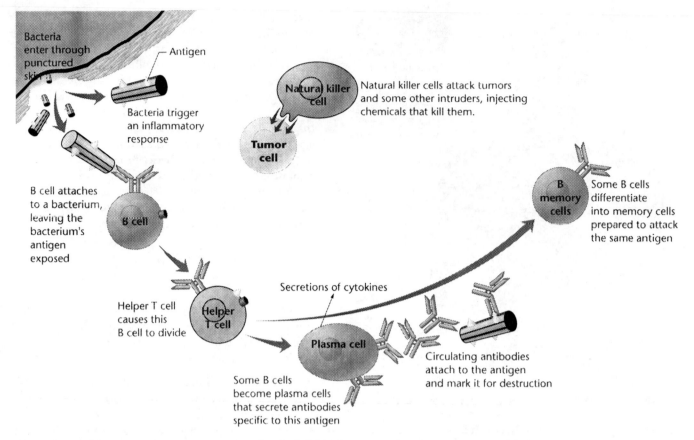

FIGURE 12.22 Immune system responses to a bacterial infection
B cells bind to bacteria and produce antibodies against the bacteria. When a helper T cell attaches to the B cell, it stimulates the B cell to generate copies of itself, called B memory cells, that immunize the body against future invasions by the same kind of bacteria. (© *Cengage Learning 2013*)

Effects of Stress on the Immune System

The nervous system has more control than we might have guessed over the immune system. The study of this relationship, called **psychoneuroimmunology**, deals with the ways experiences alter the immune system and how the immune system in turn influences the central nervous system (Ader, 2001).

Stress affects the immune system in several ways. In response to a stressful experience, the nervous system activates the immune system to increase its production of natural killer cells and the secretion of cytokines (Segerstrom & Miller, 2004). The immune system evolved to protect against the stress you might get from an injury, but in prosperous countries today it responds more often to such events as taking exams in college (L. Y. Liu et al., 2002), giving a public lecture (Dickerson, Gable, Irwin, Aziz, & Kemeny, 2009), or seeing photos of sick or injured people (Schaller, Miller, Gervais, Yager, & Chen, 2010).

The elevated cytokine levels help combat infections, but they also trigger the brain to produce the same symptoms as if one were ill. Rats subjected to inescapable shocks show symptoms resembling illness, including fever, sleepiness, and decreased appetite. The same is true for people who are under great stress (Maier & Watkins, 1998). Many of the symptoms of depression, such as loss of interest and loss of appetite, are similar to those of illness and are probably related to the increased cytokines found in depressed people (Dantzer, O'Connor, Freund, Johnson, & Kelley, 2008). In short, if you have been under much stress and start to feel ill, one possibility is that your symptoms are reactions to the stress itself.

A prolonged stress response is as draining on the body as a prolonged illness would be (Segerstrom & Miller, 2004; Zorrilla et al., 2001). A likely hypothesis is that prolonged increase of cortisol directs energy toward increasing metabolism and therefore detracts energy from synthesizing proteins, including the proteins of the immune system. For example, in 1979 at the Three Mile Island nuclear power plant, a major accident was barely contained. The people who continued to live in the vicinity during the next year had lower than normal levels of B cells, T cells, and natural killer cells. They also complained of emotional distress and showed impaired performance on a proofreading task (A. Baum, Gatchel, & Schaeffer, 1983; McKinnon, Weisse, Reynolds, Bowles, & Baum,

1989). A study of research scientists in Antarctica found that a 9-month period of cold, darkness, and social isolation reduced T cell functioning to about half of normal levels (Tingate, Lugg, Muller, Stowe, & Pierson, 1997).

In one study, 276 volunteers filled out an extensive questionnaire about stressful life events before being injected with a moderate dose of common cold virus. (The idea was that those with the strongest immune responses could fight off the cold, but others would succumb.) People who reported brief stressful experiences were at no more risk for catching a cold than were people who reported no stress. However, for people who reported stress lasting longer than a month, the longer it lasted, the greater the risk of illness (S. Cohen et al., 1998).

Prolonged stress can also harm the hippocampus. Stress releases cortisol, and cortisol enhances metabolic activity throughout the body. When metabolic activity is high in the hippocampus, its cells become more vulnerable. Toxins or overstimulation are then more likely than usual to damage or kill neurons in the hippocampus (Sapolsky, 1992). Rats exposed to high stress—such as being restrained in a mesh wire retainer for 6 hours a day for 3 weeks—show shrinkage of dendrites in the hippocampus and impairments in the kinds of memory that depend on the hippocampus (Kleen, Sitomer, Killeen, & Conrad, 2006). They also show atrophy of other brain areas (Dias-Ferreira et al., 2009). High cortisol levels may also be responsible for the deterioration of the hippocampus and decline of memory that occur in many older people (Cameron & McKay, 1999).

STOP & CHECK

20. How do the effects of prolonged stress mimic the effects of illness?

21. How does prolonged stress damage the hippocampus?

ANSWERS

20. Prolonged stress increases release of cytokines. Cytokines tell the brain to initiate responses to combat illness, such as fever, inactivity, and loss of appetite. **21.** Stress increases the release of cortisol, which enhances metabolic activity throughout the body. When neurons in the hippocampus have high metabolic activity, they become more vulnerable to damage by toxins or overstimulation.

Stress Control

Individuals vary in their reactions to a stressful experience. Studies with mice have identified genes that relate to being more vulnerable or more resilient (Krishnan et al., 2007). Individual differences also relate to life circumstances. In baboon troops, the entry of a new adult male into a troop is stressful to females, because he may attack either them or their babies. However, a female who has a male "friend" to defend her (possibly the father of her babies) shows less stress response

(Beehner, Bergman, Cheney, Seyfarth, & Whitten, 2005). In humans, resilience in the face of stress correlates with stronger connections between the amygdala and the prefrontal cortex (Kim & Whalen, 2009; St. Jacques, Colcos, & Cabeza, 2009).

People have found many ways to control their stress responses. Possibilities include special breathing routines, exercise, meditation, and distraction, as well as, of course, trying to deal with the problem that caused the stress. Social support is one of the most powerful methods of coping with stress, and researchers have demonstrated its effectiveness by brain measurements as well as people's self-reports. In one study, happily married women were given moderately painful shocks to their ankles. On various trials, they held the hand of their husband, a man they did not know, or no one. Holding the husband's hand reduced the response indicated by fMRI in several brain areas, including the prefrontal cortex. Holding the hand of an unknown man reduced the response a little, on average, but not as much as holding the husband's hand (Coan, Schaefer, & Davidson, 2006). In short, as expected, brain responses correspond to people's self-reports that social support from a loved one helps reduce stress.

Post-traumatic Stress Disorder

People have long recognized that many soldiers returning from battle are prone to continuing anxieties and distress. In the past, people called this condition *battle fatigue* or *shell shock*. Today, they call it **post-traumatic stress disorder (PTSD)**. PTSD occurs in some people who have endured terrifying experiences, such as a life-threatening attack or watching someone get killed. The symptoms, lasting at least a month after the event, include frequent distressing recollections (flashbacks) and nightmares about the traumatic event, avoidance of reminders of it, and vigorous reactions to noises and other stimuli (Yehuda, 2002).

However, not all people who endure traumas develop PTSD. For example, investigators in one study examined 218 people admitted to a hospital emergency ward after severe automobile accidents. All showed about similar stress responses at the time and 1 week later, but the responses declined over time in some and increased in others so that about one sixth of them met the criteria for PTSD 4 months after the accident (Shalev et al., 2000). The ones developing PTSD had not been in consistently worse wrecks than the others. Evidently, they were more vulnerable to PTSD. Other studies have confirmed that the people showing the greatest distress shortly after a traumatic event are not necessarily the ones who later develop PTSD (Harvey & Bryant, 2002).

What accounts for differences in vulnerability? Most PTSD victims have a smaller than average hippocampus (Stein, Hanna, Koverola, Torchia, & McClarty, 1997). It might seem natural to assume that severe stress elevated the cortisol secretion and that the high cortisol levels damaged the hippocampus. However, PTSD victims show *lower* than normal cortisol levels both immediately after the traumatic event and weeks later (Delahanty, Raimonde, & Spoonster, 2000; Yehuda, 1997). The low levels suggest another hypothesis: Perhaps people with low cortisol levels are ill-equipped to combat stress and therefore more vulnerable to the damaging effects of stress and more prone than other people to PTSD.

To determine whether certain people are predisposed to PTSD, investigators examined men who developed PTSD during war. First, they confirmed earlier reports that most PTSD victims had a smaller than average hippocampus. Then they found cases in which the PTSD victim had an identical twin who had not been in battle and who did not have PTSD. The results showed that the twin without PTSD *also* had a smaller than average hippocampus (Gilbertson et al., 2002). Presumably, both twins had a smaller than average hippocampus from the start, which increased their susceptibility to PTSD.

One further point about PTSD: A study compared Vietnam War veterans who suffered injuries that produced various kinds of brain damage. Of those whose damage included the amygdala, *none* suffered PTSD. Of those with damage elsewhere in the brain, 40% suffered PTSD (Koenigs et al.,

2008). Apparently, the amygdala, which is so important for emotional processing, is essential for the extreme emotional impact that produces PTSD.

22. How do the cortisol levels of PTSD victims compare to those of other people?

23. What evidence indicates that a smaller than average hippocampus makes people more vulnerable to PTSD?

ANSWERS

22. People with PTSD have lower than normal cortisol levels in contrast to most people, who show elevated cortisol levels in response to stress. **23.** On average, PTSD victims have a smaller than average hippocampus. For those who have an identical twin, the twin also has a smaller than average hippocampus, even if he or she does not have PTSD.

Emotions and Body Reactions

Research on stress and health provides an interesting kind of closure. Decades ago, Hans Selye argued that any stressful event leads to the general adaptation syndrome, marked by fever and other signs of illness. We now see why: The body reacts to prolonged stress by activating the adrenal cortex and the immune system, and the resulting increase in cytokines produces the

same reactions that an infection would. Research has also improved our understanding of the predispositions behind post-traumatic stress disorder and makes it possible to foresee a new era of advances in psychosomatic medicine. Emotional states, which once seemed too ephemeral for scientific study, are now part of mainstream biology.

SUMMARY

1. Hans Selye introduced the idea of the general adaptation syndrome, which is the way the body responds to all kinds of illness and stress. **380**

2. Brief stress activates the sympathetic nervous system. More prolonged stress activates the hypothalamus-pituitary-adrenal cortex axis. The adrenal cortex releases cortisol, which increases metabolism. **380**

3. Although brief stress enhances the immune response and facilitates memory formation, prolonged stress drains the body of the resources it needs for other purposes. **382**

4. Stress activates the immune system, helping to fight viruses and bacteria. The immune system releases cytokines, which stimulate the hypothalamus to initiate activities to combat illness. **382**

5. Because stress causes release of cytokines, it can lead to fever, sleepiness, and other symptoms that resemble those of illness. **382**

6. The high cortisol levels associated with prolonged stress damage cells in the hippocampus, thereby impairing memory. **383**

7. Successful methods of coping with stress, such as social support, produce measurable effects in brain responses as well as in people's self-reports. **383**

8. After a severely trying event, some people but not others develop post-traumatic stress disorder (PTSD). Evidently, people with a smaller than average hippocampus and lower than average cortisol levels are predisposed to PTSD. **383**

KEY TERMS

Terms are defined in the module on the page number indicated. They're also presented in alphabetical order with definitions in the book's Subject Index/Glossary, which begins on page 561. Interactive flashcards and crossword puzzles are among the online resources available to help you learn these terms and the concepts they represent.

adrenocorticotropic hormone (ACTH) 380

antibody 381

antigen 381

behavioral medicine 380

cortisol 380

cytokine 381

general adaptation syndrome 380

HPA axis 380

immune system 381

leukocyte 381

post-traumatic stress disorder (PTSD) 383

psychoneuroimmunology 382

stress 380

THOUGHT QUESTION

If someone were unable to produce cytokines, what would be the consequences?

CHAPTER 12 Interactive Exploration and Study

The **Psychology CourseMate** for this text brings chapter topics to life with interactive learning, study, and exam preparation tools, including quizzes and flashcards for the Key Concepts that appear throughout each module, as well as an interactive media-rich eBook version of the text that is fully searchable and includes highlighting and note taking capabilities and interactive versions of the book's **Stop & Check** quizzes and **Try It Yourself Online** activities. The site also features **Virtual Biological Psychology Labs, videos,** and **animations** to help you better understand concepts—logon and learn more at **www.cengagebrain.com**, which is your gateway to all of this text's complimentary and premium resources, including the following:

Virtual Biological Psychology Labs

Explore the experiments that led to modern-day understanding of biopsychology with the Virtual Biological Psychology Labs, featuring a realistic lab environment that allows you to conduct experiments and evaluate data to better understand how scientists came to the conclusions presented in your text. The labs cover a range of topics, including perception, motivation, cognition, and more. You may purchase access at **www.cengagebrain.com**, or login at **login.cengagebrain.com** if an access card was included with your text.

© 2013 Cengage Learning

Videos

© 2013 Cengage Learning

Facial Analysis

Also available—

- Emotional Memory
- Suspicion and Trust
- Health and Stress
- The Limbic System

Animations

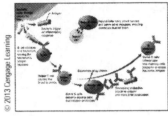

© 2013 Cengage Learning

Cells of the Immune System

Also available—

- Sympathetic and Parasympathetic Nervous System
- Amygdala and Fear Conditioning
- GABA Synapse
- CNS Depressants
- Hypothalamus and Pituitary

Suggestions for Further Exploration

Books

Damasio, A. (1999). *The feeling of what happens.* New York: Harcourt Brace. A neurologist's account of the connection between emotion and consciousness, full of interesting examples.

McEwen, B. S., with Lasley, E. N. (2002). *The end of stress as we know it.* Washington, DC: Joseph Henry Press. Readable review by one of the leading researchers.

Pfaff, D. W. (2007). *The neuroscience of fair play.* New York: Dana Press. Exploration of how the physiology of emotions, especially the amygdala, relates to moral behavior.

Websites

The Psychology CourseMate for this text provides regularly updated links to relevant online resources for this chapter, such as one concerning stress.

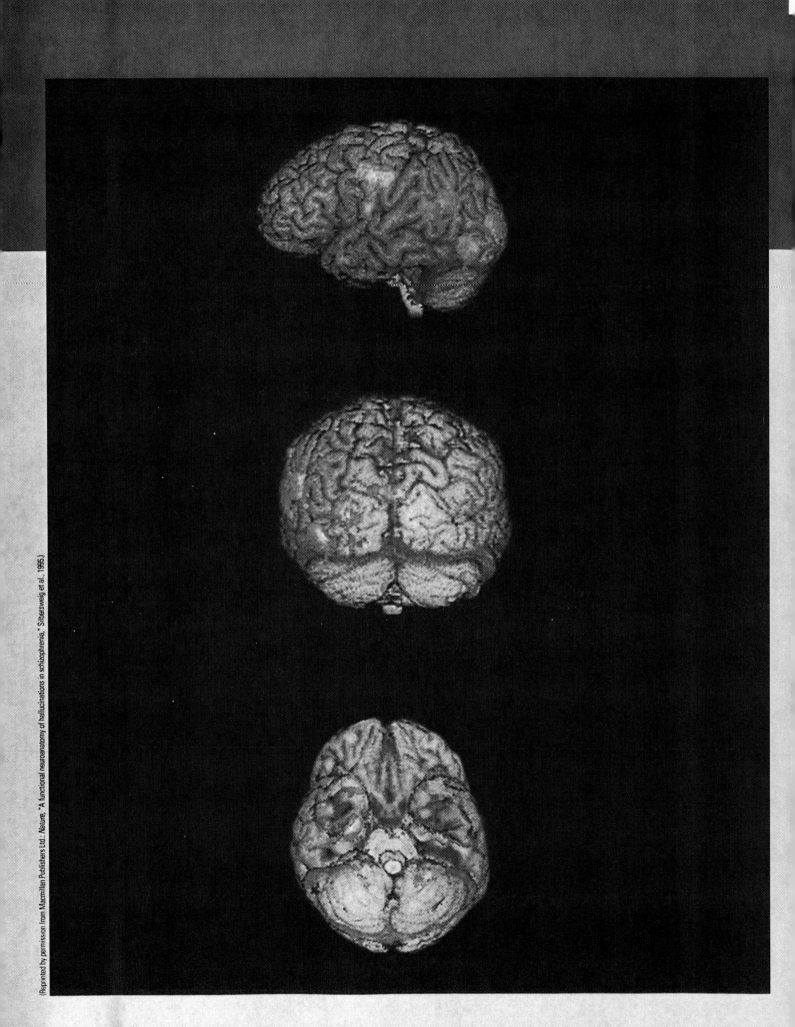

Mood Disorders and Schizophrenia

15

MAIN IDEAS

1. Psychological disorders result from a combination of environmental and biological influences, including genetics.

2. The effectiveness of certain drugs provides a clue as to the underlying basis of depression and schizophrenia, but many questions remain about how these drugs exert their effects.

3. Schizophrenia may be the result of genetic or other problems that impair early development of the brain.

OPPOSITE: PET scans show the brain areas that increase their activation during visual and auditory hallucinations by a patient with schizophrenia.

Are mental illnesses really *illnesses*, analogous to tuberculosis or influenza? Or are they normal reactions to abnormal experiences? They are not exactly either. They are outcomes that combine biological predispositions with experiences. To control them, we need a good understanding of both aspects.

Abnormal behavior comes in many varieties. *The Diagnostic and Statistical Manual of Mental Disorders, fourth edition* (American Psychiatric Association, 1994) lists hundreds of disorders. This chapter deals with mood disorders—depression and bipolar disorder—and schizophrenia. These disorders have been the focus of a huge amount of biological research. Chapter 12 discussed anxiety disorders and Chapter 3 had a section about addictions.

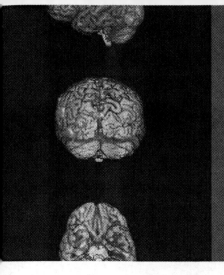

Mood Disorders

Different people can get to the same place by different routes. For example, the people in a room at any moment may have started from different cities or different parts of a city and traveled in different ways, although they all reached the same destination. Similarly, people can become depressed through different routes, including genetics, traumatic experiences, hormonal problems, substance abuse, head injuries, brain tumors, and other illnesses. Despite having different causes, or combinations of causes, these people all look and act depressed (Figure 15.1). In this module, we explore some of the many factors that contribute to depression.

▌ Major Depressive Disorder

Many people say they feel "depressed" when they feel sad or discouraged. Major depression is much more intense and prolonged. According to the *DSM-IV* (American Psychiatric Association, 1994), people with a **major depression** feel sad and helpless every day for weeks at a time. They have little energy, feel worthless, contemplate suicide, have trouble sleeping, cannot concentrate, find little pleasure, and can hardly even imagine being happy again.

Absence of happiness is a more reliable symptom than increased sadness. In one study, people carried a beeper that sounded at unpredictable times to signal them to describe their emotional reactions at the moment. People with depression reported only an average number of unpleasant experiences but far below the average number of pleasant ones (Peters, Nicolson, Berkhof, Delespaul, & deVries, 2003). In other studies, people examined photographs or films as researchers recorded their reactions. Individuals with depression reacted normally to sad or frightening depictions but seldom smiled at the comedies or pleasant pictures (Rottenberg, Kasch, Gross, & Gotlib, 2002; Sloan, Strauss, & Wisner, 2001). Additional studies found that people with depression show a decreased response to happy facial expressions (Monk et al., 2008) and a decreased response to a likely reward (McFarland & Klein, 2009).

A survey reported that about 5% of adults in the United States have a "clinically significant" depression (i.e., serious

FIGURE 15.1 The face of depression
Depression shows in a person's face, walk, voice, and mannerisms.

enough to warrant attention) within a given year, and more than 10% do at some point in life (Narrow, Rae, Robins, & Regier, 2002). Reported one-year prevalence rates vary among countries and ethnic groups, from less than 5% among Chinese-Canadians to more than 15% in India (Murali, 2001; Tiwari & Wang, 2006). It is hard to know how seriously to take these numbers. Standards for diagnosis inevitably vary from place to place, and psychiatrists have no laboratory tests to confirm a diagnosis.

Childhood depression is about equally common for boys and girls, but beyond about age 14, depression is more common in females (Twenge & Nolen-Hoeksema, 2002). Various hypotheses have been advanced to explain this tendency, but none is well established.

Although some people suffer from long-term depression (Klein, 2010), it is more common to have episodes of depression separated by periods of normal mood. The first episode is special in certain regards. The first episode is generally longer than most of the later ones, and most patients can identify a highly stressful event that triggered the first episode. For later episodes, people are less and less likely to identify a triggering event (Post, 1992). It is as if the brain learns how to be depressed and gets better at it (Monroe & Harkness, 2005). In that regard it is like epilepsy and migraine headaches: The more often you have had an episode, the easier it is to start another one (Post & Silberstein, 1994).

Genetics

Studies of twins and adopted children indicate a moderate degree of heritability for depression (Shih, Belmonte, & Zandi, 2004). However, although researchers have identified several genes linked to depression, none of the genes by itself has a large effect (Camp et al., 2005; Holmans et al., 2007).

One reason why no gene shows a strong link to depression is that when we talk about depression, we are probably lumping together at least two distinguishable syndromes. People with early-onset depression (before age 30) have a high probability of other relatives with depression (Bierut et al., 1999; Kendler, Gardner, & Prescott, 1999; Lyons et al., 1998), as well as relatives with anxiety disorders, attention-deficit disorder, alcohol or marijuana abuse, obsessive-compulsive disorder, bulimia, migraine headaches, and irritable bowel syndrome (Q. Fu et al., 2002; Hudson et al., 2003). People with late-onset depression (especially after age 45 to 50) have a high probability of relatives with circulatory problems (Kendler, Fiske, Gardner, & Gatz, 2009). Distinguishing between early-onset and late-onset cases may lead to progress in identifying genes, and perhaps in selecting effective therapies.

Still, given the difficulty so far in identifying any gene strongly linked to depression, another hypothesis arose: Perhaps the effect of a gene varies with the environment. One gene controls the serotonin transporter, a protein that regulates the ability of axons to reabsorb serotonin after its release, to recycle it for further use. Investigators examined the serotonin transporter genes of 847 young adults, identifying two types: the "short" type and the "long" type. They also asked each participant to report certain stressful events over five years, including financial setbacks, loss of job, divorce, and so forth. Figure 15.2 shows the results. For people with two short forms of the gene, increasing numbers of stressful experiences led to a big increase in the probabil-

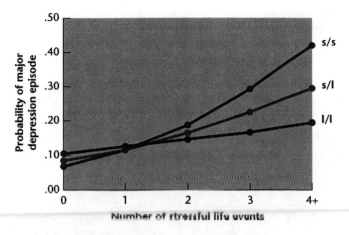

FIGURE 15.2 Genetics, stress, and depression
The effect of the serotonin transporter gene depends on the amount of stress. (*Reprinted by permission from A. Caspi, et al., "Influence of life stress on depression: Moderation by a polymorphism in the 5-HTT gene," Science, 301, pp. 386–389. © 2003 AAAS.*)

ity of depression. For those with two long forms, stressful events only slightly increased the risk of depression. Those with one short and one long gene were intermediate. In other words, the short form of the gene by itself did not lead to depression, but it might magnify the reaction to stressful events (Caspi et al., 2003).

This report provoked a great deal of excitement. However, since then most researchers have failed to replicate the result, finding no significant relationship between depression and the serotonin transporter gene itself and no interaction between effects of the gene and stress (Munafo, Durrant, Lewis, & Flint, 2009; Risch et al., 2009).

When a result in psychology, medicine, or any other field cannot be replicated, the obvious interpretation is that the first report was wrong. Given the huge number of researchers collecting studies, occasionally a random fluctuation in data suggests a relationship between variables that are in fact unrelated. However, here is another possibility: If a study finds no significant correlation between two variables, perhaps one or both of the variables was poorly measured. (We can't expect a poorly measured variable to correlate with anything else.) Our measurements of depression are probably good enough, but the measurements of stress are more doubtful. Generally researchers ask people how many stressful events they have experienced, and simply count them. Losing a job can be extremely stressful or hardly stressful at all, depending on how easily someone found an equal or better job. Similarly, divorce is much more stressful to some people than others. Also, the biochemical methods used to measure short vs. long forms of the gene have been inaccurate in many cases (Wray et al., 2009). We should await more research with more careful measurements before we draw a firm conclusion.

1. What evidence suggests two types of depression influenced by different genes?

2. What did Caspi and colleagues report to be the relationship between depression and the gene controlling the serotonin transporter protein?

3. What should we conclude from the fact that most researchers have not been able to replicate Caspi et al.'s finding?

ANSWERS been hampered by inaccurate measurement. really related to depression, or the studies so far have not increased. **3.** Either variation in this gene is not absence of stressful experiences, their probability is experiences by becoming depressed. However, in the are more likely than other people to react to stressful problems. **2.** People with the short form of the gene depression have a high probability of circulatory logical disorders. Relatives of people with late-onset have a high risk of depression and many other psycho- **1.** Relatives of people with early-onset depression

Other Biological Influences

Genetic differences partly explain why some people are more vulnerable to depression than others are, but other factors contribute also. A few cases of depression are linked to viral infections. Borna disease, a viral infection of farm animals, produces periods of frantic activity alternating with periods of inactivity (Figure 15.3). In 1985, investigators tested 370 people for possible exposure to this virus (Amsterdam et al.,

1985). Only 12 people tested positive for Borna disease virus, but all 12 were suffering from major depression or bipolar disorder. These 12 were a small percentage of the 265 depressed people tested; still, *none* of the 105 nondepressed people had the virus.

Since then, thousands of people have been tested in Europe, Asia, and North America. The Borna virus is found in about 5% of normal people and about one-third of people with severe depression or schizophrenia (Bode, Ferszt, & Czech, 1993; Bode, Riegel, Lange, & Ludwig, 1992; Nunes et al., 2008; Terayama et al., 2003). The role of this virus in psychiatric disorders remains uncertain, but the results so far suggest that viruses might be a predisposing factor in some cases.

Hormones may be another trigger for depression. Stress is accepted as an important factor in depression, and stress increases release of cortisol, as discussed in Chapter 12. About 20% of women report some degree of **postpartum depression**—that is, depression after giving birth—and many researchers suspect that hormonal fluctuations are a contributing factor. Stress hormones reach a peak late in pregnancy, and ovarian hormones go through major changes around the time of delivery. One study found that after a drug-induced drop in estradiol and progesterone levels, women with a history of postpartum depression suddenly show new symptoms of depression, whereas other women do not (M. Bloch et al., 2000). Among older men, a declining level of the hormone testosterone is associated with increased probability of depression (Almeida, Yeap, Hankey, Jamrozik, & Flicker, 2008). However, few studies have been done that directly link hormones to depression, and the relationship remains uncertain (Brummelte & Galea, 2010). We do know that the risk of postpartum depression increases in women with previous bouts of depres-

FIGURE 15.3 Symptoms of Borna disease
Animals infected with Borna disease have periods of frantic activity alternating with inactivity, much like a person with bipolar disorder. (left) Horse with Borna disease. (right) Same horse after recovery. *(Figure 2, page 174, from Bode L. and Ludwig H., (1997). "Clinical similarities and close genetic relationship of human and animal Borna disease virus."* Archives of Virology (Supplement 13), *167–182. Springer-Verlag. Photo scan by Kevin J. Nolte.)*

sion, stressful life events, and a lack of social support—that is, the same factors linked to major depression at any other time of life (O'Hara, 2009).

Abnormalities of Hemispheric Dominance

Studies of normal people have found a fairly strong relationship between happy mood and increased activity in the left prefrontal cortex (Jacobs & Snyder, 1996). Most people with depression have decreased activity in the left and increased activity in the right prefrontal cortex, and this imbalance is stable over years despite changes in symptoms of depression (Davidson, 1984; Pizzagalli et al., 2002; Vuga et al., 2006). Here's something you can try: Ask someone to solve a cognitive problem, such as, "See how many words you can think of that start with *hu-*" or "Try to remember all the ingredients you've ever seen on a pizza." Then unobtrusively watch the person's eye movements to see whether they gaze right or left. Most people gaze to the right during verbal tasks, but most individuals with depression gaze to the left, suggesting right-hemisphere dominance (Lenhart & Katkin, 1986).

TRY IT YOURSELF

STOP & CHECK

4. Some people offer to train you to use the right hemisphere of your brain more strongly, allegedly to increase creativity. If they were successful, can you see any disadvantage?

ANSWER

4. People with predominant right-hemisphere activity and decreased left-hemisphere activity show an increased tendency toward depression.

▌Antidepressant Drugs

You might assume that investigators first determine the causes of a psychological disorder and then develop medications based on the causes. The opposite order has been more common: First investigators find a drug that seems helpful, and then they try to figure out how it works. Like many other psychiatric drugs, the early antidepressants were discovered by accident.

APPLICATIONS AND EXTENSIONS

Accidental Discoveries of Psychiatric Drugs

Nearly all of the earliest psychiatric drugs were discovered by accident. Disulfiram, for example, was originally used in the manufacture of rubber. Someone noticed that workers in a certain rubber factory avoided alcohol and traced the cause to disulfiram, which had altered the workers' metabolism so they became ill after drinking al-

cohol. Disulfiram became the drug Antabuse, sometimes prescribed for people who are trying to avoid alcohol.

The use of bromides to control epilepsy was originally based on a theory that was all wrong (Friedlander, 1986; Levitt, 1975). Many people in the 1800s believed that masturbation caused epilepsy and that bromides reduced sexual drive. Therefore, they reasoned, bromides should reduce epilepsy. It turns out that bromides do relieve epilepsy but for different reasons.

Iproniazid, the first antidepressant drug, was originally marketed to treat tuberculosis, until physicians noticed that it relieved depression. Similarly, chlorpromazine, the first antipsychotic drug, was originally used for other purposes, until physicians noticed its ability to alleviate schizophrenia. For decades, researchers sought new drugs entirely by trial and error. Today, researchers evaluate new potential drugs in test tubes or tissue samples until they find one with a potential for stronger or more specific effects on neurotransmission. The result is the use of fewer laboratory animals. ∎

Types of Antidepressants

Antidepressant drugs fall into several categories, including tricyclics, selective serotonin reuptake inhibitors, monoamine oxidase inhibitors, and atypical antidepressants (Figure 15.4). The **tricyclics** (e.g., imipramine, trade name Tofranil) operate by blocking the transporter proteins that reabsorb serotonin, dopamine, and norepinephrine into the presynaptic neuron after their release. The result is to prolong the presence of the neurotransmitters in the synaptic cleft, where they continue stimulating the postsynaptic cell. However, the tricyclics also block histamine receptors, acetylcholine receptors, and certain

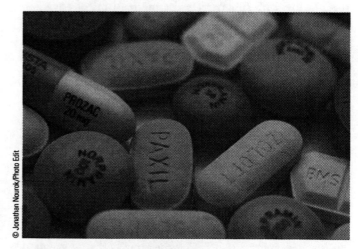

© Jonathan Nourok/Photo Edit

FIGURE 15.4 Antidepressant pills
Tricyclic drugs block the reuptake of catecholamines and serotonin by presynaptic terminals. Selective serotonin reuptake inhibitors, such as Prozac, have similar effects but are limited to serotonin. MAOIs block an enzyme that breaks down catecholamines and serotonin.

sodium channels (Horst & Preskorn, 1998). As mentioned in Chapter 9, blocking histamine produces drowsiness. Blocking acetylcholine leads to dry mouth and difficulty urinating. Blocking sodium channels causes heart irregularities, among other problems. People have to limit their use of tricyclic drugs to minimize these side effects.

The **selective serotonin reuptake inhibitors (SSRIs)** are similar to tricyclics but specific to the neurotransmitter serotonin. For example, fluoxetine (trade name Prozac) blocks the reuptake of serotonin. SSRIs produce milder side effects than the tricyclics, but their effectiveness is about the same. Other common SSRIs include sertraline (Zoloft), fluvoxamine (Luvox), citalopram (Celexa), and paroxetine (Paxil or Seroxat). Several newer drugs are **serotonin norepinephrine reuptake inhibitors (SNRIs)**, such as duloxetine (Cymbalta) and venlafaxine (Effexor). As you might guess, they block reuptake of serotonin and norepinephrine.

The **monoamine oxidase inhibitors (MAOIs)** (e.g., phenelzine, trade name Nardil) block the enzyme monoamine oxidase (MAO), a presynaptic terminal enzyme that metabolizes catecholamines and serotonin into inactive forms. When MAOIs block this enzyme, the presynaptic terminal has more of its transmitter available for release. Generally, physicians prescribe tricyclics or SSRIs first and then try MAOIs with people who did not respond to the other drugs (Thase, Trivedi, & Rush, 1995). People taking MAOIs must avoid foods containing tyramine—including cheese, raisins, and many others—because a combination of tyramine and MAOIs increases blood pressure. Figure 15.5 summarizes the mechanisms of tricyclics, SSRIs, and MAOIs.

The **atypical antidepressants** are a miscellaneous group—everything other than the types just discussed (Horst & Preskorn, 1998). One example is bupropion (Wellbutrin), which inhibits reuptake of dopamine and to some extent norepinephrine but not serotonin.

In addition, many people use St. John's wort, an herb. Because it is marketed as a nutritional supplement instead of a drug, the U.S. Food and Drug Administration does not regulate it, and its purity varies from one bottle to another. It has the advantage of being less expensive than antidepressant drugs. An advantage or disadvantage, depending on your point of view, is that it is available without prescription. People can get it easily but often take inappropriate amounts. Its effectiveness appears to be about the same as that of standard antidepressant drugs (Kasper, Caraci, Forti, Drago, & Aguglia, 2010). However, it has a potentially dangerous side effect: All mammals have a liver enzyme that breaks down plant toxins. St. John's wort increases the effectiveness of that enzyme. Increasing the breakdown of toxins sounds like a good thing, but the enzyme also breaks down most medicines. Therefore,

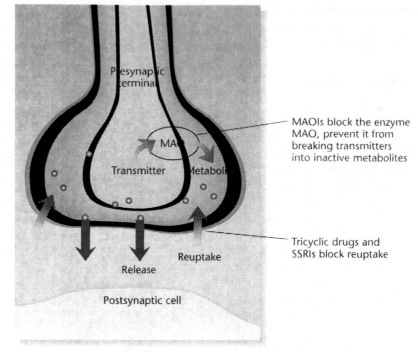

FIGURE 15.5 Routes of action of antidepressants
Tricyclics block the reuptake of dopamine, norepinephrine, and serotonin. SSRIs specifically block the reuptake of serotonin. SNRIs block reuptake of serotonin and norepinephrine. MAOIs block the enzyme MAO, which converts dopamine, norepinephrine, or serotonin into inactive chemicals. (© Cengage Learning 2013)

taking St. John's wort decreases the effectiveness of other drugs you might be taking—including other antidepressant drugs, cancer drugs, and AIDS drugs (He, Yang, Li, Du, & Zhou, 2010; Moore et al., 2000).

STOP & CHECK

5. What are the effects of tricyclic drugs?

6. What are the effects of SSRIs?

7. What are the effects of MAOIs?

ANSWERS

5. Tricyclic drugs block reuptake of serotonin and catecholamines. They also block histamine receptors, acetylcholine receptors, and certain sodium channels, thereby producing unpleasant side effects. **6.** SSRIs selectively inhibit the reuptake of serotonin. **7.** MAOIs block the enzyme MAO, which breaks down catecholamines and serotonin. The result is increased availability of these transmitters.

How Do Antidepressants Work?

Understanding how antidepressants work should shed some light on the causes of depression. The commonly used antidepressants increase the presence of serotonin or other neurotransmitters at the synapse, and so it might seem that the problem in depression is too little of the neurotransmitters. However, the story is not that simple. So far as we can tell from blood metabolites, people with depression have approximately normal levels of release of neurotransmitters. In fact, some studies show that people with depression have an *increase* in serotonin release (Barton et al., 2008). Furthermore, it is possible to decrease serotonin levels suddenly by consuming all the amino acids except tryptophan, the precursor to serotonin. For most people, this decrease in serotonin does not provoke any feelings of depression (Neumeister et al., 2004, 2006).

Furthermore, given that different drugs act in different ways on different neurotransmitters, wouldn't you expect some of them to be more effective than others? So far as we can tell, all of them are about equal in effectiveness (Montgomery et al., 2007). Two studies examined patients who failed to respond to an antidepressant drug within a few weeks. In one study the psychiatrists added a second drug, and in the other study they switched patients from one drug to the other. The result was that some patients who did not respond to the first drug did respond after a few weeks on the new regimen (Rush et al., 2006; Trivedi et al., 2006). Should we conclude, as the researchers did, that adding a drug or switching drugs helped? No. Unfortunately, neither study included a control group that stayed on the first drug for the additional time. In short, we have no clear evidence that any antidepressant drug produces any different effects from any other.

The time course of effects poses an additional threat to any explanation in terms of neurotransmitters: Antidepressant drugs produce their effects on neurotransmitters in the synapses within minutes to hours, depending on the drug, but people need to take the drugs for 2 or more weeks before they experience any mood elevation (Stewart et al., 1998). This delay of benefits strongly suggests that increasing the levels of neurotransmitters at synapses does not explain the benefits of the drugs. Perhaps the neurotransmitter effects are not even relevant.

Today, much research attention focuses on neurotrophins. As discussed in Chapter 5, neurotrophins aid in the survival, growth, and connections of neurons. Most people with depression have lower than average levels of a neurotrophin called *brain-derived neurotrophic factor* (BDNF) that is important for synaptic plasticity, learning, and proliferation of new neurons in the hippocampus (Martinowich, Manji, & Lu, 2007; Sen, Duman, & Sanacora, 2008). As a result of low BDNF, most people with depression have a smaller than average hippocampus, impaired learning, and reduced production of new hippocampal neurons. Prolonged use of antidepressant drugs generally increases BDNF production and improves learning and formation of new neurons. This process takes weeks (Drzyzga, Marcinowska, & Obuchowicz, 2009; Vetencourt et al., 2008). That is, the time course for BDNF and changes in the hippocampus matches the time course for behavioral recovery. Procedures that block neuron production also block the behavioral benefits of antidepressant drugs (Airan et al., 2007).

Apparently BDNF by itself does not automatically elevate mood, but it helps by facilitating new learning that builds new synapses and removes many old ones. That mode of action explains why antidepressants help people in depression—who might profit from substituting new thoughts for old ones—but fail to elevate mood for normal people (Castrén & Rantamäki, 2010).

Although this story may seem convincing, the conclusion remains tentative, as a few antidepressant drugs improve mood without demonstrable effects on BDNF (Basterzi et al., 2008; Matrisciano et al., 2009). Perhaps antidepressants work in more than one way.

▶ STOP & CHECK

8. In what way does the time course of antidepressants conflict with the idea that they improve mood by increasing neurotransmitter levels?

9. As opposed to an interpretation in terms of neurotransmitter levels, what is an alternative explanation for the benefits of antidepressant drugs?

ANSWERS **8.** Antidepressants produce their effects on serotonin and other neurotransmitters quickly, but their behavioral benefits develop gradually over 2 to 3 weeks. **9.** Antidepressant drugs increase production of BDNF, which gradually promotes growth of new neurons, new synapses, and new learning in the hippocampus.

How Effective Are Antidepressants?

So far we have considered explanations of how antidepressants work. How sure are we that they *do* work? Not everyone is convinced (Kirsch, 2010), and at least we have to say that the effectiveness is limited.

In most cases, depression occurs in episodes. That is, even without treatment, many people recover within a few months. Furthermore, giving someone a medication produces an expectation of improvement, thereby enhancing the probability of recovery, even if the medication itself is ineffective. To test the effectiveness of an antidepressant drug, researchers need to compare its effects to those of a placebo (a pharmacologically inactive substance).

Figure 15.6 summarizes the results of many experiments in which people were randomly assigned to receive antidepressant drugs or placebos. The horizontal axis represents the mean amount of improvement on the Hamilton Depression Rating Scale. The pink triangles represent patients receiving the drug in a study, and the gray circles represent patients receiving a placebo. The size of the triangle or circle is proportional to the number of patients in a group. Many people respond well on placebos, either because of spontaneous recovery over time or because of the expectation that a pill induced. Younger patients are particularly likely to respond to placebos (Bridge, Birmaher, Iyengar, Barbe, & Brent, 2009). For patients with mild to moderate depression, the results for placebo groups overlap those for drug groups, and the differences between the groups are, on average, too small to be of much clinical significance. Only for people with severe depression do the drugs show a meaningful advantage (Kirsch et al., 2008). Another independent analysis of the research confirmed that the drugs show no clear benefit over placebos for people with mild to moderate depression (Fournier et al., 2010). Furthermore, even at the most severe levels of depression, antidepressants help some people and not others (Uhr et al., 2008).

An alternative to antidepressant drugs is psychotherapy. Reviews of the research literature find that antidepressant drugs and psychotherapy are about equally effective for treating all levels of depression, from mild to severe, with three exceptions: First, the drugs work better for *dysthymia*, a long-term, almost life-long condition of unhappy mood. Nearly all of the research studies examined short-term therapies, and it may be that brief psychotherapy is ineffective for such a long-term condition. Second, antidepressants are generally ineffective for patients who had suffered abuse or neglect during early childhood or patients with multiple psychological disorders. Those patients usually respond better to psychotherapy (Asarnow et al., 2009; Nemeroff et al., 2003). Third, psychotherapy is more likely to have long-

term benefits, reducing the likelihood of a relapse months or years after the end of treatment (Bortolotti, Menchetti, Bellini, Montaguti, & Berardi, 2008; Imel, Malterer, McKay & Wampold, 2008).

Would a combination of antidepressant drugs and psychotherapy work better than either one alone? On average, people who improve while receiving both treatments improve more than people receiving either one alone. However, the percentage of people showing improvement increases only slightly with combined treatment (de Maat et al., 2008; Hollon et al., 2005). That is, it is not the case that many people respond better to one treatment than the other. Evidently, many people with mild to moderate depression improve with only a placebo, another group improves with either antidepressants or psychotherapy, a few respond better to one or the other, and the remainder—one-third to one-half, by most estimates—do not respond well to either one (Friedman et al., 2009; Hollon, Thase, & Markowitz, 2002; Thase et al., 1997).

The effects of antidepressants and those of psychotherapy overlap more than we might have guessed. Brain scans show that antidepressants and psychotherapy increase metabolism in the same brain areas (Brody et al., 2001; S. D. Martin et al., 2001). That similarity should not be terribly surprising if we accept the mind–body monism position. If mental activity is the same thing as brain activity, then changing someone's thoughts should indeed change brain chemistry.

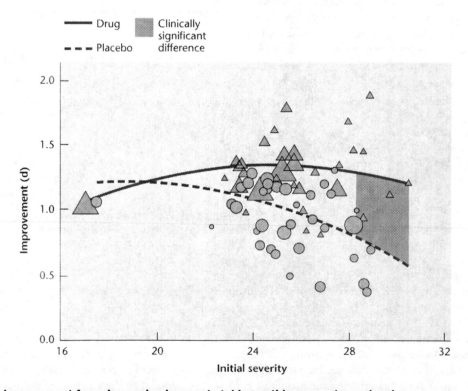

FIGURE 15.6 Mean improvement from depression by people taking antidepressants or placebos
Pink triangles represent people taking medications in a particular study. Gray circles represent people taking placebos. The size of the triangle or circle is proportional to the number of people in the study. *(From Kirsch, 2008)*

10. As depression becomes more severe, what happens to the percentage of patients showing improvement while taking antidepressant drugs or placebos?

11. What is an advantage of psychotherapy over antidepressant drugs?

ANSWERS

10. For more severe cases, the percentage of patients who improve remains about the same for patients taking antidepressant drugs, but fewer patients taking placebos show improvement. 11. People who respond well to psychotherapy have a lower risk of later relapse than people who respond to antidepressant drugs. Also, antidepressant drugs produce unpleasant side effects and appear to be less effective for people with multiple disorders or people who suffered abuse or neglect in childhood.

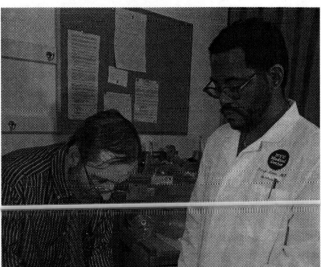

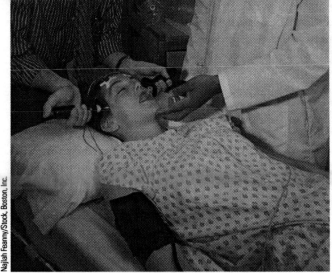

Najlah Feanny/Stock, Boston, Inc.

FIGURE 15.7 Electroconvulsive therapy (ECT)
In contrast to an earlier era, ECT today is administered with muscle relaxants or anesthetics to minimize discomfort and only if the patient gives informed consent.

Electroconvulsive Therapy (ECT)

Many people with depression do not respond well to either drugs or psychotherapy. What options are available for them? One possibility, despite its stormy history, is treatment through an electrically induced seizure, known as **electroconvulsive therapy (ECT)**. ECT originated with the observation that for people with both epilepsy and schizophrenia, as symptoms of one disorder increase, symptoms of the other often decrease (Trimble & Thompson, 1986). In the 1930s, Ladislas Meduna tried to relieve schizophrenia by inducing convulsions. Soon, other physicians were doing the same, inducing seizures with a large dose of insulin. Insulin shock is a dreadful experience, however, and difficult to control. An Italian physician, Ugo Cerletti, after years of experimentation with animals, developed a method of inducing seizures with an electric shock through the head (Cerletti & Bini, 1938). Electroconvulsive therapy is quick, and most patients awaken calmly without remembering it.

When ECT proved to be not very effective with schizophrenia, you might guess that psychiatrists would abandon it. Instead, they tried it for other mental hospital patients, despite having no theoretical basis. ECT did indeed relieve depression in many cases. However, its misuse during the 1950s earned it a bad reputation, as some patients were given ECT hundreds of times without their consent.

When antidepressant drugs became available in the late 1950s, the use of ECT declined abruptly. However, it made a partial comeback in the 1970s. ECT today is used only with informed consent, usually for patients with severe depression who have not responded to antidepressant drugs (Reisner, 2003). It is usually applied every other day for about 2 weeks. Patients are given muscle relaxants or anesthetics to minimize discomfort and the possibility of injury (Figure 15.7).

The most common side effect of ECT is memory loss, but limiting the shock to the right hemisphere reduces the memory loss. In any case, the memory impairment lasts no more than a few months, not forever (Reisner, 2003). Besides the threat of memory loss, the other serious drawback to ECT is the high risk of relapsing into another episode of depression within a few months (Riddle & Scott, 1995). After ECT has relieved depression, the usual strategy is to try to prevent a relapse by means of drugs, psychotherapy, or periodic ECT treatments (Swoboda, Conca, König, Waanders, & Hansen, 2001).

More than half a century after the introduction of ECT, no one is yet sure how it relieves depression, but like antidepressant drugs, ECT increases the proliferation of new neurons in the hippocampus (Perera et al., 2007). It also alters the expression of at least 120 genes in the hippocampus and frontal cortex alone (Altar et al., 2004).

A similar treatment is repetitive transcranial magnetic stimulation. An intense magnetic field is applied to the scalp, stimulating the axons near the surface of the brain. This procedure is moderately effective against depression, although its mechanism of behavioral effect is not known (Ridding & Rothwell, 2007).

Altered Sleep Patterns

Almost everyone with depression has sleep problems, and the sleep problems generally precede the mood changes. One study identified teenagers who reported almost daily problems in falling asleep or staying asleep. Within the next 6 to 7 years, more than half of these young people developed depression (Roane & Taylor, 2008).

The usual sleep pattern for a depressed person resembles the sleep of healthy people who travel a couple of time zones west and have to go to bed later than usual: They fall asleep but awaken early, unable to get back to sleep, and they enter REM sleep within 45 minutes after going to sleep, as Figure 15.8 illustrates. In addition, people who are depressed have more than the average number of eye movements per minute during REM sleep. Many of their relatives show these same sleep patterns, and the relatives who show these patterns are more likely to become depressed themselves than are relatives who sleep normally (Modell, Ising, Holsboer, & Lauer, 2005). In short, altered sleep is a lifelong trait of people who are predisposed to depression.

Surprisingly, although most people feel worse after a sleepless night, a night of total sleep deprivation is the quickest known method of relieving depression (Ringel & Szuba, 2001). However, the benefit is brief, as the depression usually returns after the next night's sleep. Also, while sleep deprivation helps alleviate depression, it increases sensitivity to pain (Kundermann, Hemmeter-Spernal, Huber, Krieg, & Lautenbacher, 2008).

A more practical solution is to alter the sleep schedule, going to bed earlier than usual. The person might still awaken in the very early morning, but by that time he or she would have received seven or eight hours of sleep. This procedure relieves depression for at least a week in most patients and often longer (Riemann et al., 1999).

Researchers cannot yet explain how sleep deprivation or rescheduling produces mood benefits. A better understanding might lead to other treatments for depression.

STOP & CHECK

12. How can one decrease the memory loss associated with ECT?

13. What change in sleep habits sometimes relieves depression?

ANSWERS **12.** ECT over just the right hemisphere produces less memory loss. **13.** Getting people with depression to go to bed earlier sometimes relieves depression.

Other Therapies

Each of the currently available treatments for depression has its pros and cons, and some people with depression do not respond well to any of them. The search continues for new and improved treatments.

One promising possibility is a program of regular, nonstrenuous exercise, such as brisk walking for half an hour or more per day (Leppämäki, Partonen, & Lönnqvist, 2002).

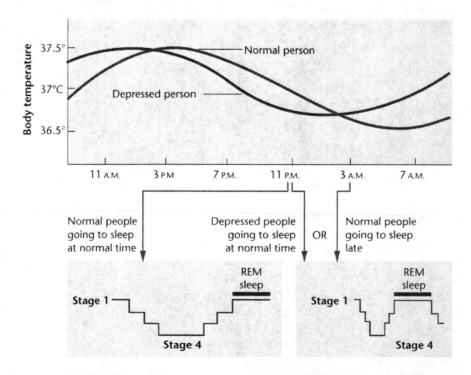

FIGURE 15.8 Circadian rhythms and depression
Most people with depression have their circadian rhythms advanced by several hours. They sleep as if they had gone to bed later than they actually did. *(Bottom graphs from* Sleep *by J. Allan Hobson, ©1989, 1995 by J. Allan Hobson. Reprinted by permission of Henry Holt and Company, LLC.)*

Many studies have shown that active people are less likely than sedentary people to become depressed. However, most of these studies are correlational in nature and do not support a cause-and-effect conclusion. A few controlled experiments have yielded inconclusive results (Teychenne, Ball, & Salmon, 2010). Still, exercise increases blood flow to the brain and provides other benefits, without the costs or risks of other treatments (Hillman, Erickson, & Kramer, 2008; Hunsberger et al., 2007). More research is necessary, but in the meantime, exercise is a good recommendation.

Bipolar Disorder

Depression can be either unipolar or bipolar. People with **unipolar disorder** vary between normality and one pole—depression. People with **bipolar disorder**, formerly known as *manic-depressive disorder*, alternate between two poles—depression and its opposite, mania. **Mania** is characterized by restless activity, excitement, laughter, self-confidence, rambling speech, and loss of inhibitions. People with mania become dangerous to themselves and others. Figure 15.9 shows the brain's increase in glucose use during mania and its decrease during depression (Baxter et al., 1985).

People who have full-blown episodes of mania are said to have **bipolar I disorder**. People with **bipolar II disorder** have milder manic phases, called hypomania, characterized by agitation or anxiety. In addition to the mood swings, most people with bipolar disorder have attention deficits, poor impulse control, and impairments of verbal memory (Quraishi & Frangou, 2002). Diagnoses of bipolar disorder have been increasing since the 1990s, especially among teenagers and young adults (Moreno et al., 2007). It is now estimated that about 1% of people will have bipolar I disorder at some time in life, another 1% will have bipolar II disorder, and 2% to 3% will have "subthreshold" bipolar disorder—a minor case not quite strong enough for a diagnosis of bipolar disorder (Merikangas et al., 2007).

Genetics

A genetic predisposition for bipolar disorder is supported by the usual types of evidence—twin studies and adoption studies. In addition, researchers have located two genes that appear to increase the probability of bipolar II disorder (Nwulia et al., 2007). They have also demonstrated that some of the same genes that predispose to major depression also predispose to bipolar disorder (Liu et al., 2011). However, the genes merely increase the risk. None of the genes shows a strong relationship to the disorder.

Treatments

The first successful treatment for bipolar disorder, and still the most common one, is **lithium** salts. Lithium's benefits were discovered accidentally by an Australian investigator, J. F. Cade, who believed uric acid might relieve mania and depression. Cade mixed uric acid (a component of urine) with a lithium salt to help it dissolve and then gave the solution to

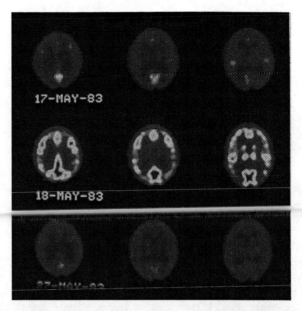

FIGURE 15.9 PET scans for a patient with bipolar disorder Horizontal planes through three levels of the brain are shown for each day. On May 17 and May 27, when the patient was depressed, brain metabolic rates were low. On May 18, when the patient was in a cheerful, hypomanic mood, the brain metabolic rate was high. Red indicates the highest metabolic rate, followed by yellow, green, and blue. *(Reprinted by permission from Macmillan Publishers Ltd: Nature, A functional neuroanatomy of hallucinations in schizophrenia, Silbersweig et al., 1995.)*

patients. It was indeed helpful, although investigators eventually realized that lithium was the effective agent, not uric acid.

Lithium stabilizes mood, preventing a relapse into either mania or depression. The dose must be regulated carefully, as a low dose is ineffective and a high dose is toxic (Schou, 1997). Two other effective drugs are valproate (trade names Depakene, Depakote, and others) and carbamazepine. If these drugs are not fully effective, physicians sometimes supplement them with antidepressant drugs or antipsychotic drugs—the ones also prescribed for schizophrenia. Antidepressant drugs are risky, as they sometimes provoke a switch from depression to mania. Antipsychotic drugs can be helpful, but they also produce unpleasant side effects.

Lithium, valproate, and carbamazepine have many effects on the brain. A good research strategy is to assume that they relieve bipolar disorder because of some effect they have in common. One effect they share is that they decrease the number of AMPA type glutamate receptors in the hippocampus (Du et al., 2008). Excessive glutamate activity is responsible for some aspects of mania. Also, the drugs that are effective against bipolar disorder block the synthesis of a brain chemical called *arachidonic acid*, which is produced during brain inflammation (S. I. Rapoport & Bosetti, 2002). Bipolar patients show an increased expression of genes associated with inflammation (Padmos et al., 2008). The effects of arachidonic acid are also counteracted by omega-3 fatty acids, such as those in

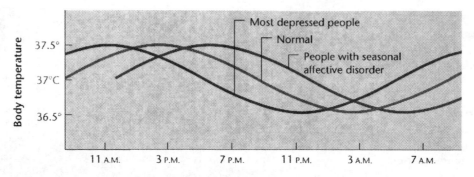

FIGURE 15.10 Circadian rhythms for major depression and seasonal affective disorder (SAD)
Patients with SAD are phase-delayed whereas most other patients with depression are phase-advanced. *(© Cengage Learning 2013)*

seafood, and epidemiological studies suggest that people who eat at least a pound (0.45 kg) of seafood per week have a decreased risk of bipolar disorder (Noaghiul & Hibbeln, 2003).

Another possible treatment relates to sleep. Patients with bipolar disorder during the depressed phase tend to stay in bed for many hours. During the manic phase, they awaken early, reach their activity peak earlier in the day than most people, and get relatively little sleep (Salvatore et al., 2008). Preliminary studies suggest that getting people to maintain a consistent sleeping schedule in a dark, quiet room reduces the intensity of mood swings (Wehr et al., 1998).

 STOP & CHECK

14. What are two common treatments for bipolar disorder?

ANSWER

14. The common treatments for bipolar disorder are lithium salts and certain anticonvulsant drugs—valproate and carbamazepine.

▌Seasonal Affective Disorder

One more form of depression is **seasonal affective disorder (SAD)**—depression that recurs during a particular season, such as winter. SAD is most prevalent near the poles, where the winter nights are long (Haggarty et al., 2002).

SAD differs from other types of depression in many ways. For example, patients with SAD have phase-delayed sleep and temperature rhythms—becoming sleepy and wakeful later than normal—unlike most other patients with depression, whose rhythms are phase-advanced (Teicher et al., 1997) (Figure 15.10). Also, SAD is seldom as severe as major depression. Many people with SAD have a mutation in one of the genes responsible for regulating the circadian rhythm, as discussed in Chapter 9 (Johansson et al., 2003).

It is possible to treat SAD with very bright lights (e.g., 2,500 lux) for an hour or more each day. The bright light treatment is effective in the morning, afternoon, or evening (Eastman, Young, Fogg, Liu, & Meaden, 1998; Lewy et al., 1998; Terman, Terman, & Ross, 1998). Although its benefits are as yet unexplained, they are substantial. Bright light is less expensive than the other antidepressant therapies and produces its benefits more rapidly, often within 1 week (Kripke, 1998).

 STOP & CHECK

15. What are the advantages of bright light treatment compared to antidepressant drugs?

ANSWER

15. It is cheaper, has no side effects, and produces its benefits more quickly.

MODULE 15.1 ■ IN CLOSING

Biology of Mood Swings

There is nothing abnormal about feeling sad or happy if something unusually bad or good has just happened to you. For people with major depression or bipolar disorder, mood becomes largely independent of events. A traumatic experience might trigger a bout of depression, but once someone has become depressed, the mood persists for months, and even the best of news provides little cheer. A bipolar patient in a manic state has boundless energy and self-confidence that no contradiction can deter. Studying these states has great potential to inform us about the brain states that correspond to moods.

SUMMARY

1. People with major depression find that almost nothing makes them happy. In most cases, depression occurs as a series of episodes. 460

2. Depression has a genetic predisposition, but no one gene has a strong effect by itself. 461

3. Uncommonly, depression can be a reaction to a virus, or possibly to hormonal changes. 462

4. Depression is associated with decreased activity in the left hemisphere of the cortex. 463

5. Several kinds of antidepressant drugs are in wide use. Tricyclics block reuptake of serotonin and catecholamines. SSRIs block reuptake of serotonin. SNRIs block reuptake of both serotonin and norepinephrine. MAOIs block an enzyme that breaks down catecholamines and serotonin. Atypical antidepressants are a miscellaneous group with diverse effects. 463

6. Antidepressants alter synaptic activity quickly, but their effects on behavior require at least 2 weeks. Although different drugs affect different neurotransmitters, they all appear to be about equally effective. It is possible that their well-known effects on neurotransmitters are not the main reason for their effects on behavior. 464

7. Most people with depression have a deficiency of the neurotrophin BDNF, which promotes development of new neurons, synapses, and learning in the hippocampus. Most antidepressant drugs produce a gradual increase in BDNF, and therefore enhance synaptic plasticity in the hippocampus. The effects on BDNF may be the main reason for the drugs' benefits. 465

8. Antidepressant drugs are ineffective for many people. For depressed patients with mild to moderate depression, antidepressants are not significantly more effective than placebos. 465

9. Psychotherapy is about as effective as antidepressant drugs for patients with all levels of severity. Psychotherapy is more likely than antipsychotic drugs to produce long-lasting benefits that prevent or delay a relapse after the end of treatment. 466

10. Other therapies for depression include electroconvulsive therapy, altered sleep patterns, and exercise. 467

11. People with bipolar disorder alternate between depression and mania. Effective therapies include lithium salts and certain other drugs. A consistent sleep schedule is also recommended. 469

12. Seasonal affective disorder is marked by recurrent depression during one season of the year. Exposure to bright lights is usually effective in treating it. 470

KEY TERMS

Terms are defined in the module on the page number indicated. They're also presented in alphabetical order with definitions in the book's Subject Index/Glossary, which begins on page 561. Interactive flashcards and crossword puzzles are among the online resources available to help you learn these terms and the concepts they represent.

atypical antidepressants 464
bipolar disorder 469
bipolar I disorder 469
bipolar II disorder 469
electroconvulsive therapy (ECT) 467
lithium 469

major depression 460
mania 469
monoamine oxidase inhibitors (MAOIs) 464
postpartum depression 462
seasonal affective disorder (SAD) 470

selective serotonin reuptake inhibitors (SSRIs) 464
serotonin norepinephrine reuptake inhibitors (SNRIs) 464
tricyclics 463
unipolar depression 469

THOUGHT QUESTIONS

1. Some people have suggested that ECT relieves depression by causing people to forget the events that caused it. What evidence opposes this hypothesis?

2. Certain people suffer from what they describe as "post-Christmas depression," a feeling of letdown after all the excitement of the holiday season. What other explanation can you offer?

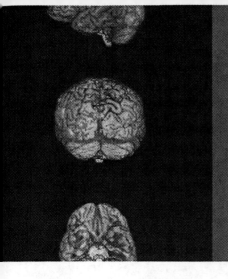

Schizophrenia

ere is a conversation between two people diagnosed with schizophrenia (Haley, 1959, p. 321):

A: Do you work at the air base?

B: You know what I think of work. I'm 33 in June, do you mind?

A: June?

B: 33 years old in June. This stuff goes out the window after I live this, uh—leave this hospital. So I can't get my vocal cords back. So I lay off cigarettes. I'm in a spatial condition, from outer space myself. . . .

A: I'm a real spaceship from across.

B: A lot of people talk that way, like crazy, but "Believe It or Not," by Ripley, take it or leave it—alone—it's in the *Examiner*, it's in the comic section, "Believe It or Not," by Ripley, Robert E. Ripley, believe it or not, but we don't have to believe anything, unless I feel like it. Every little rosette—too much alone.

A: Yeah, it could be possible.

B: I'm a civilian seaman.

A: Could be possible. I take my bath in the ocean.

B: Bathing stinks. You know why? 'Cause you can't quit when you feel like it. You're in the service.

People with schizophrenia say and do things that other people (including other people with schizophrenia) find difficult to understand. The causes of the disorder are not well understood, but they include a large biological component.

Diagnosis

Schizophrenia was originally called *dementia praecox*, which is Latin for "premature mental deterioration." In 1911, Eugen Bleuler introduced the term *schizophrenia*. Although the term is Greek for "split mind," it is *not* related to *dissociative identity disorder* (previously known as *multiple personality disorder*), in which someone alternates among different personalities. What Bleuler meant by *schizophrenia* was a split between the emotional and intellectual aspects of experience: The person's emotional expression or lack of it seems unconnected with current experiences. For example, someone might giggle or cry for no apparent reason or show no reaction to bad news. Not all patients show this detachment of emotion from intellect, but the term lives on.

Diagnosis of schizophrenia is difficult. In most areas of medicine, a physician can confirm a diagnosis with a lab test of some sort. Psychiatry has no dependable lab tests. Psychiatrists rely on behavioral observations, and many cases leave room for uncertainty.

According to the *DSM-IV* (American Psychiatric Association, 1994), to be diagnosed with **schizophrenia**, someone must have deteriorated in everyday functioning (work, interpersonal relations, self care, etc.) for at least 6 months, and must show at least two of the following, that are not attributable to other disorders:

- **Delusions** (unjustifiable beliefs, such as "Beings from outer space are controlling my actions")
- **Hallucinations** (false sensory experiences, such as hearing voices when alone)
- Disorganized speech (rambling or incoherent)
- Grossly disorganized behavior
- Weak or absent signs of emotion, speech, and socialization

Each of these is a judgment call. Sometimes a statement that appears to be a delusion ("People are persecuting me") is actually true, or at least defensible. Many healthy people have heard a voice when they knew they were alone, at least once or twice. The term "grossly disorganized behavior" encompasses a wide variety of possibilities. The symptoms vary so greatly that you could easily find several people diagnosed with schizophrenia who have almost nothing in common (Andreasen, 1999).

The first four items on the list—delusions, hallucinations, disorganized speech, and disorganized behavior—are called **positive symptoms** (behaviors that are present that should be absent). Weak or absent emotion, speech, and socialization are **negative symptoms** (behaviors that are absent that should

Nancy C. Andreasen

Being a scientist and a clinician is a double privilege. We actually get paid to spend our time asking both scientific and clinical questions that everyone would like to ask and have answered, and people grant us the trust of sharing their most intimate thoughts and experiences with us.

be present). Negative symptoms are usually stable over time and difficult to treat.

It is also useful to distinguish cognitive symptoms. The cognitive symptoms are limitations of thought and reasoning that are common in schizophrenia, even if they are not central to the diagnosis. Overall intelligence varies considerably, but on average, IQ scores are a few points below those of the rest of the population (Woodberry, Giuliano, & Seidman, 2008). The most typical type of thought disorder of schizophrenia is a difficulty understanding and using abstract concepts. Related symptoms include deficits in attention and working memory (Hanlon et al., 2005).

Which of the various symptoms, if any, is the primary problem? According to Nancy Andreasen (1999), a leading investigator of schizophrenia, the main problem is disordered thoughts that result from abnormal interactions between the cortex and the thalamus and cerebellum. The disordered thinking may lead to the hallucinations, delusions, and other symptoms.

One way to test this idea is to see whether we could make normal, healthy people talk or behave in incoherent ways if we overtaxed their working memory. Imagine yourself in the following study. The researcher shows a series of pictures for 30 seconds each, and you are supposed to tell a short story about each one. If you see the same picture a second time, you should tell a totally new story about it, unlike your first one. Furthermore, on some trials, you have an additional task to burden your memory while you are trying to tell a story: A series of letters appears on the screen, one at a time. You should pay attention to every second letter. Whenever it is the same as the last letter that you paid attention to, you should press a key. For example,

D L K F R F B L M T J T X H Q U B R B N

Attend to every second letter.

Press on these, because same as previous attended letter.

Do *not* press here. Same as previous *non*attended letter.

Most people's speech becomes less clear when they perform this memory task while trying to tell a story. If it is the second presentation of a picture, requiring them to avoid what they said the first time and tell a totally new story, the memory task causes even greater interference, and their speech becomes incoherent, somewhat like schizophrenic speech (Kerns, 2007). The implication is that memory impairment could be the central symptom.

STOP & CHECK

16. Why are hallucinations considered a positive symptom?

ANSWER

16. Hallucinations are considered a positive symptom because they are present when they should be absent. A "positive" symptom is not a "good" symptom.

APPLICATIONS AND EXTENSIONS

Differential Diagnosis of Schizophrenia

In the rules for diagnosing schizophrenia, did you notice the expression "not attributable to other disorders"? Even if someone's symptoms match the description of schizophrenia perfectly, it is important to make a **differential diagnosis**—that is, one that rules out other conditions with similar symptoms. Here are a few conditions that sometimes resemble schizophrenia:

- *Mood disorder with psychotic features:* People with depression frequently have delusions, especially delusions of guilt or failure. Some report hallucinations also.

- *Substance abuse:* Many of the positive symptoms of schizophrenia can develop from prolonged use of amphetamine, methamphetamine, cocaine, LSD, or phencyclidine ("angel dust"). Someone who stops taking the drugs is likely, though not certain, to recover from these symptoms. Substance abuse is more likely than schizophrenia to produce visual hallucinations.

- *Brain damage:* Damage or tumors in the temporal or prefrontal cortex often produce some of the symptoms of schizophrenia.

- *Undetected hearing deficits:* Sometimes, someone who is starting to have trouble hearing thinks that everyone else is whispering and starts to worry, "They're whispering about me!" Delusions of persecution can develop.

- *Huntington's disease:* The symptoms of Huntington's disease include hallucinations, delusions, and disordered thinking, as well as motor symptoms. An uncommon type of schizophrenia, catatonic schizophrenia, includes motor abnormalities, so a mixture of psychological and motor symptoms could represent either schizophrenia or Huntington's disease.

- *Nutritional abnormalities:* Niacin deficiency can produce hallucinations and delusions (Hoffer, 1973), and so can a deficiency of vitamin C or an allergy to milk proteins (not the same as lactose intolerance). Some people who cannot tolerate wheat gluten or other proteins react with hallucinations and delusions (Reichelt, Seim, & Reichelt, 1996). ∎

Demographic Data

Worldwide, about 1% of people suffer from schizophrenia at some point in life (Narrow et al., 2002; Perälä et al., 2007). The estimate rises or falls depending on how many mild cases we include. Since the mid-1900s, the reported prevalence of schizophrenia has been declining in many countries (Suvisaari, Haukka, Tanskanen, & Lönnqvist, 1999; Torrey & Miller, 2001). Is schizophrenia actually less common, or are psychiatrists just diagnosing it differently? This is not an easy question to answer. However, even when it is diagnosed today, it appears to be less severe than it often used to be. Perhaps our society is doing something to prevent schizophrenia without knowing what.

Schizophrenia occurs in all ethnic groups and all parts of the world. However, it is significantly more common in cities than in rural areas, for reasons unknown (Kelly et al., 2010). Also it is 10 to 100 times more common in the United States and Europe than in most Third World countries (Torrey, 1986). Part of that discrepancy could be due to differences in recordkeeping, but other possibilities exist, including social support and diet. A diet high in sugar and saturated fat, as is common in prosperous countries, aggravates schizophrenia, whereas a diet rich in fish alleviates it (Peet, 2004). Omega-3 fatty acids, abundant in seafood, increase production of BDNF, increase production of new cells in the hippocampus, and block apoptosis and other neural damage (V. R. King et al., 2006; Venna, 2008).

Lifetime prevalence of schizophrenia is more common for men than women by a ratio of about 7:5. On average, it is also more severe in men and has an earlier onset—usually in the teens or early 20s for men and the mid to late 20s for women (Aleman, Kahn, & Selten, 2003).

Researchers have documented several unexplained oddities about schizophrenia. The points that follow do not fit neatly into any currently prominent theory. They indicate how many mysteries remain:

- Schizophrenia is significantly less common than average among people with type 1 (juvenile-onset) diabetes, although it is more common than average in people with type 2 (adult-onset) diabetes (Juvonen et al., 2007).
- People with schizophrenia have an increased risk of colon cancer but below average probability of respiratory cancer or brain cancer (Hippisley-Cox, Vinogradova, Coupland, & Parker, 2007; Roppel, 1978).
- People with schizophrenia seldom develop rheumatoid arthritis or allergies (Goldman, 1999; Rubinstein, 1997).
- Women who have a schizophrenic breakdown during pregnancy usually give birth to daughters. However, those who have a breakdown shortly after giving birth usually give birth to sons (M. A. Taylor, 1969).
- Many people with schizophrenia have a characteristic body odor, attributed to the chemical *trans*-3-methyl-2-hexenoic acid, and decreased ability to smell that chemical themselves (Brewer et al., 2007; K. Smith, Thompson, & Koster, 1969).
- Most people with schizophrenia and many of their unaffected relatives have deficits in pursuit eye movements—the ability to keep their eyes on a moving target (Keefe et al., 1997; Sereno & Holzman, 1993).

STOP & CHECK

17. Has the reported prevalence of schizophrenia been increasing, decreasing, or staying the same?

ANSWER

17. Schizophrenia has been decreasing in reported prevalence.

Genetics

Huntington's disease (Chapter 8) can be called a genetic disease: By examining part of chromosome 4, one can predict with almost perfect accuracy who will develop the disease and who will not. At one time, many researchers believed that schizophrenia might be a genetic disease in the same sense. However, accumulating evidence indicates that although schizophrenia has a genetic basis, it does not depend on any single gene.

Twin Studies

The more closely you are biologically related to someone with schizophrenia, the greater your own probability of schizophrenia, as shown in Figure 15.11 (Gottesman, 1991). One of the most important points in Figure 15.11, confirmed by other studies (Cardno et al., 1999), is that monozygotic twins have a much higher **concordance** (agreement) for schizophrenia than do dizygotic twins. Furthermore, twin pairs who are really monozygotic, but thought they weren't, are more concordant than twin pairs who thought they were, but really aren't (Kendler, 1983). That is, *being* monozygotic is more critical than *being treated as* monozygotic.

The high concordance for monozygotic twins has long been taken as strong evidence for a genetic influence. However, note two limitations:

- Monozygotic twins have only about 50% concordance, not 100%. Monozygotic twins could differ because a gene is activated in one individual and suppressed in another (Tsujita et al., 1998), or they could differ because of environmental influences.
- In Figure 15.11, note the greater similarity between dizygotic twins than between siblings. Dizygotic twins have the same genetic resemblance as siblings but greater environmental similarity, including prenatal environment.

Percent developing schizophrenia

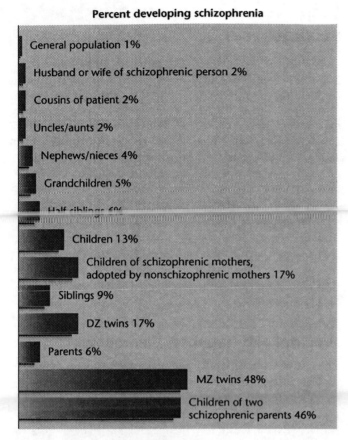

General population 1%

Husband or wife of schizophrenic person 2%

Cousins of patient 2%

Uncles/aunts 2%

Nephews/nieces 4%

Grandchildren 5%

Half-siblings 6%

Children 13%

Children of schizophrenic mothers, adopted by nonschizophrenic mothers 17%

Siblings 9%

DZ twins 17%

Parents 6%

MZ twins 48%

Children of two schizophrenic parents 46%

FIGURE 15.11 Probabilities of developing schizophrenia
People with a closer genetic relationship to someone with schizophrenia have a higher probability of developing it themselves. *(Based on data from Gottesman, 1991)*

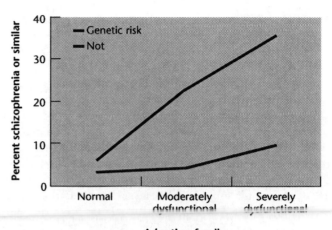

Adopting family

FIGURE 15.12 Probability of schizophrenia or similar conditions in adopted children
The probability was higher for children of a mother with schizophrenia, but growing up in a dysfunctional family magnified that risk. *(Based on data from Wynne et al., 2006)*

Adopted Children Who Develop Schizophrenia

When an adopted child develops schizophrenia, the disorder is more common in the person's biological relatives than adopting relatives. One Danish study found schizophrenia in 12.5% of the immediate biological relatives and none of the adopting relatives (Kety et al., 1994). Note in Figure 15.11 that children of a mother with schizophrenia have a moderately high probability of schizophrenia, even if adopted by mentally healthy parents.

These results suggest a genetic basis, but they are also consistent with a prenatal influence. Consider a pregnant woman with schizophrenia. True, she passes her genes to her child, but she also provides the prenatal environment. Many women with schizophrenia smoke, drink, use other drugs, and eat a less than desirable diet during pregnancy. A disproportionate number have complications during pregnancy and delivery (Jablensky, Morgan, Zubrick, Bower, & Yellachich, 2005). If some of their children develop schizophrenia, we cannot be sure that the influence is genetic.

Studies on adopted children also support a role for environmental influences. A study of adopted children in Fin-

land found a high probability of schizophrenia or related conditions among children who had a biological mother with schizophrenia *and* a severely disordered adopting family. The genetic risk itself or the disordered family itself had less effect, as shown in Figure 15.12 (Wynne et al., 2006).

Efforts to Locate a Gene

The strongest evidence for a genetic influence would be to locate a gene that is consistently linked with schizophrenia. Researchers working with various populations have identified more than a dozen genes that appear to be more common in people with schizophrenia. One that has attracted much interest, called **DISC1** (*disrupted in schizophrenia 1*), controls production of dendritic spines (Hayashi-Takagi et al., 2010) and the generation of new neurons in the hippocampus (Duan et al., 2007). Other genes linked to schizophrenia in several studies are important for brain development (Hall et al., 2006; Stefansson et al., 2009), control of transmission at glutamate synapses (Dickman & Davis, 2009), and connections between the hippocampus and the prefrontal cortex (Esslinger et al., 2009). However, researchers have not had great success at replicating the results from one population to another. A study of nearly 2,000 patients with schizophrenia and a control group found no statistically significant relationship between schizophrenia and any of the 14 genes that previous studies identified as linked to schizophrenia (Sanders et al., 2008).

In a way, these results should not be surprising. If schizophrenia depended on a single gene, it would be hard for that gene to remain in 1% of the population, given the natural selection pressures against it. People with schizophrenia die younger than other people, on average (Saha, Chant, &

McGrath, 2007). More importantly, on average they have fewer than half as many children as other people do, and their brothers and sisters do not compensate by having more children than average (Bundy, Stahl, & MacCabe, 2011). Any gene for schizophrenia should decline rapidly in prevalence, it seems.

If schizophrenia has a genetic basis but we can't find any gene with a consistent link, and any gene that leads to schizophrenia can't be passed down through many generations, what is going on? A prominent hypothesis is that many cases of schizophrenia arise from new mutations. Ordinarily, it would be ridiculous to suggest that a condition affecting 1% of the population could depend on new mutations. Mutations just aren't that common. But proper brain development depends on hundreds of genes. A mutation in one gene is a rare event, but a mutation in any of several hundred is not so rare. An even more likely possibility is deletion of a gene, a fairly common error in reproduction (International Schizophrenia Consortium, 2009). Researchers examined the chromosomes of people with and without schizophrenia and found genetic *microdeletions* and *microduplications* (i.e., elimination or duplication of parts of a gene) in 5% of the control group, 15% of people with schizophrenia, and 20% of people with onset of schizophrenia before age 18 (Walsh et al., 2008). Those microdeletions and microduplications were distributed over a great many genes. Thus, the hypothesis is that a new mutation or deletion of any of a large number of genes disrupts brain development and increases the probability of schizophrenia. As fast as natural selection weeds out those mutations or deletions, new ones arise to replace them.

One observation supporting this idea is that schizophrenia is somewhat more common among children of older fathers (Byrne, Agerbo, Ewald, Eaton, & Mortensen, 2003; Malaspina et al., 2002). Women are born with all the eggs they will ever have, but men continue making new sperm throughout life, and the possibility of mutations accumulates over time.

We need not assume that all cases of schizophrenia have a genetic predisposition. Others may depend on prenatal environment or other influences on brain development.

![STOP & CHECK arrow graphic]

18. The fact that adopted children who develop schizophrenia usually have biological relatives with schizophrenia implies a probable genetic basis. What other interpretation is possible?

19. Does the hypothesis of new mutations conflict with the results showing that an aberrant form of the gene *DISC1* is often linked to schizophrenia?

ANSWERS
18. A biological mother can influence her child's development through prenatal environment as well as genetics, even if the child is adopted early. **19.** No. Although mutations in many genes can, according to the hypothesis, lead to schizophrenia, the *DISC1* gene could be one where the mutation is more certain to cause schizophrenia.

The Neurodevelopmental Hypothesis

According to the **neurodevelopmental hypothesis** now popular among researchers, schizophrenia begins with abnormalities in the prenatal (before birth) or neonatal (newborn) development of the nervous system, based on either genetics or other influences. These early problems leave the developing brain vulnerable to other disturbances later in life, including but not limited to highly stressful experiences. The eventual results are mild abnormalities in brain anatomy and major disorders of behavior (Fatemi & Folsom, 2009; Weinberger, 1996).

The supporting evidence is that (a) several kinds of prenatal or neonatal difficulties are linked to later schizophrenia; (b) people with schizophrenia have minor brain abnormalities that apparently originate early in life; and (c) it is plausible that abnormalities of early development could impair behavior in adulthood.

Prenatal and Neonatal Environment

The risk of schizophrenia is elevated among people who had problems that could have affected their brain development, including poor nutrition of the mother during pregnancy, premature birth, low birth weight, and complications during delivery (Ballon, Dean, & Cadenhead, 2007). The risk is also elevated if the mother was exposed to extreme stress, such as the sudden death of a close relative, early in her pregnancy (Khashau et al., 2008). None of these influences by itself accounts for many cases of schizophrenia, although together their influence is greater (Cannon, Jones, & Murray, 2002). Schizophrenia has also been linked to head injuries in early childhood (AbdelMalik, Husted, Chow, & Bassett, 2003), although we do not know whether the head injuries led to schizophrenia or early symptoms of schizophrenia increased the risk of head injuries.

If a mother is Rh-negative and her baby is Rh-positive, the baby's Rh-positive blood factor may trigger an immunological rejection by the mother. The response is weak with the woman's first Rh-positive baby but stronger in later pregnancies, and it is more intense with boy than girl babies. Second- and later-born boy babies with Rh incompatibility have an increased risk of hearing deficits, mental retardation, and several other problems, and about twice the usual probability of schizophrenia (Hollister, Laing, & Mednick, 1996).

Another suggestion of prenatal influences comes from the **season-of-birth effect**: the tendency for people born in winter to have a slightly (5% to 8%) greater probability of developing schizophrenia than people born at other times of the year. This tendency is particularly pronounced in latitudes far from the equator (Davies, Welham, Chant, Torrey, & McGrath, 2003; Torrey, Miller, et al., 1997).

What might account for this effect? One possibility is complications of delivery or early nutrition (Jablensky et al., 2005). Another is viral infection. Influenza and other viral epidemics are most common in the fall. Therefore, the reasoning goes, many pregnant women become infected in the fall with a virus that impairs a crucial stage of brain development in a baby who will be born in the winter. A virus that affects the mother might or might not cross the placenta into the fetus's brain, but the mother's cytokines do cross, and excessive cytokines can impair brain development (Zuckerman, Rehavi, Nachman, & Weiner, 2003). Animal studies show that some of the effects of cytokines on brain development appear mild at first but gradually impair brain development as the individual approaches adulthood (Vuillermot, Weber, Feldon, & Meyer, 2010). The mother's infection also causes a fever, which can damage the fetal brain. A fever of just 38.5° C (101° F) slows the division of fetal neurons (Laburn, 1996). (Exercise during pregnancy does *not* overheat the abdomen and is not dangerous to the fetus. Hot baths and saunas may be risky, however.) When mice are infected with influenza during pregnancy, their offspring develop a number of behavioral abnormalities, including deficient exploration and deficient social reactions to other mice (Shi, Fatemi, Sidwell, & Patterson, 2003).

Researchers examined the records of tens of thousands of people in Scotland, England, and Denmark over several decades. They found increased schizophrenia rates among people born 2 to 3 months after major influenza epidemics, such as the one in the autumn of 1957 (Adams, Kendell, Hare, & Munk-Jørgensen, 1993). Other studies retrieved blood samples that hospitals had taken from pregnant women and stored for decades. Researchers found increased incidence of influenza virus among mothers whose children eventually developed schizophrenia (A. S. Brown et al., 2004; Buka et al., 2001). Rates of schizophrenia are also increased among offspring of mothers who had rubella (German measles), herpes, and other infections during pregnancy (A. S. Brown et al., 2001; Buka et al., 2008).

Certain childhood infections may also relate to schizophrenia. The parasite *Toxoplasma gondii* (discussed also in Chapter 12 in the context of anxiety and the amygdala) reproduces only in cats, but it can infect humans and other species also. If it infects the brain of an infant or child, it impairs brain development and leads to memory disorder, hallucinations, and delusions (Torrey & Yolken, 2005). People who develop schizophrenia in adulthood are more likely than other people to have had a pet cat in childhood (Torrey, Rawlings, & Yolken, 2000). Blood tests have found antibodies to the Toxoplasma parasite in a higher percentage of people with schizo-

phrenia than in the general population (Leweke et al., 2004; Niebuhr et al., 2008; Yolken et al., 2001).

In short, some cases of schizophrenia may develop as a result of infections. This mechanism is an alternative or supplement to genetics and other influences. Evidently, a variety of influences can lead to similar outcomes in schizophrenia.

STOP & CHECK

20. What does the season-of-birth effect suggest about a possible cause of schizophrenia?

ANSWER

20. The season-of-birth effect is the observation that schizophrenia is slightly more common among people who were born in the winter. One interpretation is that influenza or other infections of the mother during the fall impair brain development of a baby born in the winter.

Mild Brain Abnormalities

In accord with the neurodevelopmental hypothesis, some (though not all) people with schizophrenia show mild abnormalities of brain anatomy that vary from one individual to another. On average, people with schizophrenia have less than average gray matter and white matter, and larger than average ventricles—the fluid-filled spaces within the brain (Meyer-Lindenberg, 2010; Wolkin et al., 1998; Wright et al., 2000) (Figure 15.13)

Figure 15.14 summarizes 15 studies, including a total of 390 people with schizophrenia. Brain areas marked in yellow showed decreased volume in the most studies, those in various shades of red showed decreases in fewer studies, and those in gray appeared normal in all studies (Honea, Crow,

Ventricles

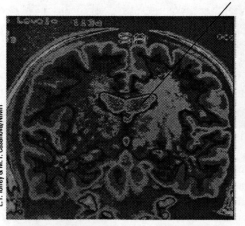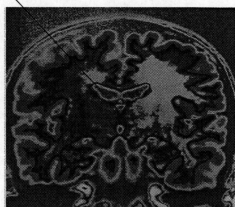

FIGURE 15.13 Coronal sections for identical twins
The twin on the left has schizophrenia; the twin on the right does not. The ventricles (near the center of each brain) are larger in the twin with schizophrenia.

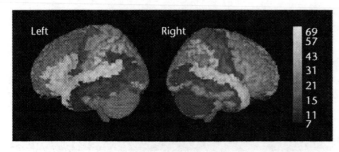

FIGURE 15.14 Cortical areas showing decreased volume in patients with schizophrenia
Areas in yellow showed decreased volume in the largest percentage of studies. Those in various shades of red showed decreases in fewer studies. *(From "Regional deficits in brain volume in schizophrenia: A meta-analysis of voxel-based morphometry studies," by R. Honea, T. J., Crow, D., Passingham, and C. E. Mackay,* American Journal of Psychiatry, *162, 2233–2245. Reprinted by permission from the* American Journal of Psychiatry, *Copyright (2005) American Psychiatric Association.)*

Passingham, & Mackay, 2005). Note that the strongest deficits were in the left temporal and frontal areas of the cortex. Note also that most cortical areas showed mild abnormalities in at least one or two studies. The thalamus, which is in the interior of the brain and therefore not shown in Figure 15.14, is also smaller than average for people with schizophrenia (Harms et al., 2007).

The areas with consistent signs of abnormality include some that mature slowly, such as the dorsolateral prefrontal cortex (Berman, Torrey, Daniel, & Weinberger, 1992; Fletcher et al., 1998; Gur, Cowell, et al., 2000). The abnormalities include weaker than average connections from the dorsolateral prefrontal cortex to other brain areas, and less than normal activity in this area during tasks requiring attention and memory (Lynall et al., 2010; van den Heuvel, Mandl, Stam, Kahn, & Pol, 2010; Weiss et al., 2009). As you might predict, people with schizophrenia perform poorly at tasks that depend on the prefrontal cortex (Goldberg, Weinberger, Berman, Pliskin, & Podd, 1987; Spindler, Sullivan, Menon, Lim, & Pfefferbaum, 1997). Most patients with schizophrenia show deficits of memory and attention similar to those of people with damage to the temporal or pre-

frontal cortex (Park, Holzman, & Goldman-Rakic, 1995) (Methods 15.1).

At a microscopic level, the most reliable finding is that cell bodies are smaller than normal, especially in the hippocampus and prefrontal cortex (Pierri, Volk, Auh, Sampson, & Lewis, 2001; Rajkowska, Selemon, & Goldman-Rakic, 1998; Selemon, Rajkowska, & Goldman-Rakic, 1995; Weinberger, 1999).

Lateralization also differs from the normal pattern. In most people, the left hemisphere is slightly larger than the right, especially in the planum temporale of the temporal lobe, but in people with schizophrenia, the right planum temporale is equal or larger (Kasai et al., 2003; Kwon et al., 1999). People with schizophrenia have lower than normal overall activity in the left hemisphere (Gur & Chin, 1999) and are more likely than other people to be left-handed (Satz & Green, 1999). All these results suggest a subtle change in brain development.

The reasons behind the brain abnormalities are not certain. Most researchers have been careful to limit their studies to patients with schizophrenia who have never taken, or who have not recently taken, antipsychotic drugs, so the deficits are not a result of treatments for schizophrenia. However, many people with schizophrenia use alcohol, marijuana, and other drugs, and it is likely that some of the brain abnormalities result from heavy drug use (Rais et al., 2008; Sullivan et al., 2000).

The results are inconsistent as to whether the brain damage associated with schizophrenia is *progressive*—that is, whether it increases over time. The brain damage associated with Parkinson's disease, Huntington's disease, and Alzheimer's disease gets worse as the person ages. Brain abnormalities are found in young people shortly after a diagnosis of schizophrenia (Lieberman et al., 2001), and many studies find that the brain abnormalities are no greater in older patients (Andreasen et al., 1990; Censits, Ragland, Gur, & Gur, 1997; Russell, Munro, Jones, Hemsley, & Murray, 1997; Selemon et al., 1995). However, other studies show a moderate degree of increased brain loss as patients age (Cahn et al., 2002; Hulshoff et al., 2001; Mathalon, Sullivan, Lim, & Pfefferbaum, 2001; Rais et al., 2008). Nevertheless, the brains of people with schizophrenia do not show the signs that accompany neuron death—proliferation of glia cells and activation of the genes responsible for repair after injury (Arnold, 2000; Benes, 1995; K. O. Lim et al., 1998). Possibly, the neurons are shrinking without dying.

METHODS 15.1

The Wisconsin Card Sorting Task

Neuropsychologists use many behavioral tests to measure the functioning of the prefrontal cortex. One is the Wisconsin Card Sorting Task. A person is handed a shuffled deck of cards that differ in number, color, and shape of objects— for example, three red circles, five blue triangles, four green squares. First the person is asked to sort them by one rule, such as separate them by color. Then the rule changes, and

the person is supposed to sort them by a different rule, such as number. Shifting to a new rule requires suppressing the old one and evokes activity in the prefrontal cortex (Konishi et al., 1998). People with damage to the prefrontal cortex can sort by whichever rule is first, but then they have trouble shifting to a new rule. People with schizophrenia have the same difficulty. (So do children.)

In any case, most of the damage is apparent early, and later changes are relatively small.

Early Development and Later Psychopathology

One question may have struck you. How can we reconcile the idea of abnormalities in early development with the fact that the disorder is usually diagnosed after age 20? The time course may not be as puzzling as it seems at first (Weinberger, 1996). Most of the people who develop schizophrenia in adulthood had shown other problems since childhood, including deficits in attention, memory, and impulse control (Keshavan, Diwadkar, Montrose, Rajarethinam, & Sweeney, 2005). Furthermore, the prefrontal cortex, an area that shows consistent signs of deficit in schizophrenia, is one of the slowest brain areas to mature. In one study, researchers damaged this area in infant monkeys and tested the monkeys later. At age 1 year, the monkeys' behavior was nearly normal, but by age 2 years, it had deteriorated markedly (P. S. Goldman, 1971, 1976). That is, the effects of the brain damage grew worse over age. Presumably, the effects of brain damage were minimal at age 1 year because the dorsolateral prefrontal cortex doesn't do much at that age anyway. Later, when it should begin assuming important functions, the damage begins to make a difference (Figure 15.15).

STOP & CHECK

21. If schizophrenia is due to abnormal brain development, why do behavioral symptoms not become apparent until later in life?

ANSWER

21. Parts of the prefrontal cortex are very slow to reach maturity; therefore, early disruption of this area's development might not produce any symptoms early in life, when the prefrontal cortex is contributing little anyway.

▌Treatments

Before antipsychotic drugs became available in the mid-1950s, most people with schizophrenia were confined to mental hospitals with little hope of recovery. Today, mental hospitals are far less crowded because of drugs and outpatient treatment.

Antipsychotic Drugs and Dopamine

In the 1950s, psychiatrists discovered that **chlorpromazine** (trade name Thorazine) relieves the positive symptoms of schizophrenia for most, though not all, patients. Researchers later discovered other **antipsychotic**, or **neuroleptic, drugs** (drugs that tend to relieve schizophrenia and similar conditions) in two chemical families: the **phenothiazines** (FEE-no-THI-uh-zeens), which include chlorpromazine, and the **butyrophenones** (BYOO-tir-oh-FEE-noans), which include haloperidol (trade name Haldol). Behavioral benefits of any of these drugs develop gradually over a month or more. Symptoms generally return after cessation of treatment.

As Figure 15.16 illustrates, each of these drugs blocks dopamine synapses. For each drug, researchers determined the mean dose prescribed for patients with schizophrenia (displayed along the horizontal axis) and the amount needed to block dopamine receptors (displayed along the vertical axis). As the figure shows, the drugs that are most effective against schizophrenia (and therefore used in the smallest doses) are the most effective at blocking dopamine receptors (Seeman, Lee, Chau-Wong, & Wong, 1976).

That finding inspired the **dopamine hypothesis of schizophrenia**, which holds that schizophrenia results from excess activity at dopamine synapses in certain brain areas. Although the concentration of dopamine in the brain is no higher than normal, the turnover is elevated, especially in the basal ganglia (Kumakura et al., 2007). That is, neurons release dopamine at a faster than average rate and synthesize more to replace the molecules that they do not reabsorb. Elevated dopamine release also occurs in people showing the first symptoms of schizophrenia (Howes et al., 2009).

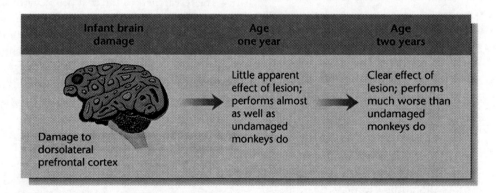

FIGURE 15.15 Delayed effects of brain damage in infant monkeys
After damage to the dorsolateral prefrontal cortex, monkeys are unimpaired at age 1 year but impaired later, when this area ordinarily matures. Researchers speculate that similar damage in humans might produce behavioral deficits not apparent until adulthood. *(Based on P. S. Goldman, 1976)*

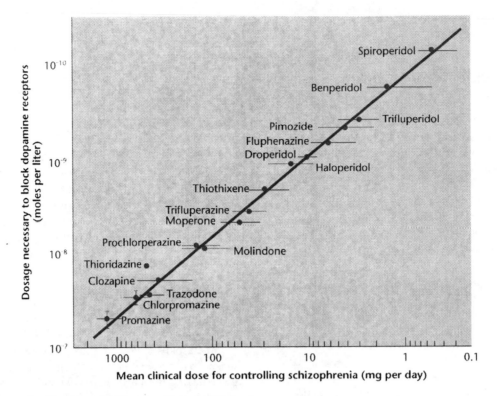

FIGURE 15.16 Dopamine-blocking effects of antipsychotic drugs
Drugs are arranged along the horizontal axis in terms of the average daily dose prescribed for patients with schizophrenia. (Horizontal lines indicate common ranges.) *Larger doses* are to the left and *smaller* doses are to the right so that *more effective* drugs are to the right. Along the vertical axis is a measurement of the amount of each drug required to achieve a certain degree of blockage of postsynaptic dopamine receptors. *Larger* doses are toward the bottom and *smaller* doses are toward the top so that the drugs on top are *more effective*. (From *"Antipsychotic Drug Doses and Neuroleptic/Dopamine Receptors," by P. Seeman, T. Lee, M. Chau-Wong, and K. Wong,* Nature, *261, 1976, pp. 717–719. Copyright © 1976 Macmillan Magazines Limited. Reprinted by permission of Nature and Phillip Seeman.)*

Further support for the dopamine hypothesis comes from the fact that large, repeated use of amphetamine, methamphetamine, or cocaine induces **substance-induced psychotic disorder**, characterized by hallucinations and delusions, the positive symptoms of schizophrenia. Each of these drugs increases or prolongs the activity at dopamine synapses. LSD, which also produces psychotic symptoms, is best known for its effects on serotonin synapses, but it also stimulates dopamine synapses.

Researchers set out to measure the number of dopamine receptors occupied at a given moment. They used a radioactively labeled drug, IBZM, that binds to dopamine type D_2 receptors. Because IBZM binds only to receptors that dopamine did not already bind, measuring the radioactivity counts the number of vacant dopamine receptors. Then the researchers used a second drug, AMPT, that blocks all synthesis of dopamine and again used IBZM to count the number of vacant D_2 receptors. Because AMPT had prevented production of dopamine, *all* D_2 receptors should be vacant at this time, so the researchers got a count of the total. Then they subtracted the first count from the second count, yielding the number of D_2 receptors occupied by dopamine at the first count:

- First count: IBZM binds to all D_2 receptors not already attached to dopamine.

- Second count: IBZM binds to all D_2 receptors (because AMPT eliminated production of dopamine).

- Second count minus first count equals the number of D_2 receptors bound to dopamine at the first count.

The researchers found that people with schizophrenia had about twice as many D_2 receptors occupied as normal (Abi-Dargham et al., 2000). Another study found that among patients with schizophrenia, the greater the amount of D_2 receptor activation in the prefrontal cortex, the greater the cognitive impairment (Meyer-Lindenberg et al., 2002).

> **STOP & CHECK**

23. The ability of traditional antipsychotic drugs to relieve schizophrenia correlates strongly with what effect on neurotransmitters?

ANSWER

22. Their ability to relieve schizophrenia correlates strongly with how well they block activity at dopamine synapses.

Role of Glutamate

Abnormalities of dopamine transmission need not be the whole story for schizophrenia. According to the **glutamate hypothesis of schizophrenia**, the problem relates in part to deficient activity at glutamate synapses, especially in the prefrontal cortex. In many brain areas, dopamine inhibits glutamate release, or glutamate stimulates neurons that inhibit dopamine release. Therefore, increased dopamine would produce the same effects as decreased glutamate. The antipsychotic effects of drugs that block dopamine are compatible with either the excess-dopamine hypothesis or the deficient-glutamate hypothesis.

Schizophrenia is associated with lower than normal release of glutamate and fewer than normal receptors in the prefrontal cortex and hippocampus (Akbarian et al., 1995; Ibrahim et al., 2000; Tsai et al., 1995). Similar abnormalities occur in people known to be at high risk for developing schizophrenia, because of their family background and early behaviors (Valli et al., 2011). Mice with a deficiency of glutamate receptors show some abnormal behaviors, including increased anxiety, impaired memory, and impaired social behaviors (Belforte et al., 2010).

Further support for the glutamate hypothesis comes from the effects of **phencyclidine (PCP)** ("angel dust"), a drug that inhibits the NMDA glutamate receptors. At low doses, it produces intoxication and slurred speech. At larger doses, it produces both positive and negative symptoms of schizophrenia, including hallucinations, thought disorder, loss of emotions, and memory loss. PCP is an interesting model for schizophrenia in other regards also (Farber, Newcomer, & Olney, 1999; Olney & Farber, 1995):

- PCP and the related drug *ketamine* produce little if any psychotic response in preadolescents. Just as the symptoms of schizophrenia usually begin to emerge well after puberty, so do the psychotic effects of PCP and ketamine.

- LSD, amphetamine, and cocaine produce temporary schizophrenic symptoms in almost anyone, and the effects are not much worse in people with a history of schizophrenia than in anyone else. However, PCP produces severe effects for someone who has recovered from schizophrenia, including a long-lasting relapse.

It might seem that the best test of the glutamate hypothesis would be to administer glutamate itself. However, recall from Chapter 5 that strokes kill neurons by overstimulating glutamate synapses. Increasing overall brain glutamate would be risky. However, drugs that stimulate particular kinds of metabotropic glutamate receptors have shown much promise in treating schizophrenia (González-Maeso et al., 2008; Patil et al., 2007).

Furthermore, the NMDA glutamate receptor has a primary site that is activated by glutamate and a secondary site that is activated by glycine (Figure 15.17). Glycine by itself does not activate the receptor, but it increases the effectiveness of glutamate. Thus, an increase in glycine can increase the activity at NMDA synapses without overstimulating glutamate throughout the brain. Although glycine is not an effective an-

tipsychotic drug by itself, it increases the effects of other antipsychotic drugs, especially with regard to negative symptoms (Heresco-Levy et al., 1999; Heresco-Levy & Javitt, 2004). Studies on laboratory mice found that extra glycine decreases the behavioral responses to phencyclidine (Yee et al., 2006).

STOP & CHECK

23. What drugs induce mainly the positive symptoms of schizophrenia? What drug can induce both positive and negative symptoms?

24. Why are the effects of antipsychotic drugs equally compatible with the dopamine hypothesis and the glutamate hypothesis?

ANSWERS

23. Repeated use of amphetamine, cocaine, or LSD induces positive symptoms, such as hallucinations and delusions. Phencyclidine induces both positive and negative symptoms. **24.** Dopamine inhibits glutamate cells in many areas, and glutamate stimulates neurons that inhibit dopamine. Therefore, the effects of increasing dopamine are similar to those of decreasing glutamate.

New Drugs

The brain has several dopamine pathways with different functions. The drugs that block dopamine synapses produce their benefits by acting on neurons in the **mesolimbocortical system**, a set of neurons that project from the midbrain tegmentum to the limbic system. However, the drugs also block dopamine neurons in the *mesostriatal system* that projects to the basal ganglia (Figure 15.18). The effect on the basal ganglia produces **tardive dyskinesia** (TARD-eev dis-kih-NEE-zhee-uh), characterized by tremors and other involuntary movements that develop gradually and to varying degrees among different patients (Kiriakakis, Bhatia, Quinn, & Marsden, 1998).

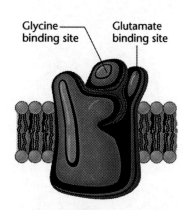

FIGURE 15.17 An NMDA glutamate receptor
NMDA glutamate receptors have a primary binding site for glutamate and a secondary binding site for glycine. Glycine increases the effect of glutamate. *(© Cengage Learning 2013)*

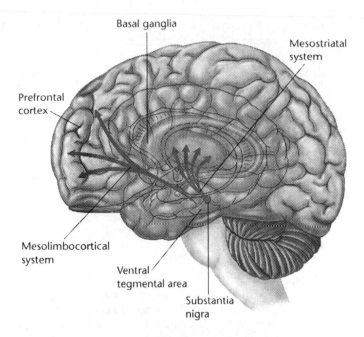

Basal ganglia

Mesostriatal system

Prefrontal cortex

Mesolimbocortical system

Ventral tegmental area

Substantia nigra

FIGURE 15.18 Two major dopamine pathways
Overactivity of the mesolimbocortical system is linked to the symptoms of schizophrenia. The path to the basal ganglia is associated with tardive dyskinesia, a movement disorder. *(Adapted from Valzelli, 1980)*

Once tardive dyskinesia emerges, it can last long after someone quits the drug (Kiriakakis et al., 1998). Consequently, the best strategy is to prevent it from starting. Certain new drugs called **second-generation antipsychotics**, or atypical antipsychotics, alleviate schizophrenia without producing movement problems (Figure 15.19). The most common of these drugs are clozapine, amisulpride, risperidone, olanzapine, and aripiprazole. They are more effective than older drugs at treating the negative symptoms of schizophrenia, and they are now used more widely (J. M. Davis, Chen, & Glick, 2003; Edlinger et al., 2005). Unfortunately, although

they avoid tardive dyskinesia, they produce other side effects, including weight gain and impairment of the immune system. All things considered, the atypical antipsychotics do not improve overall quality of life more than the older drugs (Crossley & Constante, 2010; P. B. Jones et al., 2006).

Compared to drugs like haloperidol, the second-generation antipsychotics have less effect on dopamine type D_2 receptors but more strongly antagonize serotonin type $5\text{-}HT_2$ receptors (Kapur et al., 2000; Meltzer, Matsubara, & Lee, 1989; Mrzljak et al., 1996; Roth, Willins, Kristiansen, & Kroeze, 1999). They also increase the release of glutamate (Melone et al., 2001). In short, schizophrenia is neither a one-gene disorder nor a one-neurotransmitter disorder.

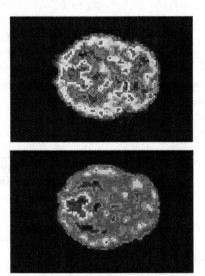

FIGURE 15.19 PET scans of a patient with schizophrenia
These PET scans of a patient with schizophrenia (a) taking clozapine and (b) during a period off the drug demonstrate that clozapine increases brain activity in many brain areas. Red indicates the highest activity, followed by yellow, green, and blue. *(Hank Morgan/Science Source/Photo Researchers)*

Many Remaining Mysteries

A great deal about abnormal psychology remains unknown. One of the most fundamental questions is whether it even makes sense to distinguish among different disorders. Some of the drugs originally approved for schizophrenia are often effective in relieving depression or bipolar disorder. Antidepressant drugs help relieve anxiety disorders. Drugs intended for bipolar disorder help many people with attention-deficit disorder. If the same treatments work for different disorders, maybe those disorders are not so different after all (Dean, 2011). Another major mystery is why concordance for schizophrenia in monozygotic twins is only about 50%. If they share their genes and presumably nearly the same environment, why isn't concordance nearly

100%? Also, why are the treatments for both depression and schizophrenia highly successful for some people and not at all for others? Perhaps you can name additional puzzles.

Research is a little like reading a good mystery novel that presents a mixture of important clues and irrelevant information. In research on schizophrenia, we have an enormous amount of information, but also major gaps and occasional points that don't seem to fit. The final chapter of our mystery novel on schizophrenia isn't complete. However, although researchers have not yet solved the mystery, it should also be clear that they have made progress. It will be fascinating to see what develops in future research.

SUMMARY

1. Positive symptoms of schizophrenia (behaviors that are not present in most other people) include hallucinations, delusions, inappropriate emotions, bizarre behaviors, and thought disorder.   472

2. Negative symptoms (normal behaviors absent that should be present) include deficits of social interaction, emotional expression, and speech.   472

3. Studies of twins and adopted children imply a genetic predisposition to schizophrenia. However, the adoption studies do not distinguish between the roles of genetics and prenatal environment.   474

4. So far, researchers have not located any gene that is strongly linked with schizophrenia in general. A promising hypothesis is that schizophrenia results from new mutations or deletions of any of the hundreds of genes that are important for brain development.   475

5. According to the neurodevelopmental hypothesis, either genes or difficulties early in life impair brain development in ways that increase vulnerability to later insults and predispose to behavioral abnormalities beginning in early adulthood.   476

6. The probability of schizophrenia is slightly higher than average for those who were subjected to difficulties before or at the time of birth or during early infancy.   476

7. Some people with schizophrenia show mild abnormalities of brain development, especially in the temporal

and frontal lobes. They also show cognitive deficits that make sense if their frontal and temporal lobes are less than fully functional.   477

8. Parts of the prefrontal cortex are very slow to mature. It is plausible that early disruption of those areas might produce behavioral symptoms that become manifest as schizophrenia in young adults.   479

9. According to the dopamine hypothesis, schizophrenia is due to excess dopamine activity. Drugs that block dopamine synapses reduce the positive symptoms of schizophrenia, and drugs that increase dopamine activity induce the positive symptoms.   479

10. According to the glutamate hypothesis, part of the problem is deficient glutamate activity. Phencyclidine, which blocks NMDA glutamate synapses, produces both positive and negative symptoms of schizophrenia, especially in people predisposed to schizophrenia.   481

11. Prolonged use of antipsychotic drugs may produce tardive dyskinesia, a movement disorder. Second-generation antipsychotic drugs relieve both positive and negative symptoms without producing tardive dyskinesia. However, these drugs apparently do not improve overall quality of life any better than the original drugs do.   481

KEY TERMS

Terms are defined in the module on the page number indicated. They're also presented in alphabetical order with definitions in the book's Subject Index/Glossary, which begins on page 561. Interactive flashcards and crossword puzzles are among the online resources available to help you learn these terms and the concepts they represent.

antipsychotic (neuroleptic) drugs 479

butyrophenones 479

chlorpromazine 474

concordance 479

delusions 472

differential diagnosis 473

DISC1 475

dopamine hypothesis of
  schizophrenia 479

glutamate hypothesis of
  schizophrenia 481

hallucinations 472

mesolimbocortical system 481

negative symptoms 472

neurodevelopmental hypothesis 476

phencyclidine (PCP) 481

phenothiazines 479

positive symptoms 472

schizophrenia 472

season-of-birth effect 476

second-generation
  antipsychotics 482

substance-induced psychotic
  disorder 480

tardive dyskinesia 481

THOUGHT QUESTION

On average, people who use much marijuana are more likely than others to develop schizophrenia. However, over the last several decades, the use of marijuana has increased substantially while the prevalence of schizophrenia has remained steady or decreased. What would be a reasonable conclusion about the relationship between marijuana use and schizophrenia?

CHAPTER 15 Interactive Exploration and Study

The **Psychology CourseMate** for this text brings chapter topics to life with interactive learning, study, and exam preparation tools, including quizzes and flashcards for the Key Concepts that appear throughout each module, as well as an interactive media-rich eBook version of the text that is fully searchable and includes highlighting and note-taking capabilities and interactive versions of the book's **Stop & Check** quizzes and **Try It Yourself Online** activities. The site also features **Virtual Biological Psychology Labs**, **videos**, and **animations** to help you better understand concepts—logon and learn more at **www.cengagebrain.com**, which is your gateway to all of this text's complimentary and premium resources, including the following:

Virtual Biological Psychology Labs

© 2013 Cengage Learning

Explore the experiments that led to modern-day understanding of biopsychology with the Virtual Biological Psychology Labs, featuring a realistic lab environment that allows you to conduct experiments and evaluate data to better understand how scientists came to the conclusions presented in your text. The labs cover a range of topics, including perception, motivation, cognition, and more. You may purchase access at **www.cengagebrain.com**, or login at **login.cengagebrain.com** if an access card was included with your text.

Videos

Emilie, a Portrait of Bipolar

Also available—

- Magnetic Stimulation to the Brain
- Andre, a Portrait of Schizophrenia

Animations

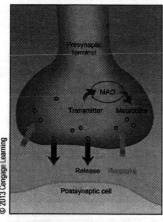

Antidepressants

Also available—

- Saccades and Schizophrenia   **xxx**

Suggestions for Further Exploration

Books

Andreasen, N. C. (2001). *Brave new brain.* New York: Oxford University Press. Excellent discussion of biological research on psychiatric disorders by one of the leading researchers dealing with schizophrenia.

Kirsch, I. (2010). *The Emperor's New Drugs.* New York: Basic Books. A highly skeptical discussion of the effectiveness or ineffectiveness of antidepressant drugs.

Websites

The Psychology CourseMate for this text provides regularly updated links to relevant online resources for this chapter concerning depression and schizophrenia.

Brief, Basic Chemistry

MAIN IDEAS

1. All matter is composed of a limited number of elements that combine in endless ways.
2. Atoms, the component parts of an element, consist of protons, neutrons, and electrons. Most atoms can gain or lose electrons, or share them with other atoms.
3. The chemistry of life is predominantly the chemistry of carbon compounds.

▌ Introduction

To understand certain aspects of biological psychology, particularly the action potential and the molecular mechanisms of synaptic transmission, you need to know a little about chemistry. If you have taken a high school or college course and remember the material reasonably well, you should have no trouble with the chemistry in this text. If your knowledge of chemistry is pretty hazy, this appendix will help. (If you plan to take other courses in biological psychology, you should study as much biology and chemistry as possible.)

▌ Elements and Compounds

If you look around, you will see an enormous variety of materials—dirt, water, wood, plastic, metal, cloth, glass, your own body. Every object is composed of a small number of basic building blocks. If a piece of wood catches fire, it breaks down into ashes, gases, and water vapor. The same is true of your body. An investigator could take those ashes, gases, and water and break them down by chemical and electrical means into carbon, oxygen, hydrogen, nitrogen, and a few other materials. Eventually, however, the investigator arrives at a set of materials that cannot be broken down further: Pure carbon or pure oxygen, for example, cannot be converted into anything simpler, at least not by ordinary chemical means. (High-power bombardment with subatomic particles is another story.) The matter we see is composed of **elements** (materials that cannot be broken down into other materials) and **compounds** (materials made up by combining elements).

Chemists have found 92 elements in nature, and they have constructed more in the laboratory. (Actually, one of the 92—technetium—is so rare as to be virtually unknown

in nature.) Figure A.1, the periodic table, lists each of these elements. Of these, only a few are important for life on Earth. Table A.1 shows the elements commonly found in the human body.

Note that each element has a one- or two-letter abbreviation, such as O for oxygen, H for hydrogen, and Ca for calcium. These are internationally accepted symbols that facilitate communication among chemists who speak different languages. For example, element number 19 is called potassium in English, potassio in Italian, kālijs in Latvian, and draslík in Czech. But chemists in all countries use the symbol K (from *kalium*, the Latin word for "potassium"). Similarly, the symbol for sodium is Na (from *natrium*, the Latin word for "sodium"), and the symbol for iron is Fe (from the Latin word *ferrum*).

A compound is represented by the symbols for the elements that compose it. For example, NaCl stands for sodium chloride (common table salt). H_2O, the symbol for water, indicates that water consists of two parts of hydrogen and one part of oxygen.

		The Elements That Compose
TABLE A.1		**Almost All of the Human Body**

Element	Symbol	Percentage by Weight in Human Body
Oxygen	O	65
Carbon	C	18
Hydrogen	H	10
Nitrogen	N	3
Calcium	Ca	2
Phosphorus	P	1.1
Potassium	K	0.35
Sulfur	S	0.25
Sodium	Na	0.15
Chlorine	Cl	0.15
Magnesium	Mg	0.05
Iron	Fe	Trace
Copper	Cu	Trace
Iodine	I	Trace
Fluorine	F	Trace
Manganese	Mn	Trace
Zinc	Zn	Trace
Selenium	Se	Trace
Molybdenum	Mo	Trace

Periodic Table of the Elements

Transition Elements

Inner Transition Elements

Period	1 IA	2 IIA	3 IIIB	4 IVB	5 VB	6 VIB	7 VIIB	8 VIIIB	9 VIIIB	10 VIIIB	11 IB	12 IIB	13 IIIA	14 IVA	15 VA	16 VIA	17 VIIA	18 VIIIA
1	1 H hydrogen 1.008																	2 He helium 4.003
2	3 Li lithium 6.941	4 Be beryllium 9.012											5 B boron 10.81		7 N nitrogen 14.007	8 O oxygen 16.0	9 F fluorine 18.999	10 Ne neon 20.179
3	11 Na sodium 22.99	12 Mg magnesium 24.305											13 Al aluminum 26.982		15 P phosphorus 30.974	16 S sulfur 32.060	17 Cl chlorine 35.453	18 Ar argon 39.948
4	19 K potassium 39.098	20 Ca calcium 40.08	21 Sc scandium 44.955	22 Ti titanium 47.90	23 V vanadium 50.941	24 Cr chromium 51.996	25 Mn manganese 54.938	26 Fe iron 55.847	27 Co cobalt 58.933	28 Ni nickel 58.70	29 Cu copper 63.546	30 Zn zinc 65.38	31 Ga gallium 69.72	germanium	33 As arsenic 74.922	34 Se selenium 78.96	35 Br bromine 79.904	36 Kr krypton 83.80
5	37 Rb rubidium 85.468	38 Sr strontium 87.62	39 Y yttrium 88.906	40 Zr zirconium 91.22	41 Nb niobium 92.906	42 Mo molybdenum 95.940	43 Tc technetium (97)	44 Ru ruthenium 101.07	45 Rh rhodium 102.905	46 Pd palladium 106.40	47 Ag silver 107.868	48 Cd cadmium 112.41	49 In indium 114.82		51 Sb antimony 121.75	52 Te tellurium 127.60	53 I iodine 126.904	54 Xe xenon 131.30
6	55 Cs cesium 132.905	56 Ba barium 137.33	57 La lanthanum 138.906	72 Hf hafnium 178.49	73 Ta tantalum 180.948	74 W tungsten 183.85	75 Re rhenium 186.207	76 Os osmium 190.20	77 Ir iridium 192.22	78 Pt platinum 195.09	79 Au gold 196.967	80 Hg mercury 200.59	81 Tl thallium 204.37		83 Bi bismuth 208.980	84 Po polonium (209)	85 At astatine (210)	86 Rn radon (222)
7	87 Fr francium (223)	88 Ra radium 226.025	89 Ac actinium (227)	104 Rf rutherfordium (261)	105 Db dubnium (262)	106 Sg seaborgium (266)	107 Bh bohrium (264)	108 Hs hassium (269)	109 Mt meitnerium (268)	110 Ds darmstadtium (271)	111 Rg roentgenium (272)	112 Cn copernicium (285)	113 Uut ununtrium (284)		115 Uup ununpentium (288)	116 Uuh ununhexium (292)	117 Uus ununseptium (?)	118 Uuo ununoctium (?)

Alkali Metals — 1 IA

Alkaline Earth Metals — 2 IIA

Halogens — 17 VIIA

Noble Gases — 18 VIIIA

† Lanthanides 6

58 Ce cerium 140.12	59 Pr praseodymium 140.908	60 Nd neodymium 144.24	61 Pm promethium (145)	62 Sm samarium 150.40	63 Eu europium 151.96	64 Gd gadolinium 157.25	65 Tb terbium 158.925	66 Dy dysprosium 162.50	67 Ho holmium 164.93	68 Er erbium 167....	69 Tm thulium 168.934	70 Yb ytterbium 173.04	71 Lu lutetium 174.97

‡ Actinides 7

90 Th thorium 232.038	91 Pa protactinium 231.036	92 U uranium 238.029	93 Np neptunium (237)	94 Pu plutonium (244)	95 Am americium (243)	96 Cm curium (247)	97 Bk berkelium (247)	98 Cf californium (251)	99 Es einsteinium (254)	100 Fm fermium (25...)	101 Md mendelevium (258)	102 No nobelium (255)	103 Lr lawrencium (260)

Key:
atomic number — 1
symbol of element — H
element name — hydrogen
atomic weight — 1.008

FIGURE A.1 The periodic table of chemistry

It is called "periodic" because certain properties show up at periodic intervals. For example, the column from lithium down consists of metals that readily form salts. The column at the far right consists of gases that do not readily form compounds. Elements 112–118 have only tentative names and symbols.

Atoms and Molecules

A block of iron can be chopped finer and finer until it is divided into tiny pieces that cannot be broken down any further. These pieces are called **atoms**. Every element is composed of atoms. A compound, such as water, can also be divided into tinier and tinier pieces. The smallest possible piece of a compound is called a **molecule**. A molecule of water can be further decomposed into two atoms of hydrogen and one atom of oxygen, but when that happens the compound is broken and is no longer water. A molecule is the smallest piece of a compound that retains the properties of the compound.

An atom is composed of subatomic particles, including protons, neutrons, and electrons. A proton has a positive electrical charge, a neutron has a neutral charge, and an electron has a negative charge. The nucleus of an atom—its center—contains one or more protons plus a number of neutrons. Electrons are found in the space around the nucleus. Because an atom has the same number of protons as electrons, the electrical charges balance out. (Ions, which we will soon consider, have an imbalance of positive and negative charges.)

The difference between one element and another is in the number of protons in the nucleus of the atom. Hydrogen has just one proton, for example, and oxygen has eight. The number of protons is the **atomic number** of the element; in the periodic table it is recorded at the top of the square for each element. The number at the bottom is the element's **atomic weight**, which indicates the weight of an atom relative to the weight of one proton. A proton has a weight of one unit, a neutron has a weight just trivially greater than one, and an electron has a weight just trivially greater than zero. The atomic weight of the element is the number of protons in the atom plus the average number of neutrons. For example, most hydrogen atoms have one proton and no neutrons; a few atoms per thousand have one or two neutrons, giving an average atomic weight of 1.008. Sodium ions have 11 protons; most also have 12 neutrons, and the atomic weight is slightly less than 23. (Can you figure out the number of neutrons in the average potassium atom? Refer to Figure A.1.)

Ions and Chemical Bonds

An atom that has gained or lost one or more electrons is called an **ion**. For example, if sodium and chloride come together, the sodium atoms readily lose one electron each and the chloride atoms gain one each. The result is a set of positively charged sodium ions (indicated Na^+) and negatively charged chloride ions (Cl^-). Potassium atoms, like sodium atoms, tend to lose an electron and to become positively charged ions (K^+); calcium ions tend to lose two electrons and gain a double positive charge (Ca^{++}).

Because positive charges attract negative charges, sodium ions attract chloride ions. When dry, sodium and chloride form a crystal structure, as Figure A.2 shows. (In water solution, the two kinds of ions move about haphazardly, occasionally attracting one another but then pulling apart.) The attraction of positive ions for negative ions forms an **ionic bond**. In other cases, instead of transferring an electron from one atom to another,

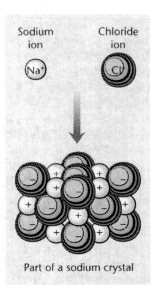

FIGURE A.2 The crystal structure of sodium chloride
Each sodium ion is surrounded by chloride ions, and each chloride ion is surrounded by sodium ions; no ion is bound to any other single ion in particular.

some pairs of atoms share electrons with each other, forming a **covalent bond**. For example, two hydrogen atoms bind, as shown in Figure A.3, and two hydrogen atoms bind with an oxygen atom, as shown in Figure A.4. Atoms that are attached by a covalent bond cannot move independently of one another.

FIGURE A.3 Structure of a hydrogen molecule
A hydrogen atom has one electron; in the compound the two atoms share the two electrons equally.

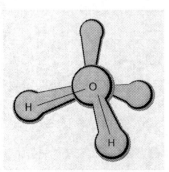

FIGURE A.4 Structure of a water molecule
The oxygen atom shares a pair of electrons with each hydrogen atom. Oxygen holds the electrons more tightly, making the oxygen part of the molecule more negatively charged than the hydrogen part of the molecule.

Reactions of Carbon Atoms

Living organisms depend on the enormously versatile compounds of carbon. Because of the importance of these compounds for life, the chemistry of carbon is known as organic chemistry.

Carbon atoms form covalent bonds with hydrogen, oxygen, and a number of other elements. They also form covalent bonds with other carbon atoms. Two carbon atoms may share from one to three pairs of electrons. Such bonds can be indicated as follows:

C—C   Two atoms share one pair of electrons.
C=C   Two atoms share two pairs of electrons.
C≡C   Two atoms share three pairs of electrons.

Each carbon atom ordinarily forms four covalent bonds, either with other carbon atoms, with hydrogen atoms, or with other atoms. Many biologically important compounds include long chains of carbon compounds linked to one another, such as:

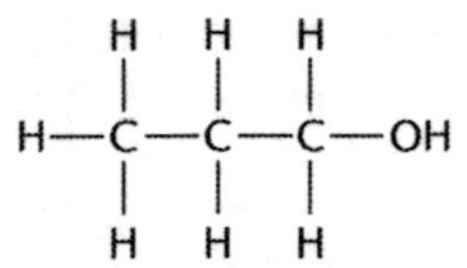

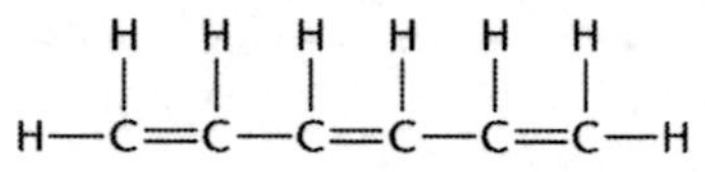

Note that each carbon atom has a total of four bonds, counting each double bond as two. In some molecules, the carbon chain loops around to form a ring:

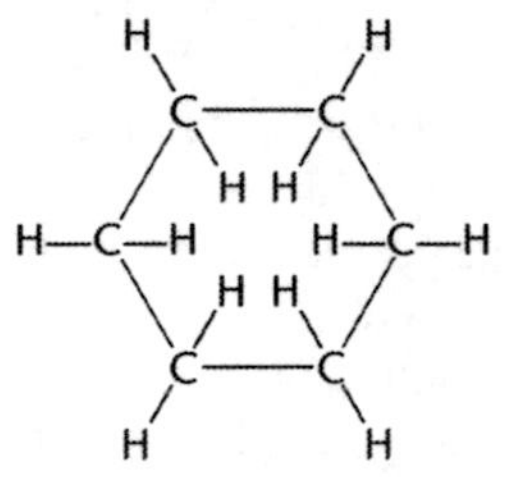

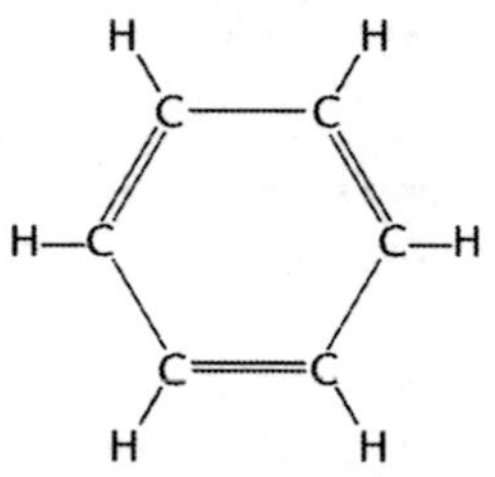

Ringed structures are common in organic chemistry. To simplify the diagrams chemists often omit the hydrogen atoms. You can simply assume that each carbon atom in the diagram has four covalent bonds and that all the bonds not shown are with hydrogen atoms. To further simplify the diagrams, chemists often omit the carbon atoms themselves, showing only the carbon-to-carbon bonds. For example, the two molecules shown in the previous diagram might be rendered as follows:

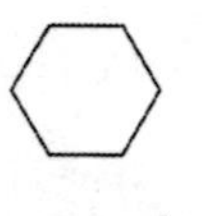

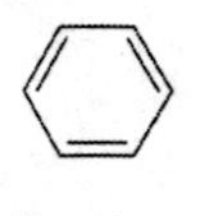

If a particular carbon atom has a bond with some atom other than hydrogen, the diagram shows the exception. For example, in each of the two molecules diagrammed below, one carbon has a bond with an oxygen atom, which in turn has a bond with a hydrogen atom. All the bonds that are not shown are carbon–hydrogen bonds.

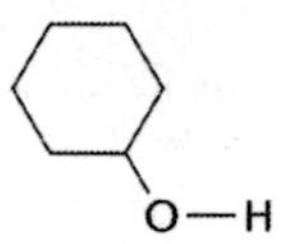

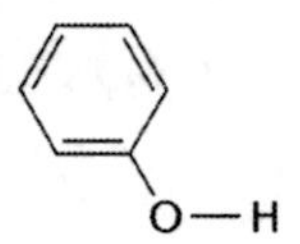

Figure A.5 illustrates some carbon compounds that are critical for animal life. Purines and pyrimidines form the central structure of DNA and RNA, the chemicals responsible for heredity. Proteins, fats, and carbohydrates are the primary types of fuel that the body uses. Figure A.6 displays the chemical structures of seven neurotransmitters that are extensively discussed in this text.

Chemical Reactions in the Body

A living organism is an immensely complicated, coordinated set of chemical reactions. Life requires that the rate of each reaction be carefully regulated. In many cases one reaction

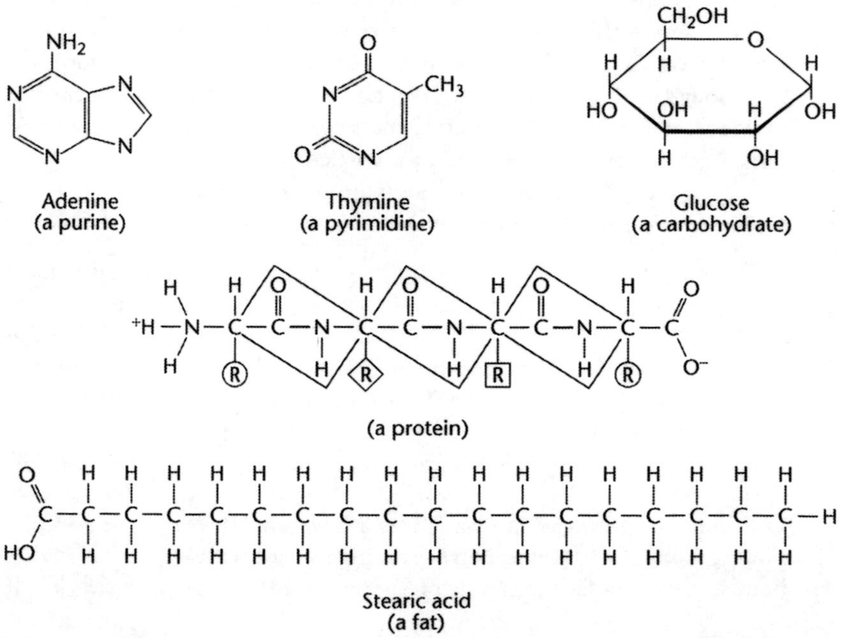

Adenine (a purine)

Thymine (a pyrimidine)

Glucose (a carbohydrate)

(a protein)

Stearic acid (a fat)

FIGURE A.5 Structures of some important biological molecules
The R in the protein represents a point of attachment for various chains that differ from one amino acid to another. Actual proteins are much longer than the chemical shown here.

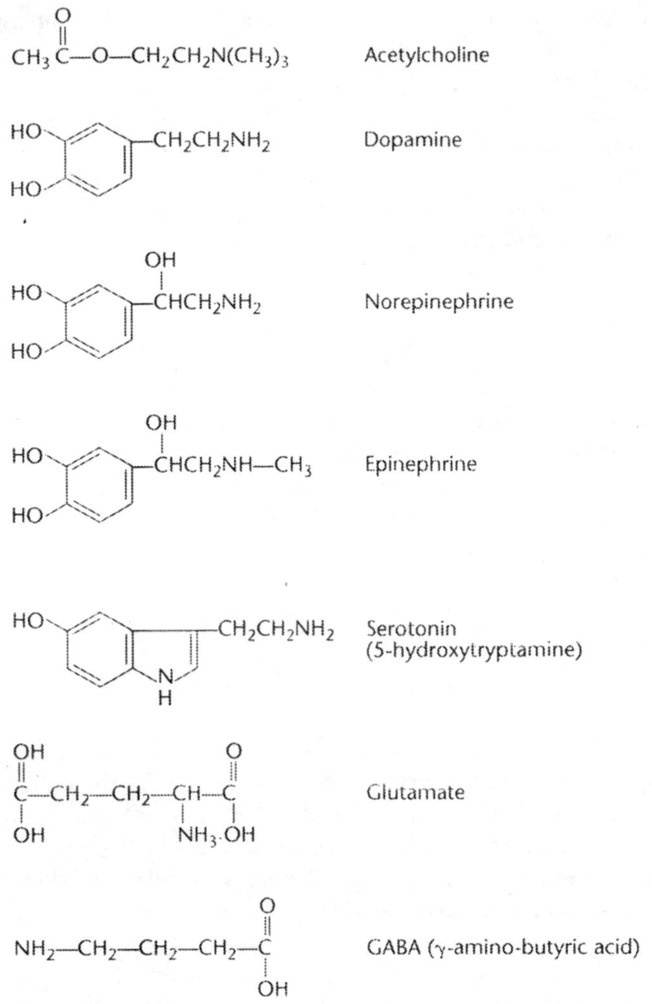

$$CH_3 \overset{\overset{O}{\|}}{C}—O—CH_2CH_2N(CH_3)_3 \quad \text{Acetylcholine}$$

Dopamine

Norepinephrine

Epinephrine

Serotonin (5-hydroxytryptamine)

Glutamate

GABA (γ-amino-butyric acid)

FIGURE A.6 Chemical structures of seven abundant neurotransmitters

produces a chemical that enters into another reaction, which produces another chemical that enters into another reaction, and so forth. If any one of those reactions is too rapid compared to the others, the chemical it produces will accumulate to possibly harmful levels. If a reaction is too slow, it will not produce enough product and the next reaction will be stalled.

Enzymes are proteins that control the rate of chemical reactions. Each reaction is controlled by a particular enzyme. Enzymes are a type of catalyst. A catalyst is any chemical that facilitates a reaction among other chemicals without being altered itself in the process.

The Role of ATP

The body relies on **ATP (adenosine triphosphate)** as its main way of sending energy where it is needed (Figure A.7). Much of the energy derived from food goes into forming ATP molecules that eventually provide energy for the muscles and other body parts.

ATP consists of adenosine bound to ribose and three phosphate groups (PO_3). Phosphates form high-energy covalent bonds. That is, a large amount of energy is required to

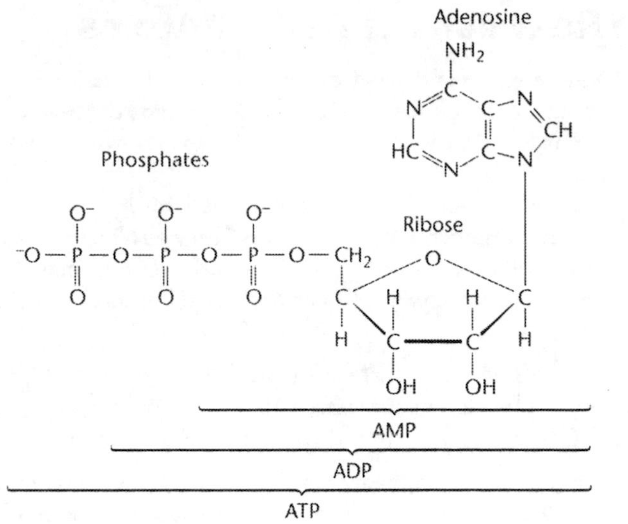

FIGURE A.7 ATP, composed of adenosine, ribose, and three phosphates
ATP can lose one phosphate group to form ADP (adenosine diphosphate) and then lose another one to form AMP (adenosine monophosphate). Each time it breaks off a phosphate group, it releases energy.

form the bonds and a large amount of energy is released when they break. ATP can break off one or two of its three phosphates to provide energy.

▌Summary

1. Matter is composed of 92 elements that combine to form an endless variety of compounds. **486**
2. An atom is the smallest piece of an element. A molecule is the smallest piece of a compound that maintains the properties of the compound. **488**
3. The atoms of some elements can gain or lose an electron, thus becoming ions. Positively charged ions attract negatively charged ions, forming an ionic bond. In some cases two or more atoms may share electrons, thus forming a covalent bond. **488**
4. The principal carrier of energy in the body is a chemical called ATP. **490**

▌Terms

atom 488
atomic number 488
atomic weight 488
ATP (adenosine triphosphate) 490
compound 486
covalent bond 488
element 486
enzyme 490
ion 488
ionic bond 488
molecule 488